introduction to gas dynamics

introduction to

gas dynamics

Ralph M. Rotty
Professor and head
Mechanical Engineering Department
Tulane University

John Wiley & Sons, Inc., New York · London · Sydney

"to Maxene"

preface

Modern devices employ energy transformations of types which were almost unheard of a few decades ago, and the transformations involved in machines currently undergoing research and development must be classed as truly exotic. These advances mean that a young engineer must have a more thorough understanding of the fundamental laws of nature, as well as a reasonable knowledge of modern applications of these laws. Furthermore, his knowledge of applications must be constantly increasing and he must make continuous effort to keep up-to-date. These same principles must apply to engineering educators. The engineering education profession, and particularly individual teachers, must re-assess current course content at regular intervals and make the necessary adjustments without hesitation.

Since the end of World War II, there has been an increasing emphasis on fundamental and engineering sciences and a concurrent increase in graduate work in engineering. While the need for more fundamental science in the educational experience of neophyte engineers cannot be discounted, it is evident that some engineering educators are in some danger of trying to educate scientists rather than engineers. I believe that there is a decided difference between the two professions and that this difference lies in the fundamental design interest of engineers. In the final analysis, the engineer uses an understanding of science to build or create a device to make life easier for his fellow man.

The education of such an engineer requires careful study of fundamental sciences, with the basic principles presented in such a way that the student can visualize the physical picture and recognize how these principles might be applied in design. Such an *education* is in contrast to the *training* of a scientist or the *training* of an engineer in current technology. The educated engineer must be taught to think from the basic principle through to a working device. This requires a continual emphasis on design throughout the curriculum, either in a sequence of courses distinct from the "science" courses, or within the science courses themselves. I prefer an approach closer to the second of these alternatives, and in this textbook I have attempted to present fundamental principles with some care and precision, trying always to make the student understand the physical pattern so that he may recognize how the principle can be applied to future design.

The problem of providing the proper selection of subject matter for the student who will be required to make new designs soon after commencement, and at the same time providing proper subject matter for the future graduate student, is a difficult one. Some compromises must be made and, through the experience of several years of trying to provide such subject matter at Michigan State University and at Tulane University, I have found that the material presented in this textbook meets with reasonable success in senior-level mechanical engineering courses at both universities.

It is assumed that such students have had at least a one-year course in fundamental thermodynamics, a course covering basic fluid mechanics, and have acquired a working knowledge of differential equations. At the undergraduate level this course may be the terminal course in this field, although at Tulane mechanical engineering seniors may elect courses in turbomachinery and/or propulsive engines, both of which build to some extent on the material in this text.

For the mechanical engineering student who is going no further, it would probably be satisfactory to treat only the case of steady flow, and yet the student who continues immediately finds himself in the midst of equations involving partial derivatives with respect to time. As a compromise, the basic equations for momentum, energy conservation, and mass conservation are all presented in the general (although one-dimensional) case with time variations included, and then simplified to the steady-flow case in analyzing adiabatic flow through nozzles, diffusers, etc., and flow of Fanno and Rayleigh line types, and flow with shock waves.

For the student who continues into graduate work and prepares himself further in mathematics, the material presented here should provide an excellent introduction to rigorous graduate courses in fluid dynamics of two- and three-dimensional flows, high-speed aerodynamics, including airfoil lift and drag at supersonic and hypersonic speeds, and courses in aerothermochemistry (combustion in high velocity flows).

Chapter 2 provides the heart of the subject as I teach it. The idea of a control volume and the mass, energy, and force balances required by the basic physical laws governing fluid flow are basic to all the special analyses presented in later chapters. For many students this is perhaps the last chance to see the significance of these laws under nonsteady conditions.

It seemed logical to include the chapter on wave motion since this is a subject frequently missing (or at least not very prominent) in the education of mechanical engineering students. In addition, this provides an excellent introduction to the idea of sonic velocity and points out the difference between particle velocity and wave velocity. I have found this gives much more meaning to the concept of Mach number.

The inclusion of material on thrust produced by a fluid moving in a duct has been found to provide motivation for mechanical engineering students who want to "make something go."

Chapters 5, 6, 7, and 8 provide an understanding of what is usually thought of as one-dimensional compressible flow of perfect gases. The treatment here is not unlike what can be found elsewhere. It is presented with the intent of providing maximum understanding for the reader while still requiring him to follow some mathematical details. The introduction of isentropic flow function and a thrust function is perhaps unique.

In the material presented here I have drawn heavily from several earlier books, published during the last decade. There is no attempt to replace or compete with any of them because all are excellent and are more detailed than this treatment. Consequently, the reader is referred to such works as *The Dynamics and Thermodynamics of Compressible Fluid Flow*, by Shapiro; *Thermodynamics of Fluid Flow*, by Hall; and *Elements of Gasdynamics*, by Liepmann and Roshko, when a more detailed description or discussion is desired.

I am indebted to many of my colleagues and former students, and acknowledging their many contributions is a sincere pleasure. Dr. Richard

L. Ditsworth and Mr. Dean E. Bluman offered much criticism in the early stages, and their contributions should add to the "teachability" of the material. Mr. Louis P. Orth assisted through the preparation of the sketches and line diagrams used throughout the text, and Mrs. James B. Kemp and Mrs. Mary P. Lyell were of great assistance in the manuscript typing.

RALPH M. ROTTY

New Orleans
January, 1962

contents

I

fundamental considerations

1.1 Introduction

With the development of jet propulsion, gas turbines, and high-speed aerodynamics, the mechanism of fluid flow has become extremely important to the engineer. For some time the relations between forces, masses, and velocities in a fluid have been known and used in the general field of fluid mechanics. Such knowledge has been necessary in the design of much modern equipment, particularly in reference to flows of incompressible fluids.

In the case of high-speed compressible flow, the analysis usually follows the same procedures as in other branches of physical science. Certain assumptions are made and applied to one or more natural laws (which have been found to be true through many years of observation). Four of the fundamental laws can be readily applied in the area of gas dynamics and are found to be sufficient for most elementary analyses when properly

1

used with intelligent assumptions. These four fundamental laws or principles, upon which all the analyses presented in this book depend directly or indirectly, are:

>   (a) Newton's second law of motion.
>   (b) The law of conservation of mass.
>   (c) The first law of thermodynamics.
>   (d) The second law of thermodynamics.

While the first two of these are sufficient for many flow problems, frequently thermodynamic principles are needed to give a complete and accurate picture of the flow. It is in this area that fluid mechanics and thermodynamics must merge. When the two fields are combined, the resulting tools become extremely powerful and the equations describing the fluid motion require a minimum of restrictions. Since this combination is so valuable in the case of compressible flow, it seems appropriate to be concerned with the dynamics and *thermodynamics* of compressible flow.

One of the assumptions which is necessary in any flow analysis is that the properties of the fluid being studied are known. This information (such as the equation of state of a perfect gas) is used in connection with one or more (or all) of the four cited fundamental laws in order to provide maximum knowledge of the flow.

Since the underlying principles rise from thermodynamics and mechanics of fluid friction, a review of this material is presented in this first chapter.

1.2 Definitions in thermodynamics

The following definitions, taken from a general elementary thermodynamics course, will be used throughout this book.

System. A system is a collection of matter or mass identified for study. In the absence of any mass-energy conversions, the mass of a system not only must remain constant, but the system must be made up of exactly the same submolecular particles.

Property. A property is any characteristic of the system which may be observed (directly or indirectly) and which describes the physical and thermal state of the system. Two or more independent properties are required to fix the state of a system.

Pressure. That property which is the force applied by the system on an infinitesimal element of boundary divided by the area of the element is called pressure.

Specific volume and density. The specific volume is that volume occupied by a unit mass of a system. Density is the inverse of specific volume—the mass contained in a unit volume of a system.

$$\rho = \frac{1}{v}$$

In fluid thermodynamics the use of density is much more common than the use of specific volume. In comparing the equations used here with those encountered in previous thermodynamics work, this change will be apparent. However, if the relation between density and specific volume is remembered, no difficulty should result.

Temperature. Temperature is that property which measures the thermal level of the fluid. In measuring temperature, some calibrated device must be brought to thermal equilibrium with the system. This causes some time delay in getting an accurate measurement of temperature. Consequently, in the case of a system with a rapidly changing thermal level, good temperature measurement is extremely difficult.

Energy. Energy is that which, when added to or removed from the system, produces a change in the properties of the system.

Heat. Heat is energy which flows to or from a system solely as a result of a temperature difference between the system and some external body.

Work. Work is energy which flows to or from a system in a form such that the sole effect external to the system may be the raising or lowering of a weight.

1.3 Units and dimensions

Whenever analyses from more than one area of physics are to be combined, it is essential that considerable care be exercised in maintaining a consistent set of units. In fluid thermodynamics, equations from mechanics of fluids and from thermodynamics are used so frequently that one consistent set of units should be used from the beginning.

The following system, which will be used throughout this course, is simple and has the advantage of easy conversion from other common engineering systems:

All systems must be consistent with Newton's Law of Motion: Force is proportional to mass times acceleration, or

$$F = kma$$

where k is a constant of proportionality. Physicists and chemists find it convenient to have $k = 1$, and the metric system establishes a dyne as a force unit.

In engineering it is commonplace to refer to both pounds of mass and pounds of force. The force of a standard gravity acting on a one-pound mass is one pound of force. Then

$$k = \frac{F}{ma} = \frac{1 \ (\text{lb}_f)}{1 \ (\text{lb}_m) \ 32.17 \ (\text{ft/sec}^2)}$$

or

$$\frac{1}{k} = g_0 = 32.17 \left(\frac{\text{ft lb}_m}{\text{lb}_f \ \text{sec}^2} \right)$$

Then Newton's law is written

$$F = \frac{ma}{g_0} \tag{1.1}$$

where (in our usual unit system):
  F is in pounds of force
  m is in pounds of mass
  a is in feet per (second)^2
  g_0 is a dimension conversion constant $= 32.17 \left(\dfrac{\text{ft lb}_m}{\text{lb}_f \ \text{sec}^2} \right)$

If the equation (1.1) is written:

$$F = \left(\frac{m}{g_0} \right) a$$

it is seen that $\dfrac{m}{g_0}$ is the mass in slugs. We then have the familiar system used in some engineering work of:

Force	pounds
Mass	slugs
Length	feet
Time	seconds

The mass in slugs $\dfrac{m}{g_0}$ can always be converted to mass in pounds by multiplying by $32.17 \left(\dfrac{\text{ft lb}_m}{\text{lb}_f \ \text{sec}^2} \right)$. A slug is equivalent to units of $\left(\dfrac{\text{lb}_f \ \text{sec}^2}{\text{ft}} \right)$, and, in general, mass may be considered as having units of force multiplied by the time squared over length.

If equation (1.1) is written

$$(g_0 F) = ma$$

it is seen that $g_0 F$ is the force in poundals, and we have a system in which:

  force is in poundals
  mass is in pounds
  length is in feet
  time is in seconds

The force in poundals, g_0F can easily be converted to force in pounds by dividing by $32.17\left(\dfrac{\text{ft lb}_m}{\text{lb}_f\text{ sec}^2}\right)$. The main objection to this system is that the number describing a practical force is extremely large: 32.17 times larger than the number required to express the same force in pounds.

If equation (1.1) is written:

$$F = m\,\frac{a}{g_0}$$

it is seen that $\dfrac{a}{g_0}$ is the acceleration in g's. To obtain acceleration in feet per (second)^2 it is necessary to multiply accelerations in g's by $32.17 \times \left(\dfrac{\text{ft lb}_m}{\text{lb}_f\text{ sec}^2}\right)$.

In summary, it should be evident that if equation (1.1) is understood, all the other systems of engineering units which are encountered can be converted with a minimum of effort and a maximum of understanding.

1.4 Laws of thermodynamics

The first law of thermodynamics states the fact of energy conservation. It is commonly written in elementary thermodynamics courses as

$$\oint \delta Q = \oint \delta W \tag{1.2}$$

if both the heat energy and work energy are expressed in the same units.

By convention in thermodynamics, heat added to a system is positive and heat rejected by a system is negative. Similarly, work done by a system is positive and work done on a system (added to a system) is negative.

Since heat may be expressed in an independently defined energy unit, Btu, and since the fundamental unit for work is the foot-pound, the first law of thermodynamics establishes a conversion between Btu's and foot-pounds.

$$J = 778.16\,\frac{\text{ft-lb}_f}{\text{Btu}}$$

J is frequently called the mechanical equivalent of heat. Further, as a consequence of the first law as stated in equation (1.2), it has been established that there must be a property of the system which is the energy content or internal energy. Both heat and work are path functions, i.e., their values depend on the path between the state points at the ends of the process. The quantities δQ and δW are inexact differentials, while the

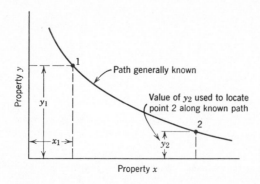

Fig. 1.1 Schematic diagram of simple thermodynamics problem.

differential of any property is an exact differential. Properties are point functions, i.e., their values depend only on the location of the state point and not on how that state point was reached. Thus the consequence of the existence of a property (point function), which is the difference of two path functions, is striking. The first law may be written:

$$dE = \delta Q - \delta W \qquad (1.3)$$

or by rearranging and integrating

$$Q = \Delta E + W$$

In thermodynamics it is customary to encounter problems in which values of two properties at the initial state point are known along with the path to be followed to a final state point where only one property is known. This is illustrated schematically in Figure 1.1.

In problems of this type the fact that equation (1.3) relates a point function to path functions proves extremely valuable.

The second law of thermodynamics is usually stated in one of its classic forms, such as "No system can pass through a complete cycle and produce net work while exchanging heat with a single heat reservoir at a uniform temperature." It is shown in elementary thermodynamics that as a direct consequence of the second law, a property, *entropy*, must exist, and is defined by

$$ds = \frac{\delta Q}{T} \qquad (1.4)$$

for any reversible process only. For an irreversible process:

$$ds > \frac{\delta Q}{T}.$$

For a reversible process the entropy change ds may be either positive, negative, or zero, depending on the amount and direction of the heat transfer. During a reversible process in which heat is transferred away from the system, the entropy decreases because the δQ is negative. In such a case the entropy of the surroundings must increase by exactly the amount that the entropy of the system has decreased. Thus, for any reversible process, the sum of the entropy changes of the system and its surroundings is zero.

Also for an irreversible process the entropy change ds may be either positive, negative or zero, depending on the amount and direction of the heat transfer. In this case, however, the sum of the entropy changes of the system and its surroundings must always be a positive value. If the entropy of the system decreases, the entropy of the surroundings must increase by a larger amount. Since all processes in the universe are at least partially irreversible, this leads to the conclusion that the total entropy of the universe must be constantly increasing.

A pure substance is defined to be any substance which is homogeneous in chemical composition and aggregation. A substance such as water is a pure substance since all the molecules are H_2O molecules, and this is true even when two phases, e.g., liquid water and steam, are present. At ordinary temperatures air may be considered to be a pure substance even though it is a mixture of approximately 21% oxygen and 79% nitrogen by volume. When air is cooled to a temperature such that two phases (liquid and gaseous) are present, the liquid phase is richer in oxygen and the gaseous phase is richer in nitrogen. Consequently, such a system is not one of homogeneous chemical composition and may not be considered a pure substance.

In a chemical reaction, such as a combustion process, the system is not made up of a pure substance and many of the familiar equations of engineering thermodynamics must be modified or made more complicated in order to describe the situation accurately. In the case of combustion in a gas turbine combustion chamber, the fuel-air ratio is so small that little error is introduced by the approximation of considering both the reactants and the products of combustion to be a pure substance with the composition of air.

For a stationary system consisting of a pure substance undergoing a *reversible process*, the first law of thermodynamics becomes: (This was shown to be the case in elementary thermodynamics.)

$$\delta Q = du + p\, dv = du + pd\left(\frac{1}{\rho}\right)$$

Then combining the first and second laws:

$$ds = \frac{du + p\, d\left(\frac{1}{\rho}\right)}{T} \tag{1.5}$$

This is sometimes taken to be the definition of entropy. Since this equation involves only properties (point functions), it is completely independent of the path of the process. Hence it is valid for either reversible of irreversible process. While equation (1.5) is extremely useful and must be remembered for easy reference, equation (1.4) is more general and, hence, is the more important definition. The student is urged to think of (1.5) as an important consequence of definition (1.4).

Thus the first law establishes the existence of a property internal energy, and the second law establishes the property entropy. It is necessary in fluid thermodynamics to make extensive use of still another property, which in contrast to internal energy and entropy is not established by one of the laws of thermodynamics, but is defined for convenience to be a certain mathematical grouping of other properties: enthalpy, h. Thus,

$$h = u + pv = u + \frac{p}{\rho} \tag{1.6}$$

$$dh = du + \frac{1}{\rho} dp + pd\left(\frac{1}{\rho}\right)$$

Then equation (1.5) can be written:

$$ds = \frac{dh - \frac{1}{\rho} dp}{T} \tag{1.7}$$

The equivalence of (1.5) and (1.7) should be apparent. Both are widely used.

1.5 Properties of fluids

A fluid is a substance which deforms continuously under the action of shearing forces. Solids undergo certain deformations which do not change so long as the forces remain constant. Fluids, on the other hand, experience relative motions between their elementary parts as long as shearing forces are present.

In general, a fluid will be either a liquid or a gas, but attempts to establish a rigorous distinction between liquids and gases have proved futile. It is easier to refer to compressible and incompressible fluids, with an incompressible fluid corresponding to our usual ideas of a liquid, and a compressible fluid exhibiting properties expected of gases.

The ideal incompressible fluid is one of constant density. However, most common liquids have a density variation with temperature which is not always negligible. We may define incompressible fluids as ones in which the density is not changed with a change in pressure. There are two possibilities:

(a) $\rho = $ constant

(b) $\rho = \rho_0[1 - \beta(T - T_0)]$ $\hspace{2cm}$ (1.8)

where β is the coefficient of volumetric thermal expansion.

$$\beta = \frac{1}{v}\left(\frac{\partial v}{\partial T}\right)_p = -\frac{1}{\rho}\left(\frac{\partial \rho}{\partial T}\right)_p \hspace{2cm} (1.9)$$

The ideal compressible fluid is one which follows the equation of state of a perfect gas:

$$pv = RT \hspace{0.5cm} \text{or} \hspace{0.5cm} p = \rho RT \hspace{2cm} (1.10)$$

R is the well known gas constant, and any gas which obeys equation (1.10) is said to be a perfect gas. Where interactions between the molecules of a gas become frequent (for example, at high densities where the molecules are more closely packed), deviations from the perfect gas law are encountered. Such situations are frequently handled by using a compressibility factor in the equation of state.

$$p = \rho ZRT \hspace{2cm} (1.11)$$

In equation (1.11), Z is the compressibility factor, and is near one for states well removed from the critical state. Data for Z for various gases under a wide range of conditions have been established as a result of recent research. As a result of the research of Nelson and Obert, a generalized chart good for all gases, using reduced pressure and reduced temperature, has been developed and is presented in the appendix.

Situations requiring modifications in the perfect gas equation of state are also frequently analyzed by using the Van der Waals equation:

$$\left(p + \frac{a}{v^2}\right)(v - b) = RT$$

or

$$(p + a\rho^2)(1 - b\rho) = \rho RT \hspace{2cm} (1.12)$$

a and b are constants which differ for different substances. Values for a and b may be found in appropriate handbooks.

For perfect gases,

$$du = c_v \, dT \hspace{2cm} (1.13)$$

$$dh = c_p \, dT \hspace{2cm} (1.14)$$

Then
$$c_p \, dT = c_v \, dT + R \, dT$$

$$c_p = c_v + R \tag{1.15}$$

Letting $\dfrac{c_p}{c_v} = k$

$$(k - 1)c_v = R \quad \text{or} \quad c_v = \frac{R}{(k - 1)} \tag{1.16}$$

Then

$$c_p = \frac{Rk}{k - 1} \tag{1.17}$$

The kinetic theory of gases shows that for a simple molecular model

$$k = \frac{n + 2}{n}$$

where n is the number of degrees of freedom of the molecule. For monatomic gases, e.g., helium, there are three degrees of freedom (the ordinary three directions for linear translation) and $k = \frac{5}{3}$. For diatomic gases, e.g., oxygen or nitrogen, there are five degrees of freedom (three for linear translation and two for rotation) and $k = \frac{7}{5}$. For triatomic gases, $n = 6$, $k = \frac{8}{6}$, and for higher numbers of atoms per molecule the number of degrees of freedom becomes very large and k approaches unity.

In dealing with real gases, frequently it is satisfactory to assume the equation of state, $pv = RT$, but the assumption of constant specific heat capacity in integrating equations (1.13) and (1.14) is not suitable. The variation in the specific heat capacity results from the molecules not being the simple model assumed in kinetic theory, and from an increase in the number of degrees of freedom as the temperature increases. This inadequacy of the assumption of constant specific heat capacities may be minimized by considering both c_v and c_p to be functions of temperature. That is,

$$c_p = f_1(T)$$
$$c_v = f_2(T)$$

If these equations are to be of sufficient accuracy to describe the specific heat capacities satisfactorily, they usually result in tedious and clumsy equations in describing internal energy and enthalpy changes. A preferable procedure in modern practice is to use gas tables whenever the variation of specific heat capacity is great enough to make the assumption of constant values impractical.

For an example of gas tables, see Table A.1 in the Appendix where internal energy and enthalpy are functions of temperature only and may be easily read from the table. Entropy changes are a function of two independent properties and, hence, a simple tabulation as a function of temperature is not possible. Substituting equation (1.14) into (1.7) for dh and employing the assumption $pv = RT$,

$$ds = c_p \frac{dt}{T} - R \frac{dp}{p} \tag{1.18}$$

In establishing a table for entropy, the zero level may arbitrarily be assumed. If zero entropy is taken at the absolute zero of temperature and a given pressure p_s, then the entropy at any point may be written as

$$s = \int_{0, p_s}^{T, p} ds = \int_0^T c_p \frac{dT}{T} - R \ln \frac{p}{p_s} \tag{1.19}$$

Defining

$$\phi = \int_0^T c_p \frac{dT}{T} \tag{1.20}$$

then the entropy change from p_1, T_1, to p_2, T_2, is

$$\Delta s = s_2 - s_1 = \phi_2 - \phi_1 - R \ln \frac{p_2}{p_1} \tag{1.21}$$

It should be noted that ϕ is a function of temperature only and hence may be tabulated just as internal energy or enthalpy.

Tabulations of enthalpy, internal energy, and the ϕ function have been made and published for air and for the products of combustion of various mixtures. It is therefore possible and relatively easy to use data which is much more accurate than that obtained by assumption of constant specific heat capacity.

1.6 Viscosity

In the previous section a fluid was defined as a substance which deforms continuously under the action of shearing forces. A Newtonian fluid is one which has a linear relation between the magnitude of the applied shear stress and the angular deformation of the fluid.

Consider the fluid between two parallel plates that are so large compared with the distance between them that conditions at the edges may be neglected. (See Figure 1.2.)

Apply a constant force, F, to the upper plate and consider the lower plate fixed. Because the fluid immediately adjacent to a solid has no motion relative to that solid, the fluid in contact with the upper plate will move with

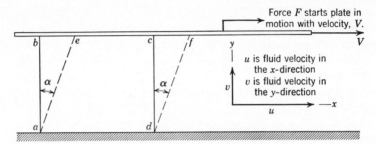

Fig. 1.2 Deformation of a fluid between two parallel plates.

that plate while that in contact with the lower plate will remain stationary with that plate. The force, F, no matter how small, will cause the upper plate to be set in motion with some velocity, V. If this is not the case, then the substance between the plates is not a fluid. Also, the particles of fluid in contact with the upper plate must move with that plate and, hence, have a velocity V.

The rate of angular deformation of the fluid may be obtained by considering the fluid element $abcd$. After a time δt, the element has the shape and position $aefd$. The distance be is equal to $V\delta t$. The particles of fluid along ab are deformed during δt to the line ae. Since the angle is usually small, the angular deformation can be expressed as

$$\alpha \approx \tan \alpha = \frac{be}{ab} = \frac{V\delta t}{ab}$$

Fluid at a position between the plates has a velocity proportional to the distance from the lower plate. Since the deformation takes place in time δt, the rate of angular deformation is $\dfrac{V}{ab}$. Keeping in mind that V is really the change in fluid velocity from the stationary plate to the moving plate, in the limit as the fluid element is taken to be very small, in differential form for one dimensional flow, the rate of angular deformation is

$$\frac{du}{dy}$$

where u is the velocity in the x-direction and y is the coordinate perpendicular to the flow.

Then for a Newtonian fluid, the shear stress,

$$\tau = \mu \frac{du}{dy} \tag{1.22}$$

μ is a coefficient of proportionality which is called the *viscosity* or *coefficient of viscosity.* Viscosity is independent of velocity and position (in an iso-thermal fluid element), but does change significantly with temperature for most common fluids. Fluids for which equation (1.22) is not valid are non-Newtonian fluids. Most gases and the common liquids used in power-producing devices are sufficiently close to being Newtonian that little error is encountered in this assumption. (In this book only Newtonian fluids are considered.)

In engineering units, from the defining equation, viscosity is measured in $\dfrac{lb_f \ sec}{ft^2}$. This is a very convenient unit in engineering practice, but frequently (especially in heat transfer) it is desirable to use pounds of mass. By multiplying by g_0, viscosity can be expressed in $\left(\dfrac{lb_m}{ft \ sec}\right)$ or $\left(\dfrac{lb_m}{ft \ hr}\right)$. While either $\left(\dfrac{lb_f \ sec}{ft^2}\right)$ or $\left(\dfrac{lb_m}{ft \ sec}\right)$ are most useful in engineering calculations, viscosity is frequently found tabulated in centipoises. A poise is a unit equivalent to $\left(\dfrac{gm}{cm \ sec}\right)$. A centipoise is $1/100$ of a poise and therefore equivalent to $\left(\dfrac{gm}{m \ sec}\right)$.

Kinematic viscosity, $\nu = \dfrac{\mu}{\rho}$, is commonly encountered in discussions of fluid friction. In engineering practice ν is usually expressed in (ft²/sec), but again, kinematic viscosity is frequently found tabulated in metric units. Most tabulations are in centistokes. A stoke is equivalent to (cm²/sec); or a poise divided by density in grams per cubic centimeter. A centistoke is $1/100$ of a stoke. Conversions from poises or centistokes to engineering units are found in many engineering handbooks.

The *viscosity of liquids* is usually found by using one of several types of viscosimeters to determine the kinematic viscosity. These viscosimeters are used to determine the time required for a given fixed quantity to pass through a certain size hole or orifice. Then the kinematic viscosity is given by:

$$\nu = At - \frac{B}{t} \tag{1.23}$$

where t is the time in seconds determined with the viscosimeter, and A and B are constants which differ for each different type of viscosimeter.

At ordinary pressures the *viscosity of gases* has been found to be nearly independent of pressure but to change with temperature. Several semi-theoretical formulas have been suggested as methods for determining μ for a gas, but for our purposes it will be sufficient to obtain values for the

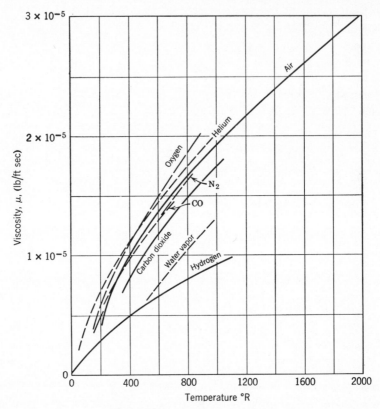

Fig. 1.3 Viscosity of common gases.

viscosity of a certain gas from Figure 1.3. This figure presents viscosity in lb_m/ft sec as a function of temperature for most of the commonly encountered gases.

1.7 Dimensional analysis and the Buckingham pi theorem

As discussed in section 1.3, a system of units is not completely defined until the constant in Newton's second law is determined as in equation (1.1). Then both mass and force cannot be varied independently, but, rather, fixing the value of one also fixes the value of the other. Thus, from Newton's second law of motion, mass or force (but not both) can be independently varied for a given system of units. Then it is possible to think of primary quantities or dimensions and for a given mechanics problem, these could be taken to be MLt (M means mass, L means length, and t means time) or FLt, force-length-time. In thermodynamics it is necessary to also include temperature, T.

All quantities must have dimensions which can be expressed in terms of the primary dimensions for the system chosen. If we choose the *MLtT* system,

force is ML/t^2
work is force $\times$ distance, ML^2/t^2
power is work per unit time, ML^2/t^3
energy must be in the same units as work, ML^2/t^2
pressure is force per unit area, M/Lt^2
velocity is length per unit time, L/t
heat is in energy units, ML^2/t^2
entropy is in energy units per unit temperature, ML^2/t^2T
viscosity is in M/Lt.

Correspondingly, if we choose the *FLtT* system,

mass $= Ft^2/L$
heat, work, energy $= FL$
power $= FL/t$
pressure $= F/L^2$
velocity $= L/t$
entropy $= FL/T$
viscosity $= Ft/L^2$.

On this basis *all* equations must be dimensionally correct. This principle of dimensional homogeneity, as it is called, is fundamental to our whole system of physical and engineering mathematics. In the attempt to establish an equation for an unknown quantity, the dimensional form of the equation is extremely valuable. The name "dimensional analysis" is given to the process of determining the correct dimensional form of the equation.

The most valuable theorem in dimensional analysis is the Buckingham pi theorem which states:

Any complete homogeneous equation expressing the relationship between n fundamental variables and dimensional constants of r primary dimensions in the form $f(a, b, c, \ldots, n) = 0$, has a solution in the form:

$$\phi(\pi_1, \pi_2, \ldots, \pi_{n-r}) = 0$$

where the π's are independent dimensionless groupings.

For example, suppose the pressure gradient in a fluid due to friction in a duct is assumed to depend on such things as density, velocity, duct diameter, fluid viscosity, and duct roughness. Then we have the following six fundamental variables:

> pressure drop, dp/dx in F/L^3
> density, ρ in Ft^2/L^4
> velocity, V in L/t
> diameter, D in L
> viscosity, μ in Ft/L^2
> duct roughness, ϵ in L

Since the six variables are expressed in F, L, and t—three primary dimensions—there must be 6-3 or 3 dimensionless π groups.

The general form of the π groups is

$$\pi = \left(\frac{dp}{dx}\right)(\rho)^b(V)^c(D)^d(\mu)^e(\epsilon)^f$$

or

$$\pi = \left(\frac{F}{L^3}\right)^a\left(\frac{Ft^2}{L^4}\right)^b\left(\frac{L}{t}\right)(L)^d\left(\frac{Ft}{L^2}\right)^e(L)^f$$

Since π must be dimensionless:

> for $F \to a + b + e = 0$
> for $L \to -3a - 4b + c + d - 2e + f = 0$
> for $t \to 2b - c + e = 0$

Hence there are three equations with six unknowns. This means that three variables can be chosen arbitrarily. Since an expression for dp/dx is desired, it will be convenient to let $a = 1$. The simplest possibility is to let two of the other exponents be zero; say $e = 0$, and $f = 0$. Then: $a = 1$, $b = -1$, $c = -2$, $d = 1$, $e = 0$, $f = 0$ and

$$\pi_1 = \left(\frac{dp}{dx}\right)\frac{D}{\rho V^2}$$

Making another arbitrary selection, $a = 0$ (so that the desired quantity appears only once in our final solution) and $b = 1$, and $f = 0$.

Then $a = 0$, $b = 1$, $c = 1$, $d = 1$, $e = -1$ and $\pi_2 = \dfrac{\rho V D}{\mu}$. Note that this second dimensionless group is the familiar Reynolds number.

Making a third selection, $a = 0$, $b = 0$, and $f = 1$ (since f has been zero in each of the other groups), then:

$$a = 0, b = 0, c = 0, d = -1, e = 0, f = 1$$

and

$$\pi_3 = \frac{\epsilon}{D}$$

From the π-theorem

$$\phi\left(\frac{dp}{dx}\frac{D}{\rho V^2}, \frac{\rho VD}{\mu}, \frac{\epsilon}{D}\right) = 0$$

or,

$$\frac{dp}{dx}\frac{D}{\rho V^2} = F\left(\frac{\rho VD}{\mu}, \frac{\epsilon}{D}\right)$$

where F is an arbitrary function of Reynolds number and the relative roughness. Now let $f = 2F$ (still a *function* of *Reynolds number and roughness*), and the usual expression for the pressure drop due to friction results:

$$dp = -\frac{\rho V^2}{2g_0}f\frac{dx}{D} \tag{1.24}$$

Here the g_0 has been inserted so that instead of density in the more awkward $\text{lb}_f \, \text{sec}^2/\text{ft}^4$ units, the more common pounds of mass per cubic foot can be used. Note that $\frac{\text{lb}_f \, \text{sec}^2}{\text{ft}^4}$ multiplied by g_0 yields lb/ft^3. Thus $\frac{\rho}{g_0}$ is density in $\frac{Ft^2}{L^4}$, if ρ alone is to be in $\frac{M}{L^3}$. Equation (1.24) gives the pressure drop in pounds of force per square foot, and the negative sign has been inserted to indicate a pressure decrease with a positive length. It must be remembered that f is a function of both Reynolds number and the relative roughness.

In the case of a gas or other compressible fluid moving at a velocity at which compressibility effects are important, the density alone is not sufficient to define the thermodynamic state of the fluid. The analysis must then be expanded to include either temperature and gas constant or absolute pressure as a fundamental variable, and the result will be 8-4 (or 7-3, if absolute pressure is selected) or 4 dimensionless π groups. The added π group which results is the ratio of the fluid velocity to the velocity of sound in the fluid. Therefore, for a compressible fluid, the friction factor, f, must be a function not only of relative roughness and Reynolds number, but also of this additional quantity which we shall later define as Mach number.

1.8 Fluid friction

When a fluid is moving slowly in a duct, the viscous forces govern the flow with the velocity at the wall being zero as required by the notions of section 1.6, and the velocity being a maximum at the center of the duct. In such a flow, each fluid particle is moving in the same direction, and if

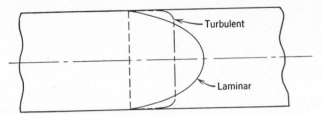

Fig. 1.4   Velocity profiles for laminar and turbulent flows.

we draw a line joining the subsequent positions of one element, we obtain a line parallel to the walls of the duct. Such would be the case for all fluid elements—all such lines would be parallel because all the velocities are parallel; only different in magnitude. A flow of this type is frequently called streamline flow and the lines described above are streamlines. It is common in engineering to call this laminar flow.

As the velocity increases, the viscosity is no longer able to maintain laminar flow. Inertia forces become so large that instability results and eddies are produced. Except in the immediate vicinity of the wall, the velocity along the duct is nearly uniform. This type of flow is called turbulent and is more frequently encountered in engineering than is laminar flow. Figure 1.4 shows a typical velocity variation with radius at a given cross section.

With either laminar or turbulent flow, the friction results in a loss in pressure—that is, the pressure downstream is less because of the friction forces attempting to hold the fluid back. In the absence of acceleration of the fluid element, the forces resulting from a pressure difference is balanced by the shear forces at the walls. (See Figure 1.5.)

$$[p - (p + dp)]\frac{\pi}{4} D^2 = -\pi D \, dx \, \tau_0 \qquad (1.25)$$

where τ_0 is the shear stress at the wall. Then

$$\tau_0 = \frac{1}{4} D \frac{dp}{dx} \qquad (1.26)$$

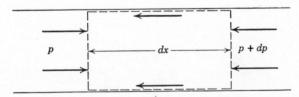

Fig. 1.5   Forces acting on a fluid element.

and employing equation (1.24) for dp/dx

$$\tau_0 = -\frac{1}{4} D\left[\rho \frac{V^2}{2g_0} \frac{f}{D}\right] = -\frac{1}{8g_0} \rho V^2 f \tag{1.27}$$

This equation (1.27) makes it possible to determine the friction factor, f, in terms of flow conditions for both laminar and turbulent flow. Thus (1.27) is a fundamental equation which is very valuable in analyzing flow with friction.

Frequently a friction factor is defined to be the ratio of the shear stress at the wall to the dynamic head, $\dfrac{V^2}{2g_0}$. That is,

$$f' = \frac{-\tau_0}{\dfrac{\rho V^2}{2g_0}}, \quad \text{or} \quad \tau_0 = -\frac{\rho V^2}{2g_0} f' \tag{1.28}$$

Thus f' is equal to the f, as defined in this text, divided by 4:

$$f' = \frac{f}{4} \tag{1.29}$$

The friction factor f' is called the Fanning friction factor and is used with the Fanning equation for pressure loss:

$$dp = -4f \frac{\rho V^2}{2g_0} \frac{dx}{D} \tag{1.30}$$

The factor f, as we use it here, is sometimes called the D'Arcy friction factor and is used with the D'Arcy equation (1.24) which was previously developed by dimensional analysis. Care must be taken in interpreting the literature on this subject to be sure which way the friction factor is defined.

1.9 Laminar flow

The condition for equilibrium of forces when there is no acceleration of the flow,

$$dp\left[\frac{\pi}{4} D^2\right] = \pi D\, dx\, \tau$$

as developed in the previous section, must be valid at any radius in the case of laminar flow. Thus,

$\pi r^2\, dp = 2\pi r\, \tau\, dx$, for any radius r

$\pi a^2\, dp = 2\pi a \tau_0\, dx$, for complete cylinder in duct of radius a

Then

$$\frac{r^2}{a^2} = \frac{r}{a} \frac{\tau}{\tau_0} \quad \text{or} \quad \frac{r}{a} = \frac{\tau}{\tau_0} \tag{1.31}$$

By the definition of viscosity

$$\tau = \mu \frac{du}{dy} = -\mu \frac{du}{dr} \quad \text{since } y = a - r$$

$$\frac{du}{dr} = -\frac{\tau}{\mu} = -\frac{\tau_0 r}{\mu a} \tag{1.32}$$

Integrating the differential equation, we obtain the velocity distribution for laminar flow in a duct.

$$u = \frac{\tau_0}{2a\mu}(a^2 - r^2) \tag{1.33}$$

This equation gives the velocity at any radius r. The mean velocity can be obtained by adding a series of annular rings of thickness dr. Thus, by integrating over the whole cross section and dividing by the total area, the average velocity is found.

$$V = \frac{1}{\pi a^2} \int_0^a u(2\pi r \, dr) \tag{1.34}$$

$$= \frac{\tau_0}{a^3 \mu} \int_0^a (a^2 - r^2) r \, dr \tag{1.35}$$

$$= \frac{\tau_0}{\mu}\left[\frac{a}{2} - \frac{a}{4}\right] = \frac{\tau_0 a}{4\mu} \tag{1.36}$$

Eliminating the shear stress at the wall by using equation (1.27),

$$V = \frac{\rho V^2 a f}{32 g_0 \mu}$$

or

$$f = \frac{64 g_0 \mu}{VD} = \frac{64}{Re} \tag{1.37}$$

where $Re = \dfrac{\rho VD}{g_0 \mu}$ is the common dimensionless Reynolds number. It must be emphasized that this is valid for *laminar flow* only. Here the friction factor is independent of the relative roughness because the viscous forces are dominant.

1.10 Turbulent flow

For higher Reynolds numbers, inertia forces become dominant and the viscous forces are secondary. The velocity distribution is complicated by the random eddy motion within the fluid. Certainly the fluid density is a factor in determining where laminar flow breaks down and turbulent eddies develop. The wall roughness also contributes to disturbing the flow and causing the development of eddies. Thus there can be no distinct division between laminar and turbulent flow on the basis of fluid properties. In general, for a fluid flowing in a duct with Reynolds numbers under 2000, the flow will be laminar; and for Reynolds numbers over about 3500 the flow will be turbulent. At values between 2000 and 3500 for Reynolds numbers the flow may be either laminar or turbulent, depending on other physical factors—particularly the wall roughness.

In the case of turbulent flow, no simple expression for velocity distribution is available as with laminar flow, equation (1.33). Therefore it is not possible to evaluate the friction factor by the same techniques as in the section for laminar flow. For incompressible fluids or for compressible fluids with velocities low in comparison with the speed of sound, a partly theoretical, partly empirical procedure has led to the customary friction-factor chart.

For compressible fluids with supersonic flow, no thorough understanding of friction-factor variation with flow parameters has yet been attained. It has been found that friction factors for the supersonic flow of gases are, in general, lower than the value for incompressible flow at the same Reynolds number. Some investigators have suggested that one-half the value for incompressible flow be used in working in the supersonic regime, although this may not always lead to a conservative answer.

1.11 Configuration and drag losses

It was shown in section 1.7 that, for a fluid flowing in a duct, the pressure drop resulting from friction is given in equation (1.24) as

$$dp = \frac{\rho V^2}{2g_0} f \frac{dx}{D} \tag{1.24}$$

At any bend or elbow, at orifices and T's, at a sudden enlargement or contraction, the flow pattern must undergo extensive adjustments which result in a pressure drop just as in the case of a length of duct with friction. The same is true if a strut or airfoil is placed in a stream of moving air. The air must flow around the solid object and a certain force is established which tends to "hold-back" the fluid. This is the common "drag" force which is so important in airfoil design. The simplest way to account for these forces is to lump them together (for each flow disturbance separately) in terms of a drag coefficient, C_D, such that the pressure loss resulting from the interference is

$$\Delta p = \frac{\rho V^2}{2g_0} C_D$$

It is very convenient to combine the pressure loss from friction with that caused by a flow interruption and,

$$dp = \frac{\rho V^2}{2g_0}\left(f\frac{dx}{D} + dC_D\right) \qquad (1.38)$$

The symbol dC_D is difficult to visualize, since C_D is a discontinuous quantity—existing at the flow interruption and then becoming zero until another interruption is encountered. The symbol dC_D is meant to include all the C_D's in the very short flow element of length dx over which there is the pressure drop dp.

Problems

1.1 A certain pump delivers 10,000 gpm of water when pumping it to a height of 50 ft. What horsepower is required to drive this pump?

1.2 One cu ft of a gas is expanded slowly without friction from 100 psia to 25 psia, according to the relationship $pv^{1.3} = $ const. How much heat must be added or rejected during the expansion in order that the internal energy decrease by 10 Btu?

1.3 Air is flowing in a 3-in. diameter round pipe with a mass flow rate of 15 lb/sec. The temperature is 0°F and the pressure is 100 psia. What is the flow velocity?

1.4 A steel tank with a volume of 100 cu ft contains air at a pressure of 100 psia and a temperature of 200°F. Heat is transferred from the air by radiation until the temperature is 40°F. Find: (*a*) the heat transferred; (*b*) the pressure after heat transfer; (*c*) the entropy change.

1.5 Show that the compressibility factor, Z, for a Van der Waals gas with small density is given by:

$$Z = 1 + \left(b - \frac{a}{RT}\right)\rho$$

1.6 It is frequently desirable to relate pressure, density, and *entropy* instead of the usual p, ρ, T relation. Show that for a perfect gas this relationship may be written:

$$\frac{p}{p_1} = \left(\frac{\rho}{\rho_1}\right)^k e^{(k-1)(s-s_1)/R}$$

1.7 Two parallel plates are 0.04 in. apart. One plate is moving relative to the other at a rate of 2.0 ft/sec. The shear stress on one plate is 0.72 psi.
(*a*) What is the rate of angular deformation of the fluid between the plates?
(*b*) What is the viscosity? (Use consistent engineering units.)

1.8 Find the following viscosities in units of (*i*) lb sec/ft²; (*ii*) lb_m/ft sec.
(*a*) 0.8 centipoise
(*b*) 4.5×10^{-7} slug/ft sec (Air at 200°F)
(*c*) 1.65 lb_m/ft hr (Water at 100°F)

1.9 Air with a density 0.075 lb_m/ft^3 is flowing at 500 ft/sec. The shear stress on the walls of the duct is 0.01 psi. Find the "friction factor" for this flow.

1.10 For laminar flow in a circular duct, show that the average velocity is one-half the maximum velocity (velocity at the center). Show that the velocity at any point can be expressed as a function of the average velocity at that cross section and the radius to that point, as

$$V = 2V_{av}\left(1 - \frac{r^2}{a^2}\right)$$

1.11 Find the pressure loss due to friction in a 12-in. diameter duct, 100 ft long, carrying 1000 cfm of air at 70°F and 14.7 psia. ($f = 0.02$.)

1.12 A pipe 500 ft long is to deliver 50 ft³/min of air (assume 70°F). Assume the pressure at the exit to be atmospheric and determine the minimum size pipe which will give no more than 10 psi pressure loss. (Assume isothermal flow and $f = 0.0275$.)

1.13 A given tail pipe of a turbojet engine is 10 ft long and 1 ft in diameter. Average velocity is 2000 ft/sec. Average temperature is 1200°F. Assume an average pressure of 0.8 atm, and find the friction pressure loss in this tail pipe. ($f = 0.015$.)

1.14 A solid cylinder of radius r is rotated at constant speed, ω rpm, inside a circular tube of radius $r + \delta r$. This arrangement may be used to determine the viscosity of any fluid by filling the space between the solid cylinder and the concentric tube with that fluid and measuring the torque which is exerted on the tube. Develop an expression for the fluid viscosity, μ, in terms of ω, r, δr, and T/l, where T/l is the torque per unit length of the cylinder or tube.

References

1. J. C. Hunaker and B. G. Rightmire: *Engineering Applications of Fluid Mechanics*, McGraw-Hill, New York, 1947.
2. D. A. Mooney: *Mechanical Engineering Thermodynamics*, Prentice-Hall, Englewood Cliffs, N.J., 1953.
3. J. H. Keenan: *Thermodynamics*, John Wiley and Sons, New York, 1941.
4. A. H. Shapiro: *The Dynamics and Thermodynamics of Compressible Fluid Flow*, Vol. I, Ronald Press, New York, 1953.
5. N. A. Hall: *Thermodynamics of Fluid Flow*, Prentice-Hall, Englewood Cliffs, N.J., 1951.
6. L. C. Nelson and E. F. Obert: Generalized *pvT* Properties of Gases, ASME paper No. 53-A-194. *Transactions of the ASME*, Oct. 1954.

2

conservation laws in fluid flow

2.1 Introduction

In Chapter 1, it was pointed out that the analysis of a gas dynamics problem is always based on the use of one or more of the four cited laws governing fluid flow. Each of these four laws is usually stated in such a manner that the definition of a system is inherent in the statement (verbal or mathematical). As defined in thermodynamics (and in the brief review of Chapter 1), a system is a collection of identified matter. It is frequently much more convenient to discuss energy, mass, and velocity changes as they occur in a particular region of space rather than in regard to a particular mass.

This is particularly true in connection with such analyses of moving fluids. Instead of basing the discussion on a *system* of constant mass, it is much easier to use the concept of a *control volume*. A control volume may be defined as any volume in space bounded by a (real or imaginary) control surface. By setting up monitoring stations along the control surface and noting all energy, mass, and momentum as it crosses the surface, it is possible to obtain statements (again, either verbal or mathematical) for the fundamental laws governing fluid flow which are predicated on changes relative to the control volume.

It is the major goal of this chapter to point out how the transformation from an analysis based on a *system* to one based on a *control volume* may be accomplished. In some respects added insight into the physical terms involved can be obtained only through such a procedure. The procedures used in sections 2.2, 2.3, and 2.4 are patterned after those found in Shapiro's *The Dynamics and Thermodynamics of Compressible Fluid Flow*. The treatment here is limited to one-dimensional problems with the hope that this will make it both possible and convenient for the reader to observe and grasp the physical meaning of the changes.

2.2 Conservation of mass; continuity equation

The principle of the conservation of mass states simply that mass may be neither created nor destroyed. Thus, for a fluid *system* which we shall consider, the mass remains constant.

Consider a fluid to be flowing through (or into, or out of, or both) a control volume bounded by a control surface. (See Figure 2.1.) Take as the *system* the fluid within the control volume plus that which will enter the control volume in the next δt interval of time. At time t the system is located in position indicated by the dotted lines in Figure 2.1. At time δt later, the system will have moved so that its boundary is as indicated by

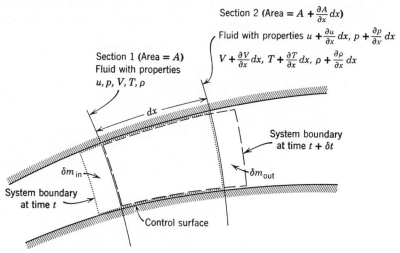

Section 2 (Area $= A + \frac{\partial A}{\partial x} dx$)

Fluid with properties $u + \frac{\partial u}{\partial x} dx$, $p + \frac{\partial p}{\partial x} dx$

Section 1 (Area $= A$)
Fluid with properties
u, p, V, T, ρ

$V + \frac{\partial V}{\partial x} dx$, $T + \frac{\partial T}{\partial x} dx$, $\rho + \frac{\partial \rho}{\partial x} dx$

dx

System boundary
at time $t + \delta t$

δm_{in}

δm_{out}

System boundary
at time t

Control surface

Fig. 2.1 Motion of system relative to a control surface.

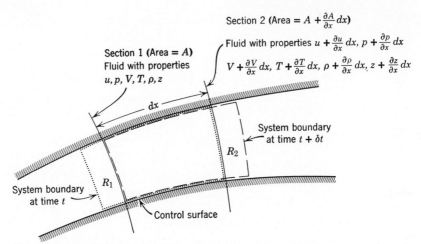

Fig. 2.2 Motion of system relative to a control surface.

Consider a fluid to be flowing through a certain control volume bounded by its control surface. Define a system as the fluid within the control surface, plus the fluid in region R_1. (See Figure 2.2.) Region R_1 contains exactly the mass of fluid that will enter the control volume in the next δt interval of time. At some time later, $t + \delta t$, the system will have moved downstream so that it now fills the space within the control surface, plus filling region R_2.

If the time interval is very short, the properties of the fluid in region R_1 may be considered to be the same as the properties of the fluid as it crosses section 1, and similarly the properties of the fluid in region R_2 may be considered to be the same as the properties of the fluid as it crosses section 2.

Now from the first law, for the system in question,

$$\frac{dE}{dt} = \lim_{\delta t \to 0} \frac{(E_{R2} + E_{\text{cv}})_{t+\delta t} - (E_{R1} + E_{\text{cv}})_t}{\delta t} = \delta \dot{Q} - \delta \dot{W} \quad (2.13)$$

where $\delta \dot{Q} = $ *Rate* of heat addition

$\delta \dot{W} = $ *Rate* of work done

With some rearranging:

$$\delta \dot{Q} - \delta \dot{W} = \lim_{\delta t \to 0} \left[\frac{(E_{\text{cv}})_{t+\delta t} - (E_{\text{cv}})_t}{\delta t} \right] + \lim_{\delta t \to 0} \left[\frac{(E_{R2})_{t+\delta t} - (E_{R1})_t}{\delta t} \right] \quad (2.14)$$

or,

$$\delta\dot{Q} - \delta\dot{W} = \frac{dE_{cv}}{dt}$$

$$+ \lim_{\delta t \to 0} \left[\frac{m_{R2}(u + du) + m_{R2}\dfrac{(V + dV)^2}{2g_0} + \dfrac{m_{R2}g(z + dz)}{g_0}}{\delta t} \right]$$

$$- \lim_{\delta t \to 0} \left[\frac{m_{R1}u + m_{R1}\dfrac{V^2}{2g_0} + \dfrac{m_{R1}gz}{g_0}}{\delta t} \right] \tag{2.15}$$

where m_{R2} is the mass of fluid in region R_2 at time $t + \delta t$

m_{R1} is the mass of fluid in region R_1 at time t.

In the limit as δt becomes extremely small, $m_{R2}/\delta t$ becomes the mass flow rate out of the control volume, and $m_{R1}/\delta t$ is the mass flow rate into the control volume. Then the first law of thermodynamics for our system becomes:

$$\delta\dot{Q} - \delta\dot{W} = \frac{dE_{cv}}{dt} + w_{out}\left[(u + du) + \frac{(V + dV)^2}{2g_0} + g\frac{(z + dz)}{g_0} \right]$$

$$- w_{in}\left[u + \frac{V^2}{2g_0} + \frac{gz}{g_0} \right] \tag{2.16}$$

It is now necessary to break $\delta\dot{W}$ into its several parts. Note that for any system, $\delta W = p\,dV + \delta W_0$, where $p\,dV$ is the system work for a reversible process and δW_0 includes all forms of work other than $p\,dV$. At its upstream boundary, the system has $p\,dV$ work done on it, and the rate at which this work is done is $w_{in}pv$. At its downstream boundary the system does $p\,dV$ work at a rate $w_{out}(p + pd)(v + dv)$. Then the total work rate of the system is

$$\delta\dot{W} = -w_{in}pv + w_{out}pv + w_{out}p\,dv + w_{out}v\,dp + \delta\dot{W}_0 \tag{2.17}$$

where the higher order infinitesimals have been neglected.

Note that all the terms on the right side of equation (2.17), with the exception of the $\delta\dot{W}_0$, represent a part of the work rate of the system which cannot be utilized externally since it is the work required to move the fluid. It is sometimes referred to as "flow work." It should be emphasized that $\delta\dot{W}_0$ is not a $p\,dV$ work and cannot be evaluated by any such technique.

Returning now to the first law, i.e., equation (2.16), and substituting from (2.17):

$$\delta\dot{Q} - \delta\dot{W}_0 = \frac{dE_{cv}}{dt}$$

$$+ w_{out}\left[(u + pv + du + p\,dv + v\,dp) + \frac{(V + dV)^2}{2g_0} + \frac{g(z + dz)}{g_0}\right]$$

$$- w_{in}\left[(u + pv) + \frac{V^2}{2g_0} + \frac{gz}{g_0}\right] \tag{2.18}$$

or, more simply

$$\delta\dot{Q} - \delta\dot{W}_0 = \frac{dE_{cv}}{dt} + w_{out}\left[(h + dh) + \frac{(V + dV)^2}{2g_0} + \frac{g(z + dz)}{g_0}\right]$$

$$- w_{in}\left[h + \frac{V^2}{2g_0} + \frac{gz}{g_0}\right] \tag{2.19}$$

This is the "general energy equation" for a control volume. Although $\delta\dot{Q}$ is the rate at which heat crosses the boundaries of the system, it is evident that as δt approaches zero the system boundaries become identical with the control surface which bounds the control volume. Similarly, $\delta\dot{W}_0$ may be considered to be the rate at which external work crosses the control surface.

In cases where the rate of mass flow is constant, i.e., $w_{in} = w_{out} = w$, equation (2.19) becomes

$$\delta\dot{Q} - \delta\dot{W}_0 = \frac{dE_{cv}}{dt} + w\left(dh + \frac{dV^2}{2g_0} + \frac{g\,dz}{g_0}\right) \tag{2.20}$$

The other condition for steady flow is that conditions are invariant with time. Then $\dfrac{dE_{cv}}{dt}$ becomes zero, and the first law of thermodynamics for a control volume with a fluid passing through it in steady flow is

$$\delta\dot{Q} - \delta\dot{W}_0 = w\left(dh + \frac{dV^2}{2g_0} + \frac{g\,dz}{g_0}\right) \tag{2.21}$$

or dividing by the mass flow rate

$$\delta Q - \delta W_0 = dh + \frac{dV^2}{2g_0} + \frac{g\,dz}{g_0} \tag{2.22}$$

where δQ is the heat addition per unit mass of fluid and δW_0 is the external work done per unit mass of fluid.

The two forms of the "steady-flow energy equation" given by equations (2.21) and (2.22) should be familiar to students from an elementary thermodynamics course. It is of some importance to note that the "steady-flow energy equation" is a special case of the general and classical statement of the first law of thermodynamics for a system. It should be remembered that equation (2.19) is the more general equation for a control volume.

2.4 Momentum equation

Newton's second law of motion is the basis for the dynamics of fluid motion. In essence, this law says that force exerted at a certain instant on a body is equal to the rate of change in momentum of the body at that instant. Consider the body to be a fluid *system*.

As in sections 2.2 and 2.3, define the *system* as the fluid within the control volume, plus that which will enter the control volume in the next δt interval of time. At time $t + \delta t$, the system occupied the control volume plus region R_2 instead of the control volume plus region R_1, as it does at time t. (See Figure 2.3.)

From Newton's second law:

$$\sum F = \frac{1}{g_0} \frac{d}{dt} (mV) \qquad (2.23)$$

The right hand side of the equation can be transformed by considering

$$\frac{d}{dt} (mV) = \lim_{\delta t \to 0} \frac{[(mV)_{R2} + (mV)_{\mathrm{cv}}]_{t+\delta t} - [(mV)_{R1} + (mV)_{\mathrm{cv}}]_t}{\delta t} \qquad (2.24)$$

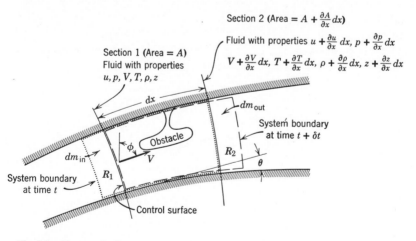

Fig. 2.3 Motion of a fluid system relative to a control surface at any instant of time.

We must recognize that, for very small δt, region R_1 is very small and the fluid in it may be considered to have the same velocity as the fluid crossing section 1. Similarly the fluid in region R_2 will have the same velocity as fluid crossing section 2. Some rearrangement gives:

$$\frac{d}{dt}(mV) = \lim_{\delta t \to 0} \frac{[(mV_{cv}]_{t+\delta t} - [(mV)_{cv}]_t}{t}$$

$$+ \lim_{\delta t \to 0} \frac{m_{R2}(V + dV) - m_{R1}V}{\delta t} \qquad (2.25)$$

Since in the limit as δt becomes extremely small, $m_{R2}/\delta t$ becomes w_{out}, and $m_{R1}/\delta t$ becomes w_{in},

$$\frac{d}{dt}(mV) = \frac{d(mV)_{cv}}{dt} + w_{out}(V + dV) - w_{in}V \qquad (2.26)$$

Equation (2.23) may then be written as

$$\sum F = \frac{1}{g_0}\frac{d(mV)_{cv}}{dt} + \frac{1}{g_0}[w_{out}(V + dV) - w_{in}V] \qquad (2.27)$$

The term $\sum F$ is the algebraic summation of all forces instantaneously exerted on the given system in the direction of flow by the surroundings. These forces may be divided into two classes, i.e., body forces and surface forces. Body forces are those involved with the whole volume or mass of the body (system). These forces involve action at a distance from the system. For example, body forces arise from force fields such as gravitational and electromagnetic.

Consider here that the electromagnetic forces and all other body forces, other than gravitational, are negligible. Therefore, for body forces, only an expression for the gravitational force on the system of Figure 2.3 need be developed. In general the gravitational force is equal to the mass times the acceleration of gravity. Or, in consistent units,

$$F_g = \frac{gm}{g_0}$$

The mass of this system is the average density multiplied by the system volume. The average density may be taken as $\rho + d\rho/2$, and the volume is $(A + dA/2)\,dx$. Then the mass is

$$(\rho + d\rho/2)(A + dA/2)\,dx \approx \rho A\,dx$$

where products involving more than one differential are neglected. Then

$$F_g = \frac{g\rho A\,dx}{g_0}$$

The component of this force in the direction of motion is

$$-\left(\frac{g}{g_0}\, \rho A\, dx\right) \cos \phi$$

and since $dx \cos \phi = dz$:

$$F_g \text{ (in the direction of motion)} = -\frac{g\rho A\, dz}{g_0}$$

Surface forces are those which act on the system at its surface as a result of material outside the system. Surface forces are usually divided into normal forces and shearing forces. For the system in question, the normal forces involved are pressure forces:

pressure force at section $1 = Ap$

pressure force at section $2 = -(A + dA)(p + dp)$

sidewall pressure force (in direction of motion) $= (p + dp/2)\, dA_w \sin \theta$

where dA_w is the side wall area and $dA_w \sin \theta$ is dA. Then the total normal forces are

$$Ap - (A + dA)(p + dp) + (p + dp/2)\, dA = -A\, dp$$

if second order terms, $(dA\, dp)$ are disregarded. The shearing forces are a result of friction and internal drag. From sections 1.7 and 1.11 these are:

$$\underset{\text{(In direction of motion)}}{\text{Force}} = -\frac{A\rho V^2}{2g_0}\, f \frac{dx}{D} - \frac{A\rho V^2}{2g_0}\, dC_D$$

Even though the final term above is written in terms of a dC_D, it should be pointed out that C_D is not a continuous function. When an equation involving this term is integrated between two points in the fluid stream there may or may not be any flow interruptions. Hence this term may or may not be required in the equation. In general this integration can be performed by including a separate integrated term, $\dfrac{A\rho V^2}{2g_0}\, C_D$, for each discontinuity.

Adding all the surface forces and the gravitational force (which is usually small when applied to gases), equation (2.27) may be written:

$$-A\, dp - \frac{A\rho V^2}{2g_0}\left(f \frac{dx}{D} + dC_D\right) - \frac{g}{g_0}\, A\rho\, dz$$
$$= \frac{1}{g_0}\frac{d(mV)_{\text{cv}}}{dt} + \frac{1}{g_0}\left[w_{\text{out}}(V + dV) - w_{\text{in}}V\right] \quad (2.28)$$

This is the most general one-dimensional form of the momentum equation for a control volume. In its use, it is usually found convenient to use one of the specialized forms which follow.

is sometimes called the external entropy change), and ds_i is the internal entropy change caused by irreversibility in the process.

$$ds_e = \frac{\delta Q}{T} \tag{2.36}$$

and

$$ds_i \geq 0 \tag{2.37}$$

where the equality holds for reversible process and the inequality for irreversible processes. The nature of the internal entropy increase will be apparent in subsequent paragraphs.

The enthalpy change of a fluid may now be expressed from equation (1.7) as

$$dh = T \, ds_e + T \, ds_i + \frac{1}{\rho} \, dp \tag{2.38}$$

The steady-flow energy equation (2.22) may be written for a mass flow of 1 lb/sec

$$dh + \frac{d(V^2)}{2g_0} + \frac{g \, dz}{g_0} = \delta Q - \delta W_0$$

For no external work, and substituting (2.38) into the energy equation,

$$T \, ds_e + T \, ds_i + \frac{1}{\rho} \, dp + \frac{d(V^2)}{2g_0} + \frac{g \, dz}{g_0} = \delta Q \tag{2.39}$$

From equation (2.36), $T \, ds_e = \delta Q$, so (2.39) becomes

$$dp + \frac{\rho \, dV^2}{2g_0} + \frac{g\rho \, dz}{g_0} + \rho T \, ds_i = 0 \tag{2.40}$$

This is sometimes called the pressure-energy equation, but it is actually a more generalized statement of the common Bernoulli equation. If the flow process is reversible, $ds_i = 0$; and

$$dp + \frac{\rho \, dV^2}{2g_0} + \frac{g\rho \, dz}{g_0} = 0 \tag{2.41}$$

The term $\rho T \, ds_i$ may be thought of as the loss of pressure resulting from irreversibility, and with an ideal flow (reversible), the simpler equation (2.41) results.

It is interesting to compare the generalized Bernoulli equation (2.40) with the momentum equation developed in section 2.3. Equation (2.34) is repeated here for easy reference.

$$dp + \frac{g\rho \, dz}{g_0} + \frac{1}{2g_0} \rho V^2 \left(f \frac{dx}{D} + dC_D \right) + \frac{\rho \, dV^2}{2g_0} = 0 \tag{2.34}$$

From a comparison of equation (2.34) with (2.40), it is seen that

$$\rho T \, ds_i = \frac{1}{2g_0} \, \rho V^2 \left(f \frac{dx}{D} + dC_D \right) \tag{2.42}$$

Thus the pressure loss due to irreversibility is exactly the same as the pressure loss because of friction and flow interruptions.

Frequently it is convenient to refer to an internal entropy coefficient defined so that

$$\rho T \, ds_i = \frac{1}{2g_0} \, \rho V^2 \left(f \frac{dx}{D} + dC_D \right) = \frac{\rho V^2}{2g_0} \, dC_s \tag{2.43}$$

Then the momentum equation for steady flow may be written in terms of the entropy coefficient C_s as

$$dp + \frac{g\rho \, dz}{g_0} + \frac{\rho \, dV^2}{2g_0} + \frac{\rho V^2}{2g_0} \, dC_s = 0 \tag{2.44}$$

2.6 Stagnation states

When discussing the properties of a fluid which is in motion, it is necessary to have a reference state on which to base the discussion. Frequently it is convenient to use the concept of stagnation enthalpy:

$$h_0 = h + V^2/2g_0 + gz/g_0 \tag{2.45}$$

or for cases where elevation changes are small:

$$h_0 = h + V^2/2g_0$$

The stagnation enthalpy may be thought of as the value of the enthalpy which would result when the elevation and the velocity are reduced to zero.

The idea of stagnation state is probably best seen on an h–s diagram. (See Figure 2.4.)

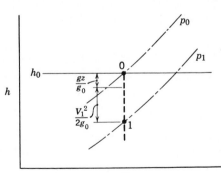

Fig. 2.4 Mollier chart, showing relation between state point and the corresponding stagnation state.

2.5 Thirty pounds of air are contained in a tank at a pressure of 15 psia and a temperature of 545°R. There is a large hole in the tank so that the pressure inside the tank is always kept equal to that of the atmosphere (15 psia) by allowing mass to pass in or out through the hole. If heat is added at the rate of 500 Btu/min, find the temperature of the air in the tank after 1 min.

2.6 If the heat transfer of problem 2.5 is in the opposite direction, i.e., cooling the contents of the tank at a steady rate of 500 Btu/min, what is the temperature after one minute?

2.7 In rocketry, all the fuel and oxidizing agents are contained within the rocket initially and after combustion they are accelerated out the tail pipe. For 1 lb/sec being discharged at 5000 ft/sec, find the thrust on the rocket.

2.8 The general Bernoulli equation frequently must be integrated to be of maximum utility. In this integration it is convenient to use a mean density such that:

$$\rho_m = \frac{p_2 - p_1}{\displaystyle\int_1^2 \frac{dp}{\rho}}$$

Then the Bernoulli equation may be written:

$$\frac{1}{\rho_m}\int_1^2 dp + \frac{1}{2g_0}\int_1^2 dV^2 + \frac{g}{g_0}\int_1^2 dz + \frac{V^2}{2g_0}\int_1^2 dC_s = 0$$

In this equation each term may be more easily integrated. For a perfect gas, $p = \rho R T$, with an isentropic flow such that $p = a\rho^k$, show that the mean density is given by:

$$\rho_m = \frac{p_2 - p_1}{c_p(T_2 - T_1)}$$

2.9 Show that the mean density as defined in problem 2.8 is:

$$\rho_m = \frac{n-1}{n}\left(\frac{\rho_2^{\,n} - \rho_1^{\,n}}{\rho_2^{\,n-1} - \rho_2^{\,n-1}}\right)$$

for a fluid whose state varies along a general polytropic path such that

$$p = a + b\rho^n$$

2.10 Steam flows in a pipe with a gravity head of 50 ft at a velocity of 300 ft/sec. The pressure is 300 psia and the temperature is 500°F.
(a) Find the difference between the static and stagnation enthalpies.
(b) Find the stagnation pressure.
(c) Find the stagnation temperature.

2.11 The atmospheric temperature is 0°F at the altitude where a turbojet aircraft is flying at 600 mph. Find the stagnation temperature entering this aircraft.

2.12 Air flows through a ventilating system in which the sum of several loss coefficients or drag coefficients is 5.0. The air is at a temperature of 70°F and flows at 40 ft/sec. Assume the pressure varies from atmospheric by a negligible amount and compute the internal entropy increase.

References

1. A. H. Shapiro: *The Dynamics and Thermodynamics of Compressible Fluid Flow*, Vol. I, Ronald Press, New York, 1953.
2. N. A. Hall: *Thermodynamics of Fluid Flow*, Prentice-Hall, Englewood Cliffs, N.J., 1951.

3

wave motion, Mach number

3.1 Pressure waves and sonic velocity

A small pressure wave moving through a fluid is propagated by the elastic properties of the fluid. The vibration or movement of a solid may set up such a small pressure variation, which is transmitted through a fluid and which may eventually reach our ear. The vibration caused in the ear results in our hearing a "sound." The transmission of sound through any fluid is accomplished by the motion of small pressure waves in the fluid. Hence the velocity with which sound is transmitted is precisely the same as the velocity of small pressure fluctuations and is determined by the elastic properties of the fluid. The sonic velocity is frequently taken to be an additional state property of the fluid. The advantages of this approach will be apparent in later chapters.

It should be kept in mind that only small (weak) pressure waves are propagated with sonic velocity. Large, intense pressure waves, usually called

42

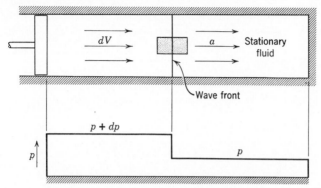

Fig. 3.1 Propagation of a small pressure wave.

shock waves, may have velocities several times the acoustic velocity. As shown below, the sonic velocity is calculated on the assumption of a reversible isentropic process, and this assumption is quite good for sound waves (weak or small pressure waves). For large and strong waves, the assumption of reversibility cannot be made and it will be shown later that these waves must move with a higher velocity. Consider a body of fluid with a pressure impulse moving through it with a velocity, a, as in Figure 3.1. The pressure to the left of the discontinuity is dp higher than the pressure to the right. The fluid to the left must be moving toward the discontinuity with some velocity dV in order for the wave front to move into the stationary fluid with velocity a. Now consider a control volume such as the shaded section along the wave front in Figure 3.1. If the coordinate system is chosen so that it moves with the control volume, then relative to this coordinate system the fluid to the right of the wave front moves toward the left with a velocity a and the fluid to the left of the wave front moves with a velocity $a - dV$. (See Figure 3.2.)

Since there are no elevation changes and no friction or flow obstructions (hence isentropic conditions are properly assumed), the steady flow momentum equation may be written for this control volume as:

$$A\, dp + \frac{w}{g_0}(-dV) = 0 \qquad (3.1)$$

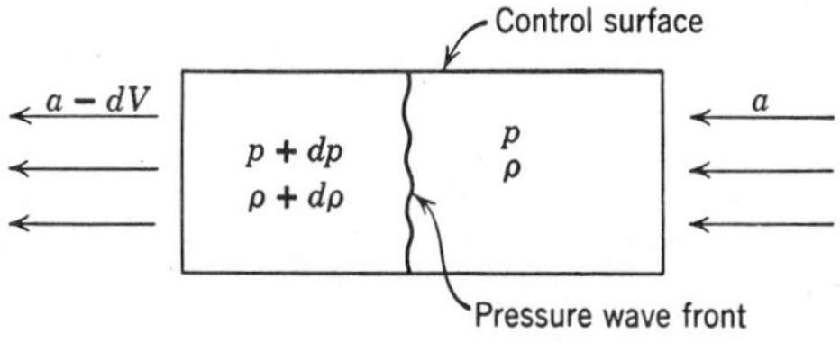

Fig. 3.2 Control volume for flow through a pressure wave.

but from the continuity equation for steady flow

$$w = \rho A a \tag{3.2}$$

Then the momentum equation becomes

$$dp = \frac{a\rho \, dV}{g_0} \tag{3.3}$$

Since $\rho A a = w = (\rho + d\rho)A(a - dV)$

$$1 = \left(1 + \frac{d\rho}{\rho}\right)\left(1 - \frac{dV}{a}\right)$$

and if the second order term is neglected,

$$\frac{d\rho}{\rho} = \frac{dV}{a} \tag{3.4}$$

Substituting into equation (3.3) for dV as obtained from equation (3.4)

$$dp = \frac{a^2 \, d\rho}{g_0} \tag{3.5}$$

or solving for a, the acoustic velocity is

$$a = \sqrt{g_0 \left(\frac{\partial p}{\partial \rho}\right)_s} \tag{3.6}$$

where the derivative, $dp/d\rho$, is indicated as a partial derivative with the entropy held constant because, for very small variations in pressure (and other properties), the process is essentially isentropic, and the pressure-density relation across an acoustic wave is the same as that for an isentropic compression.

In an isentropic process for a perfect gas, the relation between pressure and density is

$$p = (\text{const.})(\rho^k) \tag{3.7}$$

Taking the logarithm of both sides and differentiating

$$\frac{dp}{p} = k \frac{d\rho}{\rho} \tag{3.8}$$

Then

$$\left(\frac{\partial p}{\partial \rho}\right)_s = k \frac{p}{\rho} = kRT \tag{3.9}$$

and the expression for the acoustic velocity in a perfect gas may be written

$$a = \sqrt{kg_0 RT} \tag{3.10}$$

For any fluid with a constant density, the pressure may change by any amount whatever with still no density change. Therefore, in an incompressible fluid, the sonic velocity must be infinite. Actual liquids are not truly constant density fluids, as was pointed out in Chapter 1. With water, for example, the little change in density makes the sonic velocity less than infinite but still very large compared with fluid velocities. In common liquids the speed of sound is of the order of 5000 ft/sec.

3.2 Acoustic waves

For a true wave the conditions are constantly changing with time and the momentum equation in the form of (2.30) must be used.

$$\frac{1}{\rho}\frac{\partial p}{\partial x} + \frac{1}{g_0}\frac{\partial V}{\partial t} + \frac{V}{g_0}\frac{\partial V}{\partial x} = 0 \tag{3.11}$$

Also, from continuity (including the variation of density with time):

$$\frac{\partial \rho}{\partial t} + V\frac{\partial \rho}{\partial x} + \rho\frac{\partial V}{\partial x} = 0 \tag{3.12}$$

The term $\partial A/\partial x$ in equation (2.8) may be considered zero for fluid motion associated with waves moving through a medium. Equations (3.11) and (3.12) describe the conditions which must hold for any point on a wave, as in Figure 3.3, being propagated into a stationary fluid.

Equations (3.11) and (3.12) are extremely difficult to solve because they are nonlinear. They contain a mixture of partial derivatives of the two variables ρ and V, and products of these partial derivatives and the variables themselves. (Note that for small, adiabatic waves p is not independent of ρ, and hence the equations may be transformed to include only ρ and V.) While dealing with these equations for the most general case is quite difficult, there are some conditions for which these equations can be made linear and then a solution obtained.

Let it be assumed that only "small perturbations" are present. That is, the variations in each fluid property are small compared with the value of

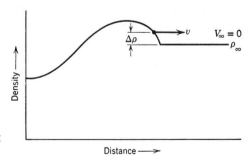

Fig. 3.3 Simple wave propagating into stationary fluid.

To be sure that this is truly a solution, it is necessary to differentiate twice with respect to both x and t:

$$\frac{\partial^2 \left(\frac{\Delta\rho}{\rho_\infty}\right)}{\partial x^2} = f_1''(x - a_\infty t) + f_2''(x + a_\infty t)$$

and

$$\frac{\partial^2 \left(\frac{\Delta\rho}{\rho_\infty}\right)}{\partial t^2} = a_\infty{}^2 f_1''(x - a_\infty t) + a_\infty{}^2 f_2''(x + a_\infty t)$$

Thus equation (3.23) is satisfied and (3.25) must be a solution.

To investigate the nature of this solution, consider the two parts separately. Then

$$\left(\frac{\Delta\rho}{\rho_\infty}\right)_1 = f_1(x - a_\infty t) \tag{3.26}$$

and at time, $t = 0$, the relative density change is

$$\left(\frac{\Delta\rho}{\rho_\infty}\right)_{1,\, t=0} = f_1(x)$$

and this defines the shape of the wave. When $t \neq 0$, the shape must be the same but the wave is displaced in space by an amount $a_\infty t$. (See Figure 3.4.) Thus it is evident that the wave defined by $f_1(x - a_\infty t)$ moves in the positive x-direction and hence is called a rightward propagating wave.

Similarly the second part of the general solution in equation (3.25),

$$\left(\frac{\Delta\rho}{\rho_\infty}\right)_2 = f_2(x + a_\infty t) \tag{3.27}$$

describes a wave whose shape is defined by the function f_2 and which is propagated in the negative x-direction and thus is a leftward propagating wave. The complete solution of the wave equation is a combination of

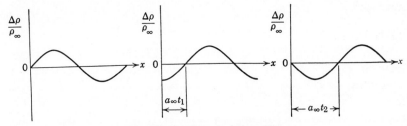

Fig. 3.4 Simple wave propagation.

these two simple waves. If the leftward propagating wave is superposed with the rightward propagating wave, the result is the most general acoustic wave.

Consideration of the foregoing also leads to the following three observations:

1. The velocity of propagation of either the leftward or the rightward propagating acoustic wave is evidently a_∞ which was initially used to replace $g_0 \sqrt{\left(\dfrac{\partial p}{\partial \rho}\right)_{s,\infty}}$ and, therefore, is consistent with the previous section in which the acoustic velocity was determined by a less elegant analysis.

2. The velocity increment has a similar solution

$$v = f_3(x - a_\infty t) + f_4(x + a_\infty t) \tag{3.28}$$

and if equations (3.21) and (3.22) are to be satisfied, it is required that

and

$$a_\infty^2 f_1' + a_\infty^2 f_2' - a_\infty f_3' + a_\infty f_4' = 0 \tag{3.29}$$

$$-a_\infty f_1' + a_\infty f_2' + f_3' + f_4' = 0 \tag{3.30}$$

Multiplying equation (3.30) by a_∞ and subtracting from (3.29)

which is satisfied if

$$a_\infty^2 f_1' = a_\infty f_3'$$

and similarly,

$$f_3 = a_\infty f_1 \tag{3.31}$$

$$f_4 = -a_\infty f_2 \tag{3.32}$$

This leads to the conclusion that not only is the velocity increment propagated with a speed of a_∞, but also the magnitude of the velocity increment is exactly a_∞ times the magnitude of the relative density change.

3. If lines of constant $\Delta\rho/\rho_\infty$ (or of constant v) are plotted on an x–t plane, these lines are found to be straight, thus having constant slope. Further, the value of this constant slope is either $+a_\infty$ or $-a_\infty$. For $\Delta\rho/\rho_\infty =$ const., $x = \pm a_\infty t$. Here the positive sign is for the rightward propagating simple wave, and the negative sign is for the leftward propagating simple wave. These lines of constant $\Delta\rho/\rho_\infty$ are called characteristics of the wave equation. Figure 3.5 shows the characteristics for both leftward and rightward propagating waves.

3.3 Finite waves

In the previous section it was necessary to assume that the wave amplitude was small in order to reduce the general equations of motion to a linear form which could be handled by ordinary methods. With waves of finite amplitude the assumption of "small perturbations" is not possible and the solution of the resulting nonlinear equations requires mathematics much more involved than what seems proper for this book. It should be

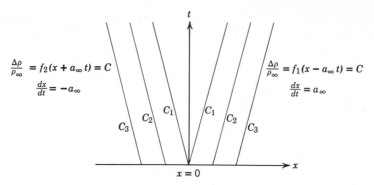

Fig. 3.5 Characteristics of the wave equation.

noted that the solution of the nonlinear equations was first presented by Riemann in 1860.

Instead of the detailed mathematical procedures, it will suffice here to think in terms of physical observations. Along a finite wave, the regions of higher density (and higher temperature) must move with a velocity greater than the sonic velocity in the undisturbed fluid. Similarly, the regions of lower density must move with a velocity less than the sonic velocity in the undisturbed fluid.

To illustrate the foregoing remarks, consider the finite compression wave in Figure 3.6 to be made up of several smaller (considered infinitesimal) waves or steps. In Figure 3.6, the first step increase in density is propagated to the right with a velocity equal to the acoustic velocity at that point along the wave, i.e., a_1. The second step increase is propagated with a velocity equal to the acoustic velocity at that point along the wave, say, $a_1 + \delta a$. This must be a greater velocity since the density is greater (and hence temperature and pressure also, for an adiabatic wave). The third step is propagated with a velocity $a_1 + 2\delta a$, and so on. Thus the portion of the wave at higher density tends to overtake the portion at lower density. The net effect is to steepen the wave until the temperature gradients and velocity gradients become so large that heat transfer and momentum transfer between fluid elements become appreciable and, at the point where these effects just balance the steepening tendency, the wave shape becomes fixed. In nature this balance between the diffusive effects and the steepening effect does not result until the increase in density (and other fluid properties) is quite sharp. A finite discontinuity then moves through the undisturbed fluid, and this is known as a shock wave. Shock waves are discussed in greater detail in Chapters 7 and 9.

In contrast, a finite expansion wave tends to flatten, as shown in Figure 3.7. The first step decrease is propagated with a velocity a_1, the second

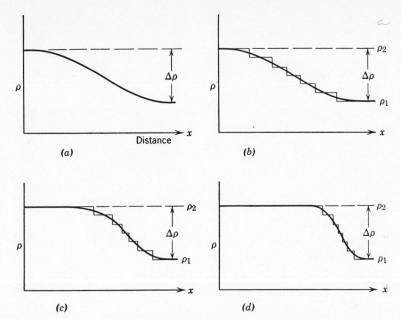

Fig. 3.6 Compression wave moving in the positive x-direction. (*a*) Wave form. (*b*) Wave made up of small steps at time $t = t_0$. (*c*) Wave at time $t = t_1$. (*d*)Wave at time $t = t_2$.

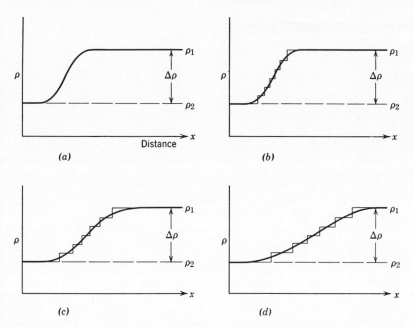

Fig. 3.7 Simple expansion wave moving in the positive x-direction. (*a*) Wave form. (*b*) Wave made up of finite steps at time $t = t_0$. (*c*) Wave at time $t = t_1$. (*d*) Wave at time $t = t_2$.

with a velocity $a_1 - \delta a$, the third with a velocity $a_1 - 2\delta a$, and so on. The first step tends to "run-away" from the rest of the wave. The velocity and temperature gradients within the wave are decreased and the assumption of isentropic conditions for a finite expansion wave can be made with no resulting difficulty. There can never be a stationary wave form resulting from a balance in steepening and diffusive effects; hence, there can be no "expansion shocks." This will be pointed out in more detail in Chapter 7.

The similarity of the waves discussed here and waves in two-dimensional, high velocity flow will be apparent in Chapters 9 and 10.

3.4 Mach number

The properties of a compressible fluid flow may be shown to depend on the ratio of the fluid stream velocity to the sonic velocity. Therefore, it is convenient to define the *Mach number* to be equal to this ratio.

$$M = \frac{V}{a} \tag{3.33}$$

where a is the velocity of sound at the local temperature and density of the stream. The sonic velocity is not a constant—this point is evident from consideration of equation (3.10)—but varies with the thermodynamic state of the fluid. Thus it is possible for the velocity to remain constant even with a change in Mach number.

In the previous sections, waves were studied as they propagated through a stationary medium. Under the conditions of various Mach numbers, the wave patterns and, hence, the fluid properties are found to have distinct differences. It is now most essential to keep in mind the distinction between the fluid velocity, V, and the wave velocity, a (for sound waves). Consider a stationary object emitting small pressure impulses (sound) as a fluid moves over it with various velocities, as in Figure 3.8.

Figure 3.8(a) shows the situation with the fluid moving very slowly or not at all. In this case the pressure impulses spread uniformly in all directions. This is the case for any fluid with a very large sonic velocity, i.e., incompressible fluid. When the Mach number is small, either the velocity may be small or the acoustic velocity may be large, and for either case the fluid may be considered to be incompressible for many calculations.

Figure 3.8(b) indicates that for Mach numbers less than unity, but not negligible, the pressure impulses are felt in all directions but the intensity is not symmetrical.

Figure 3.8(c) is the case where the fluid velocity is the same as the acoustic velocity. Here the infinitesimal pressure wave can never move

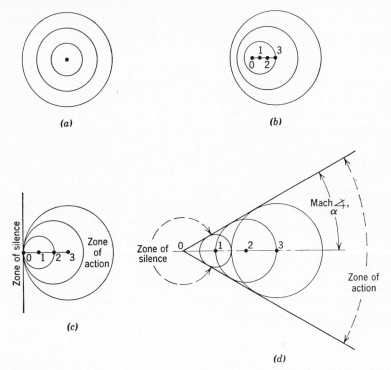

Fig. 3.8

(a) Incompressible Fluid

$$\frac{V}{a} = 0$$

(b) Subsonic Flow

$$\frac{V}{a} = \frac{1}{2}$$

1. Position of object (with reference to fluid bulk) 1 sec ago.
2. Position of object 2 sec ago.
3. Position of object 3 sec ago.

(c) Transonic Flow

$$\frac{V}{a} = 1$$

1. Position of object 1 sec ago.
2. Position of object 2 sec ago.
3. Position of object 3 sec ago.

(d) Supersonic Flow

$$\frac{V}{a} = 2$$

1. Position of object 1 sec ago.
2. Position of object 2 sec ago.
3. Position of object 3 sec ago.

upstream against the fluid stream, since the fluid is moving to the right at exactly the same velocity as the pressure impulse moves through the fluid.

Figure 3.8(d) indicates that the situation is entirely different at fluid velocities when the Mach number is greater than unity. All the pressure mpulses are limited to a cone. The pressure signals cannot be observed upstream since the cone has its apex at the stationary source of the impulses and the orientation is such that the apex points into the flow. This cone is called the Mach cone; inside the cone is the zone of action, and outside is the zone of silence.

Based on Figure 3.8 and on the assumption that disturbances in the fluid are small, i.e., acoustic waves, von Kármán (in Ref. 1) postulated the following three rules:

(*a*) *The rule of forbidden signals*

It is evident that slight pressure changes, produced in the moving fluid by a stationary source, cannot reach points upstream of the body if the velocity of flow is greater than the speed of sound. Similarly, if the fluid is stagnant and the body moving with a velocity greater than sonic, the pressure fluctuation cannot reach points ahead of the body. In this respect there is a fundamental contrast between subsonic and supersonic flow.

(*b*) *The zone of action and the zone of silence*

A small source in a stream of fluid with supersonic velocity produces effects only on points that lie on or inside the Mach cone extending downstream from the source. Similarly in a stagnant fluid, conditions at an arbitrary point can be influenced by disturbances which are moving with supersonic speed only if the disturbance is on or in a cone of the same vertex angle extending upstream from the chosen arbitrary point.

(*c*) *The rule of concentrated action*

This rule concerns the distribution of the pressure effect in the fluid relative to the body. The distance between the circles (spheres in three dimensions) which represent pressure impulses in Figure 3.8 is an inverse measurement of the strength of the pressure disturbance in that region. The closer the circles are, the stronger the wave in that region; and the farther apart they are, the weaker the impulse becomes. For the case of incompressible flow (or stationary fluid and source), the field is symmetrical about the source. For subsonic flow, the field is unsymmetrical; and for supersonic flow, the pressure disturbance is concentrated in the vicinity of the Mach cone which bounds the zone of action.

The semi-angle of the Mach cone is called the Mach angle. This angle is seen from Figure 3.8(*d*) to be

$$\alpha = \text{arc sin } \frac{1}{M} \qquad (3.34)$$

Note that the Mach angle cannot exist for subsonic flow. (It is imaginary.) The concept of Mach angle is extremely valuable in analyzing two-dimensional supersonic flow.

The lines which bound the Mach cone, having an inclination of x with the direction of flow, are called *Mach lines*, and in some of the literature, Mach waves. In this book the word *wave* will be used only to denote a variation in a fluid property, and since the fluid properties are unchanged (if the source of the impulses becomes vanishingly small, there will be no stimulus to change any flow property or pattern and yet the analysis can follow the same development), the term *Mach line* is preferable to Mach wave. This new concept will prove to be a valuable tool in later chapters.

In a plane (two-dimensional flow) there are two lines emanating from any point in the flow. Each of the lines makes an angle α with the streamline and, if we look down the streamline, it is evident that one line runs to the left and the other to the right. Consequently, it is possible to refer to left-running Mach lines and right-running Mach lines. These lines are *characteristic* of the flow, or of the mathematics describing the flow, and hence have been given the name *characteristics*. Notice that these characteristics are analogous to the characteristics of the wave equation discussed in section 3.2. A characteristic pattern in the two-dimensional flow (x–y plane) will have the same appearance as the characteristics of the one dimensional flow in the x–t plane. Just as the characteristics in section 3.2 had a constant slope (straight lines) as long as the acoustic velocity was constant in the undisturbed fluid, the characteristics in two-dimensional flow are straight lines as long as the flow is at a constant Mach number, and become curves or change direction with changing Mach numbers.

In three-dimensional flow there are an infinite number of Mach lines. These Mach lines define the Mach cone, and any straight line in the surface of the Mach cone must be a Mach line.

3.5 One-dimensional steady flow equations in terms of Mach number

Mach number is such an important parameter in controlling the pattern that it will be very convenient to be able to use the fundamental equations developed in Chapter 2 with Mach number as one of the primary variables rather than velocity. For *steady flow conditions*, it is relatively easy to obtain these valuable relations as shown in the succeeding paragraphs.

The continuity equation

$$w = \rho A V \tag{3.35}$$

may be expressed as

$$w = \frac{pAV}{RT} \cdot \sqrt{\frac{kg_0}{kg_0}} \tag{3.36}$$

However, $\sqrt{kg_0 RT} = a$, and $V/a = M$. Therefore,

$$w = \frac{pAM}{\sqrt{\dfrac{RT}{kg_0}}} \tag{3.37}$$

which is the continuity equation for a perfect gas expressed in terms of Mach number.

The energy equation

$$dh_0 = \delta Q - \delta W_0 \qquad (3.38)$$

may also be expressed in terms of Mach number

$$d\left[h + \frac{V^2(kRT)}{2g_0(kRT)}\right] = \delta Q - \delta W_0 \qquad (3.39)$$

$$d\left[h + \frac{k-1}{2} M^2 \frac{kR}{k-1} T\right] = \delta Q - \delta W_0 \qquad (3.40)$$

$$d\left[h\left(1 + \frac{k-1}{2} M^2\right)\right] = \delta Q - \delta W_0 \qquad (3.41)$$

$$\left(1 + \frac{k-1}{2} M^2\right) dh + \frac{k-1}{2} h\, dM^2 = \delta Q - \delta W_0 \qquad (3.42)$$

The steady flow momentum equation, neglecting the gravity forces, is

$$dp + \frac{\rho}{2g_0} dV^2 + \frac{\rho V^2}{2g_0}\left(f\frac{dx}{D} + dC_D\right) = 0 \qquad (3.43)$$

Dividing by pressure,

$$\frac{dp}{p} + \frac{k}{2} \frac{dV^2}{kg_0RT} + \frac{k}{2} M^2\left(f\frac{dx}{D} + dC_D\right) = 0 \qquad (3.44)$$

The second term,

$$\frac{k}{2} \frac{dV^2}{kg_0RT} = \frac{kd(a^2M^2)}{2kg_0RT} = \frac{k}{2} dM^2 + \frac{k}{2} M^2 \frac{dT}{T} \qquad (3.45)$$

Substituting in equation (3.44), the momentum equation is

$$\frac{dp}{p} + \frac{k}{2} dM^2 + \frac{k}{2} M^2 \frac{dT}{T} + \frac{k}{2} M^2\left(f\frac{dx}{D} + dC_D\right) = 0 \qquad (3.46)$$

It is also desirable to express the stagnation properties in terms of Mach number. By definition, omitting the gravity term,

$$h_0 - h = \frac{V^2}{2g_0} \qquad (3.47)$$

Since,

$$h_0 - h = c_p(T_0 - T) = \frac{kR}{k-1}(T_0 - T) \qquad (3.48)$$

equation (3.47) becomes

$$(T_0 - T) = \frac{k-1}{kR} \frac{V^2}{2g_0} \tag{3.49}$$

$$\left(\frac{T_0}{T} - 1\right) = \frac{k-1}{2}\left(\frac{V^2}{kg_0RT}\right) = \frac{k-1}{2}\frac{V^2}{a^2} \tag{3.50}$$

$$T_0 = T\left(1 + \frac{k-1}{2}M^2\right) \tag{3.51}$$

Since there must be an isentropic process between the static state and the stagnation state,

$$\frac{p_0}{p} = \left(\frac{T_0}{T}\right)^{k/k-1} \tag{3.52}$$

and

$$p_0 = p\left(1 + \frac{k-1}{2}M^2\right)^{k/k-1} \tag{3.53}$$

Problems

3.1 Across a given small compression pulse the pressure rises 0.1 psia. What is the velocity of the air following this pulse, if the pulse is moving into still air at 14.7 psia and 70°F?

3.2 Calculate the pressure differential on the two sides of a pressure wave in air, if the air velocity changes by 20 ft/sec. Assume the air to be at 14.7 psia and 40°F.

3.3 Show that the maximum velocity that can result from the flow of a perfect gas from a reservoir is

$$V_m = \sqrt{\frac{2}{k-1}}\, a_0$$

where a_0 is the acoustic velocity in the gas at reservoir conditions. Is the corresponding Mach number $\sqrt{\dfrac{2}{k-1}}$? Explain.

3.4 Assuming air to be a perfect gas, show that for the acoustic velocity to be expressed in feet per second,

$$a \approx 49.02\sqrt{T}$$

3.5 Find the value of the constant C in the equation,

$$a = C\sqrt{T}$$

in order that the acoustic velocity be given in miles per hour for air.

3.6 The compressibility of a substance is defined in thermodynamics as

$$\beta = -\frac{1}{v}\left(\frac{\partial v}{\partial p}\right)_T$$

For common liquids $\left(\dfrac{\partial p}{\partial \rho}\right)_s \approx \left(\dfrac{\partial p}{\partial \rho}\right)_T$. Show that for this condition, $a = \sqrt{\dfrac{g_0}{\rho\beta}}$.

3.7 Using the expression $\left(\dfrac{\partial p}{\partial \rho}\right)_s = k\left(\dfrac{\partial p}{\partial \rho}\right)_T$, develop an expression for the acoustic velocity in a van der Waals gas.

3.8 For a perfect gas, show that the relative pressure change across a compression pulse is

$$\frac{dp}{p} = k\frac{dV}{a}$$

and that the relative temperature change is

$$\frac{dT}{T} = (k-1)\frac{dV}{a}$$

3.9 Air at 80°F is flowing at a Mach number of 1.9. (*a*) Find the air velocity in feet per second. (*b*) What is the Mach angle?

3.10 What is the velocity in feet per second of 40°F air which gives a Mach angle of 30°?

3.11 Show that

$$\rho = \rho_\infty[1 + 0.01\sin(x - a_\infty T) + 0.02\cos 2(x - a_\infty t)]$$

is a solution to the acoustic wave equation.

3.12 Is $v = 50e^{a_\infty t - x} - 25e^{2(x - a_\infty t)}$ a solution to the acoustic wave equation?

3.13 Reynolds number and Mach number are both dimensionless numbers, depending on velocity and fluid properties. The ratio Re/M must be a function of the fluid properties since the velocity is linear in each. Find this ratio for air flowing in a circular duct 1 ft in diameter with a temperature and pressure of 70°F and 14.7 psia, respectively.

3.14 The Mach number of the air leaving a compressor rotor in a turbojet engine is 1.15. The stagnation pressure is 50 psia, and the stagnation temperature is 800°R. (*a*) What is the static temperature, and (*b*) what is the static pressure?

3.15 For flow in a wind tunnel at a Mach number of 5.0, what must be the ratio (*a*) p/p_0, and (*b*) T/T_0?

References

1. Th. von Kármán: Supersonic Aerodynamics—Principles and Applications, *J. Aero. Sci.*, **14**, No. 7 (1947).

2. A. H. Shapiro: *The Dynamics and Thermodynamics of Compressible Fluid Flow*, Vol. I, Ronald Press, New York, 1953.
3. H. W. Liepmann and A. Roshko: *Elements of Gasdynamics*, John Wiley and Sons, New York, 1957.
4. Georg Joos: *Theoretical Physics*, 2nd ed., Hafner, New York, 1950.
5. A. G. Webster: *Partial Differential Equations of Mathematical Physics*, Dover, New York, 1955.
6. A. B. Cambel and B. H. Jennings: *Gas Dynamics*, McGraw-Hill, New York, 1958.
7. Newman A. Hall: *Thermodynamics of Fluid Flow*, Prentice-Hall, Englewood Cliffs, N.J., 1951.

4

force balance and thrust

4.1 Introduction

In many engineering problems involving compressible fluid flow, particularly in the area of jet propulsion, it is necessary to calculate the forces exerted by the fluid stream on the solid boundaries confining that stream.

In a jet propulsion device in steady motion, the propulsive force, or *thrust*, is the sum of all the forces exerted on the device by the fluid flowing through or around the device. In general, this total force against solid boundaries is the sum of the pressure forces on the confining walls plus the friction and drag forces. In the absence of friction and drag forces, the propulsive thrust can be evaluated by integrating the local fluid pressure over the entire surface on which it acts. Usually it is easier to obtain the propulsive force by carefully analyzing the fluid flow and determining the forces required for certain accelerations or decelerations.

4.2 Calculation of propulsive forces

As a fluid moves through or over a solid body it has certain forces exerted on it and the momentum equation describes the balance between these forces and the momentum change of the fluid. All forces exerted by the solid boundaries on the fluid are countered by equal forces exerted in the opposite direction by the fluid on the solid boundaries. The total force exerted by the fluid against such solid boundaries is the force tending to move or propel the solid body. This force is called the *thrust* produced by the fluid.

The net force on the fluid must be in the direction of flow, if the fluid is accelerating (dV is positive). This is evident from equation (3.22). Thus it is conventional to take forces acting on the fluid as positive when they are in the direction of flow. The corresponding forces acting on the solid boundary are taken as positive when they are in the direction opposite to the flow. A *thrust* is therefore positive when the net force on the boundary acts in the direction opposite to the fluid flow.

In general, the thrust, F, or the total force against the solid boundaries is the sum of the pressure force on the sidewalls, friction forces, and drag forces. Since the forces exerted on the solid body are identical in magnitude but opposite in direction to those exerted on the fluid by the solid body, and because of the factors used for sidewall pressure, friction, and drag in the development of the momentum equations (see Chapter 3), the net thrust can be written:

$$dF = p\,dA - \rho\,\frac{AV^2}{2g_0}\left(f\frac{dx}{D} + dC_D\right) \tag{4.1}$$

It should be noted that most modern propulsive engines, i.e., turbojets, ramjets, and rockets, have a greater mass flow leaving than entering the device because the propelling fluid, or a portion of it, is carried by the device, e.g., fuel, (or fuel and oxidizer in a rocket). The friction and drag forces exerted on the fluid by the solid boundary may be evaluated by the indirect process of substituting the equivalent terms, which are dependent on the more easily measured fluid properties. The momentum equation in the form allowing for changing flow rate must be used to allow for the fuel (or fuel and oxidizer) additions. From equation (2.32) these friction and drag forces are expressible in terms of the fluid properties.

$$-\rho\,\frac{AV^2}{2g_0}\left(f\frac{dx}{D} + dC_D\right)$$
$$= A\,dp + \frac{g}{g_0}\,\rho A\,dz + \frac{d(wV)}{g_0}$$

Then equation (4.1) may be written:

$$dF = p \, dA + A \, dp + \frac{g}{g_0} \rho A \, dz + \frac{d(wV)}{g_0}$$

$$= d(Ap) + \frac{g}{g_0} \rho A \, dz + \frac{d(wV)}{g_0} \tag{4.2}$$

Since ρ is small for any gas used as propelling medium, and in a propelling device dz cannot be large enough to make the term $\dfrac{\rho A \, dz}{g_0}$ appreciable as compared with the other terms, it is customary (in working with gases) to write

$$dF = d(Ap) + \frac{d(wV)}{g_0} = d\left(Ap + \frac{wV}{g_0}\right) \tag{4.3}$$

Then the net thrust developed by the fluid *internal* to the solid boundary of the duct between any two sections in that duct is

$$F = p_2 A_2 + \frac{w_2 V_2}{g_0} - \left(p_1 A_1 + \frac{w_1 V_1}{g_0}\right)$$

$$= p_2 A_2 + \frac{\rho_2 A_2 V_2^2}{g_0} - p_1 A_1 - \frac{\rho_1 A_1 V_1^2}{g_0} \tag{4.4}$$

The quantity, $\left(\dfrac{wV}{g_0} + pA\right)$ can be considered as a fluid *impulse function*.

$$I = \frac{wV}{g_0} + pA \tag{4.5}$$

The impulse imparted to a fluid is $F \, dt$, and thus the impulse per unit time is $F = \int dI$. Therefore, the thrust resulting from the fluid flowing from station 1 to station 2 is the difference in the impulse function at the two stations.

$$F = \int_1^2 dI = I_2 - I_1 \tag{4.6}$$

This describes the net *internal* thrust or thrust produced by the fluid flowing interior to a propulsive duct. In this situation the use of the impulse function, I, is very convenient as illustrated by the following problem.

A turbojet has air entering through an intake 4 sq ft in area at a temperature of 0°F and a relative velocity of 400 ft/sec. The exit area is 6 sq ft and the combustion products leave the engine at a relative velocity of 1100 ft/sec and at ambient pressure of 0.8 atm. Assume the products of combustion have the same properties as air and the mass of fuel added is negligible. Find the net

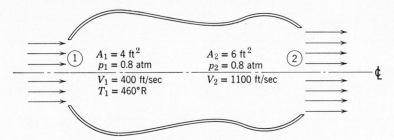

Fig. 4.1 Schematic diagram of propulsive duct of turbojet.

thrust developed as a result of the fluid flowing through the engine. (See Figure 4.1.)

Solution:

$$\rho_1 = \frac{p_1}{RT_1} = \frac{0.8 \times 14.7 \times 144}{53.34 \times 460} = 0.069 \ \mathrm{lb}_m/\mathrm{ft}^3$$

$$w = w_1 = w_2 = \rho_1 A_1 V_1 = 0.069 \times 4 \times 400 = 110.5 \ \mathrm{lb/sec}$$

$$F = \left(p_2 A_2 + \frac{wV_2}{g_0}\right) - \left(p_1 A_1 + \frac{wV_1}{g_0}\right) = I_2 - I_1$$

$$= 0.8 \times 14.7 \times 144(6 - 4) \times \frac{110.5}{32.17}(1100 - 400)$$

$$= 3385 + 2400 = 5785 \ \mathrm{lb}_f$$

Notice that this is positive thrust and will tend to move the engine into (or against) the fluid.

As a second example consider:

Find the net internal thrust produced by 1 lb/sec of air entering the nozzle shown in Figure 4.2 at a pressure of 20 psia and a temperature of 140°F, and leaving at a pressure of 15 psia and a temperature of 100°F.

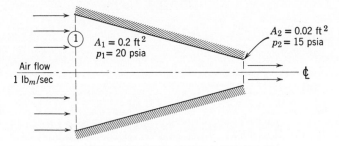

Fig. 4.2 Air flow through a convergent nozzle.

Solution:

Assuming air to be a perfect gas,

$$\rho_1 = \frac{p_1}{RT_1} = \frac{20 \times 144}{53.34 \times 600} = 0.090 \; \text{lb}_m/\text{ft}^3$$

$$V_1 = \frac{w}{\rho_1 A_1} = \frac{1}{0.09 \times 0.2} = 55.55 \; \text{ft/sec}$$

$$\rho_2 = \frac{p_2}{RT_2} = \frac{15 \times 144}{53.34 \times 56} = 0.0724 \; \text{lb}_m/\text{ft}^3$$

$$V_2 = \frac{w}{\rho_2 A_2} = \frac{1}{0.0724 \times 0.02} = 691 \; \text{ft/sec}$$

$$F = \left(\frac{wV_2}{g_0} + p_2 A_2\right) - \left(\frac{wV_1}{g_0} + p_1 A_1\right) = I_2 - I_1$$

$$= \frac{691 - 55.55}{32.17} + 144(15 \times 0.02 - 20 \times 0.2)$$

$$F = -513.1 \; \text{lb}_f$$

Thus, if the nozzle in this example were free to move, the thrust resulting from the air flowing inside the nozzle would tend to push the nozzle to the right (in the direction of the air flow).

In cases of rocket propulsion, the mass flow entering the control volume is, of course, zero. The thrust produced by the rocket propellants still may be evaluated by using equation (4.6). In this case $I_1 = 0$ since there is no flow area A_1 and no mass flow w_1. As an illustration, consider the rocket shown in Figure 4.3 which consumes w_p lb/sec of propellants and discharges the products of combustion at a velocity V_e. The thrust developed by the rocket's propellants is

$$F = I = \left(p_e A_e + \frac{wV_e}{g_0}\right)$$

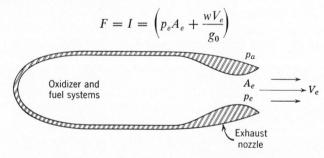

Fig. 4.3   Schematic diagram of rocket engine.

It will be found convenient in some of the future developments to use the impulse function in terms of Mach number.

$$I = pA + \frac{wV}{g_0} = A\left(p + \frac{\rho V^2}{g_0}\right) \tag{4.7}$$

but $V^2 = a^2 M^2 = kg_0 RTM^2$, so

$$I = A(p + k\rho RTM^2) \tag{4.8}$$

and for a perfect gas,

$$I = pA(1 + kM^2) \tag{4.9}$$

This is frequently a much more convenient form to use, particularly in the case of adiabatic flows, as will be seen in Chapter 5.

4.3 External thrust and drag

In addition to the thrust developed by a fluid flowing through a propulsive duct, there are forces acting on the outside surface of the duct which tend either to add to or to subtract from the internal propulsive thrust. The additional forces stem from the ambient pressure forces on the outer surfaces.

Figure 4.4 shows a propulsive duct with an inlet area A_1 and an exhaust area A_2. Ambient pressure, p_a, acts on the entire outer surface of the duct. The total force from the external (ambient) pressure has a component in the direction of the fluid flow (negative thrust) of an amount $p_a(A_{max} - A_1)$, and a component opposite to the fluid flow direction (positive thrust) of an amount, $p_a(A_{max} - A_2)$. Then the external pressure results in a thrust of:

$$p_a(A_{max} - A_2) - p_a(A_{max} - A_1) = p_a(A_1 - A_2)$$

Thus the net propulsive thrust of this duct is equal to the internal thrust plus the external pressure forces

$$F = \frac{wV_2}{g_0} + A_2(p_2 - p_a) - \left[\frac{wV_1}{g_0} + A_1(p_1 - p_a)\right] \tag{4.10}$$

or

$$dF = d\left(\frac{wV}{g_0} + Ap\right) - p_a \, dA = dI - p_a \, dA \tag{4.11}$$

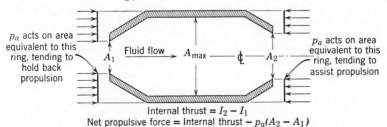

p_a acts on area equivalent to this ring, tending to hold back propulsion

Fluid flow A_1 A_{max} ¢ A_2

p_a acts on area equivalent to this ring, tending to assist propulsion

Internal thrust = $I_2 - I_1$
Net propulsive force = Internal thrust − $p_a(A_2 - A_1)$

Fig. 4.4 Relation of internal thrust to net propulsive thrust.

Consider the same examples as in section 4.2. In the case of the turbojet engine (Figure 4.1), not all the 5785 pounds of force are available to overcome the drag of the airframe. Some of the force must be used to counteract the ambient pressure forces. By equation (4.10) the net propulsive thrust of the engine is:

$$F = I_2 - I_1 - p_a(A_2 - A_1)$$

or

$$F = 5785 - 0.8 \times 14.7 \times 144(6 - 4) = 2400 \text{ lb}_f$$

A force of 2400 lb is the net amount of thrust available to propel the airframe.

In the case of the convergent nozzle (Figure 4.2), consider the ambient pressure to be 15 psia, and find the net propulsive thrust on this nozzle.

$$F = I_2 - I_1 - p_a(A_2 - A_1)$$
$$= -513.1 - 15 \times 144(0.02 - 0.2)$$
$$= -513.1 + 388.8 = -124.3 \text{ lb}_f$$

Thus it is evident that the atmosphere supplies 388.8 lb of force to tend to hold back the nozzle. To hold the nozzle stationary, however, an additional external force of 124.3 lb must be applied. Similarly in the case of the rocket engine, Figure 4.3. If the rocket exhausts at pressure $p_e = p_{\text{amb}}$, the net propulsive thrust is found to be

$$F = I - p_{\text{amb}} A_e = \frac{w V_e}{g_0}$$

If the rocket consumes 10 lb/sec of propellants and discharges the products of combustion at 6000 ft/sec, the net propulsive thrust developed is

$$F = \frac{10 \times 6000}{32.17} = 1862 \text{ lb}_f$$

The net propulsive thrust is given by equations (4.10) or (4.11). This is the force which is available (when it is positive) to overcome all external aerodynamic drag forces on both the propulsive power plant and the device to which it is attached. In constant speed propulsion the value for F as computed from equation (4.10) must have exactly the same magnitude as the sum of all the external drag forces. In order to accelerate a device, the net propulsive thrust must be greater than all the drag forces, and hence an unbalanced force will exist which will tend to accelerate the device. Similarly when the external drag forces exceed the net propulsive thrust the device will undergo a deceleration.

4.4 Special considerations of rocket thrust

A rocket is a device which burns fuel with an oxidizer in a pressure chamber and exhausts the products of combustion through a nozzle. Under ideal conditions the combustion gases are exhausted at the pressure of the surroundings, but as the altitude of the rocket or missile changes in flight, the ambient pressure changes. If other variables are held constant, this results in a change in the rocket thrust. From the previous section,

$$F = I - p_a A_e = \frac{w V_e}{g_0} + (p_e - p_a) A_e \qquad (4.12)$$

Instead of describing a given rocket as producing a certain quantity of thrust, it is more meaningful, at least thermodynamically, to refer to *effective exhaust velocity*. Effective exhaust velocity may be defined as the velocity the exhaust gases would be required to have in order to produce the measured thrust when the exit pressure and the ambient pressure are equal. The symbol c is used for effective exhaust velocity in equation (4.13) and throughout the rest of this section.

$$F = \frac{wc}{g_0} \qquad (4.13)$$

Then

$$c = \frac{F g_0}{w} = V_e + \frac{(p_e - p_a) A_e}{w/g_0} \qquad (4.14)$$

In the developmental stages of a rocket, it is this effective exhaust velocity that measures the relative merits of various designs.

In modern technology it has become commonplace to hear values for *specific impulse* quoted for certain rockets or for certain propellant combinations. Specific impulse is defined as the net thrust produced by the rocket divided by the rate of consumption of the propellants.

$$I_{sp} = \frac{F}{w} \qquad (4.15)$$

The units most commonly used are pounds of force divided by pounds of mass over seconds, or $\frac{lb_f \sec}{lb_m}$. In some instances specific impulse is quoted with units of seconds. Such usage is incorrect and should be discouraged.

From equation 4.15 it is evident that specific impulse and effective exhaust velocity are related.

$$I_{sp} = \frac{I - p_a A_e}{w} = \frac{V_e}{g_0} + \frac{(p_e - p_a) A_e}{w}$$

$$I_{sp} = \frac{c}{g_0} \qquad (4.16)$$

In rocket design there are two basic problems. One is to assure, as nearly as possible, smooth and complete combustion in the combustion chamber, and the other is to provide a nozzle for the expansion of the combustion gases that will result in maximum thrust. It is not surprising to find that additional performance parameters have been established which measure the effectiveness of the solutions to each of these basic problems.

Rocket thrust coefficient is used to determine the quality of the nozzle. It is defined by equation (4.17).

$$C_F = \frac{F}{p_c A_{\text{th}}} \tag{4.17}$$

As the pressure in the combustion chamber, p_c increases, it should be possible to obtain greater thrust. Similarly, as the nozzle throat area, A_{th}, is increased, greater mass rate of flow and hence greater thrust should result. Dividing the measured thrust by the combustion chamber pressure and the nozzle throat area gives a measure of the effectiveness of the expansion of the combustion gases. The quality of the nozzle controls the expansion process, and hence is indicated by C_F.

Rocket characteristic velocity is a measure of the quality of the combustion of the propellants in the combustion chamber. Using the symbol c^* for the characteristic velocity, equation (4.18) defines this quantity

$$c^* = \frac{p_c A_{\text{th}}}{w/g_0} \tag{4.18}$$

Through techniques to be developed later in this text it is simple to show that the rocket characteristic velocity may be expressed in terms of a combustion temperature.

$$c^* = \left[\left(\frac{k+1}{2} \right)^{(k+1)/(k-1)} \frac{g_0 R T_c}{k} \right]^{1/2} \tag{4.19}$$

The ideal combustion temperature can be computed from considerations of combustion chemistry. Equation (4.19) then gives an "ideal" (or theoretical) value for c^* which can be compared with the actual value given by equation (4.18). The combustion chamber pressure, the throat area of the nozzle, and the mass flow rate are the commonly (and relatively easily) measured quantities in an experiment, and equation (4.18) gives "experimental" c^*, whereas (4.19) gives "theoretical" c^*.

It is evident that the rocket characteristic velocity may be related to parameters previously defined through simple algebraic manipulations.

$$c^* = \frac{p_c A_{\text{th}}}{w/g_0} = \frac{F}{C_F w/g_0} = \frac{c}{C_F} \tag{4.20}$$

Then,

$$c = c^* C_F \tag{4.21}$$

which indicates that the effective exhaust velocity (an over-all rocket performance parameter) is equal to the product of the nozzle parameter and the combustion parameter.

4.5 Thrust as a pressure integral

In a propulsive duct, schematically repeated in Figure 4.5, in the absence of friction and drag forces, the thrust produced by the fluid may be computed by adding the forces produced by the fluid pressure on each elemental area, dA_w.

Obviously, if the duct is symmetrical about the center line, all the pressure forces except those in the direction of fluid flow (or opposite to it) will cancel themselves out. The resultant force acting on the inside of the duct as a result of the fluid in the duct is then the sum of the pressure times the *projected* area for each element of the wall. Thus,

$$dF = p \, dA$$

where dA is the projected area (area perpendicular to the axis of the duct).

Integrating, the net internal thrust is

$$F = \int p \, dA$$

where the integral must be taken over the entire inner surface of the propulsive duct.

Comparing this with equations (4.3)

$$dF = p \, dA = d\left(Ap + \frac{wV}{g_0} \right) = dI \qquad (4.22)$$

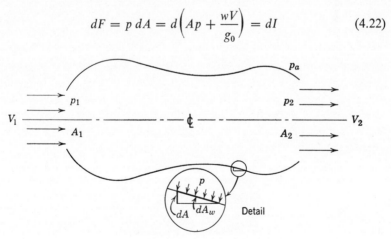

Fig. 4.5 Propulsive thrust.

and hence,

$$d(Ap) - p\,dA + \frac{d(wV)}{g_0} = 0$$

or
$$A\,dp + \frac{d(wV)}{g_0} = 0 \qquad\qquad (4.23)$$

which is the same as the momentum equation for no friction or drag.

It is evident that adding the pressure area product for the entire inner surface of a duct will give a valid procedure for calculating thrust, regardless of whether the rate of mass flow is constant or changing. That is, for a rocket $\int p\,dA$ taken over the inner walls of the rocket will give the same numerical result as I_2, while in the case of air flow through a nozzle, the value of $\int p\,dA$ will equal $I_2 - I_1$.

4.6 The thrust function

In order to compare the effectiveness or desirability of the designs of several propulsive devices, it is proper to measure the thrust produced by each and compare on this basis. In designing a particular component of a propulsive unit, it is frequently desirable to build and test several models which may be tested under a variety of conditions and in a variety of sizes. In order to analyze the thrust-producing capability of these component models (especially exhaust nozzles), it is necessary to reduce the experimental data to some common parameter.

Obviously, the larger the mass flow through a model, the larger the thrust will be. Because the scale of one model is smaller than that of another, the mass flow may be smaller and hence the measured thrust will be also. Yet under these conditions the design of the smaller model may be superior because it would give greater thrust when used with the prototype size.

Similar arguments hold in comparing test results when the tests are run with fluids at different temperatures or of different composition from that to be used in the final propulsive device.

In order to make intelligent comparisons of test data from many sources, to compare model tests with "full-scale" tests, and to compare "cold" tests with "hot" tests, the *thrust* function has been found to be very useful. Defining

$$f_F = \frac{F_g}{w\sqrt{T_0}}\sqrt{\frac{g_0}{R}} \qquad\qquad (4.24)$$

makes it possible to compare the actual measured thrust, F_g, for each of several different test set-ups. If an exhaust nozzle is being designed, use of the function f_F for a model which has been tested will prove more valuable than the "raw" parameter F_g, measured thrust.

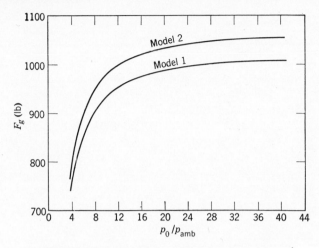

Fig. 4.6 Thrust curves for exhaust nozzle models.

As an illustration, consider the data for models of two exhaust nozzles as shown in Figure 4.6. Model 1 has a throat diameter of 6.615 in. and was tested "cold," with $T_0 = 530°R$, and with a mass flow rate of 15.4 lb/sec. Model 2 has a throat diameter of 7.5 in. and was tested with $T_0 = 550°R$ and a mass flow of 16.7 lb/sec. Both nozzles were tested over the entire pressure range by reducing the back pressure, with thrust measurements made at proper pressure ratios to determine the curves of Figure 4.6. Suppose that the critical design point for the prototype nozzle is at a pressure ratio of 20 and that the full-scale prototype is to operate with a T_0 of 3500°R and will pass 90 lb/sec. How much thrust would each of the designs produce at this design point? Which design is superior over a wide operating range?

To determine the thrust of the full scale nozzle under design-operating conditions, use the thrust function f_F. For nozzle model 1, at $P_0/P_{amb} = 20$, $F_g = 990$ lb.

$$f_F = \frac{F_g}{w\sqrt{T_0}} \sqrt{\frac{g_0}{R}} = \frac{990}{15.4} \sqrt{\frac{32.2}{530 \times 53.34}} = 2.165$$

$$F_g \text{ (full scale)} = \frac{f_F w\sqrt{RT_0}}{\sqrt{g_0}} = 2.165 \times 90 \sqrt{\frac{53.34 \times 3500}{32.2}} = 14{,}850 \text{ lb}_f$$

For nozzle model 2, at $P_0/P_{amb} = 20$, $F_g = 1038$ lb.

$$f_F = \frac{F_g}{w\sqrt{T_0}} \sqrt{\frac{g_0}{R}} = \frac{1038}{16.7} \sqrt{\frac{32.2}{550 \times 53.34}} = 2.056$$

$$F_g \text{ (full scale)} = \frac{f_F w\sqrt{RT_0}}{\sqrt{g_0}} = 2.056 \times 90 \sqrt{\frac{53.34 \times 3500}{32.2}} = 14{,}090 \text{ lb}_f$$

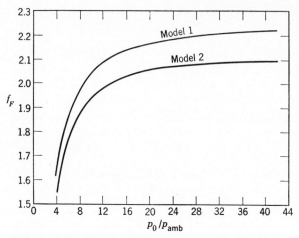

Fig. 4.7 *Thrust function* curves for exhaust nozzle models.

Hence, although the actual test on model 1 showed less thrust than the test on model 2, at the design point in question in full scale operation model 1 will give more thrust and, therefore, it is considered the superior of the two.

Similarly, if the values for the thrust function f_F are plotted over the entire pressure range instead of measured thrust (see Figure 4.7), it is evident that the design of model 1 is superior throughout the entire range of P_0/P_{amb}.

Problems

4.1 A certain rocket engine produces 1000 lb of internal thrust when consuming 5 lb per sec of propellants and expanding them to atmospheric pressure. The exit diameter of the exhaust nozzle is 2.5 in. Find the velocity of the exit gases.

4.2 In problem 4.1 find the *net* thrust which may be used for propulsive purposes.

4.3 The area of the intake scoop on a turbojet is 4 sq ft, and the area of the tail pipe is 6 sq ft. The aircraft is travelling at 400 mph and the combustion products leave the tail pipe with $M = 1.0$. The atmospheric pressure is 0.8 atm and the temperature is 0°F. Find the net thrust which may be used to overcome friction and drag forces.

4.4 Propulsive power may be defined as the propulsive force or thrust multiplied by flight speed. For an airplane with equal intake and exhaust areas and with the gases leaving the exhaust nozzle at atmospheric pressure, show that propulsive power is at its maximum when the exhaust gases leave the nozzle with a velocity equal to twice the flight velocity.

4.5 An aircraft flying at 600 mph inducts 80 lb/sec of air at atmospheric pressure of 0.6 atm and a temperature 0°F. Fuel is burned at the rate of 4 lb/sec, and the products of combustion (having properties essentially the same as air) leave the engine with a stagnation temperature of 2500°F, a Mach number of 1.5, and a static pressure equal to the surrounding atmosphere. Find the internal thrust produced and the net thrust which may be used to propel the airframe.

4.6 A test on a thrust stand shows a thrust of 2000 lb when 32 lb/sec of air flow from an exhaust nozzle. Just ahead of the nozzle the temperature is 1200°F and the velocity at this point is 350 ft/sec. Estimate the thrust from this engine if more fuel is added (i.e., an afterburner) until the T_0 entering the nozzle is 3000°F. How much must the flow rate be increased (bigger engine) in order to produce a thrust of 4000 lb, if the afterburner raises the energy level of all the flow so that $T_0 = 3000°F$?

References

1. M. J. Zucrow: *Aircraft and Missile Propulsion*, Vol. I, John Wiley and Sons, New York, 1958.
2. George P. Sutton: *Rocket Propulsion Elements*, 2nd ed., John Wiley and Sons, New York, 1956.
3. A. H. Shapiro: *The Dynamics and Thermodynamics of Compressible Fluid Flow*, Vol. I, Ronald Press, New York, 1953.
4. A. B. Cambel and B. H. Jennings: *Gas Dynamics*, McGraw-Hill, New York, 1958.
5. C. W. Smith: *Aircraft Gas Turbines*, John Wiley and Sons, New York, 1956.

5

adiabatic flow

5.1 Introduction

A flow in which all fluid properties are uniform over any cross section is said to be a one-dimensional flow. The assumption of one-dimensional flow is frequently made in the calculation of practical engineering problems because of its tremendous simplicity. With proper care and analysis the information obtained by assuming a one-dimensional flow may be quite accurate and reliable and hence extremely useful to the engineer.

More carefully defined, one-dimensional flow is such that the rate of change of fluid properties in a direction normal to the streamlines is negligible compared with the rate of change along the streamlines. The one-dimensional flow treatment may be used by an engineer in two kinds of problems: flow in stream tubes and flow in ducts.

(a) *Flow in stream tubes.* For flow around solid objects, there are stream tubes which are completely removed from the boundary layer

74

around the object, and for these stream tubes heat conduction and viscous forces have been shown by experiment to be negligible. Flow through an infinitesimal stream tube must be one-dimensional.

(b) *Flow in ducts.* Certainly, in the case of flow through ducts, there may be a variation in each fluid property over the flow cross section. For such cases it is customary to deal with average values of properties and study the rate of change of these average values along the duct.

It must be remembered that the one-dimensional treatment of fluid flow does not give information as to the variation of properties normal to the streamlines. When such information is desired, the more laborious methods of two- or three-dimensional analyses must be employed.

In most fluid flow systems (particularly in duct flow) variations in the passage cross section are quite common. Nozzles and diffusers are typical examples of flow devices in which change in passage cross section is necessary to accomplish the purpose of the device. In most cases the flow in these devices is such that heat transfer may be considered negligible. Thus the flow is "adiabatic." If the frictional and drag effects are relatively small, the flow may also be considered reversible and hence isentropic. Even with friction or drag effects which are not negligible, an analysis made on the basis of isentropic flow will give the *ideal* conditions and will serve as a standard for comparison for the actual flow problem. Isentropic flow defines the ideal conditions to be used in computing efficiencies for flow devices, such as nozzles and diffusers.

In flow through a stream tube, viscous forces and heat conduction are negligible, as pointed out above. In the absence of discontinuities, such as shock, or in the portion of flows between discontinuities, such flows must be isentropic and equations based on isentropic flow must be exact without considering an efficiency.

5.2 Fluid properties in adiabatic flow

The variation of fluid properties under adiabatic conditions can be obtained from the energy equation for adiabatic, no-work flow

$$dh_0 = 0 \tag{5.1}$$

Then for a perfect gas,

$$dT_0 = d\left[T\left(1 + \frac{k-1}{2}M^2\right)\right] = 0 \tag{5.2}$$

$$\left(1 + \frac{k-1}{2}M^2\right)dT + T\,d\left(1 + \frac{k-1}{2}M^2\right) = 0 \tag{5.3}$$

or

$$\frac{dT}{T} = -\frac{d\left(1 + \dfrac{k-1}{2} M^2\right)}{1 + \dfrac{k-1}{2} M^2} \tag{5.4}$$

Also for a perfect gas,

$$ds = \frac{kR}{k-1} \frac{dT}{T} - \frac{dp}{\rho T}$$

$$= \frac{kR}{k-1} \frac{dT}{T} - R\frac{dp}{p} \tag{5.5}$$

Then,

$$\frac{dp}{p} = \frac{k}{k-1} \frac{dT}{T} - \frac{ds}{R} \tag{5.6}$$

Substituting from equation (5.4) for dT/T in equation (5.6)

$$\frac{dp}{p} = -\frac{k}{k-1} \frac{d\left(1 + \dfrac{k-1}{2} M^2\right)}{1 + \dfrac{k-1}{2} M^2} - \frac{ds}{R} \tag{5.7}$$

Figure 5.1 shows an adiabatic process and illustrates that when T_0 is constant (as for adiabatic flow), the definition of stagnation state requires that the change in stagnation pressure be negative, or (for the case $\Delta s = 0$) zero.

$$ds = ds_0 = \frac{dh_0 - \dfrac{1}{\rho_0} dp_0}{T_0} \tag{5.8}$$

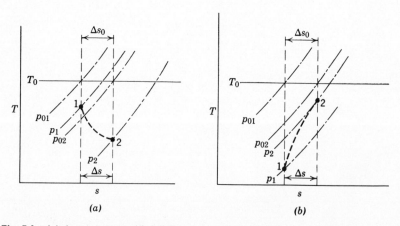

Fig. 5.1 Adiabatic process. (a) Adiabatic expansion. (b) Adiabatic compression.

Since $dh_0 = 0$

$$\frac{dp_0}{\rho_0 T_0} = -ds \qquad (5.9)$$

or, using $p_0 = \rho_0 R T_0$,

$$\frac{dp_0}{p_0} = -\frac{ds}{R} \qquad (5.10)$$

Since the entropy change ds is always zero or more than zero in an adiabatic process as shown in Figure 5.1, the stagnation pressure must decrease.

Also, for a perfect gas, the density change may be expressed:

$$\frac{d\rho}{\rho} = \frac{dp}{p} - \frac{dT}{T} \qquad (5.11)$$

Then, substituting from equations (5.4) and (5.7),

$$\frac{d\rho}{\rho} = \left(1 - \frac{k}{k-1}\right) \frac{d\left(1 + \frac{k-1}{2}M^2\right)}{1 + \frac{k-1}{2}M^2} - \frac{ds}{R}$$

$$= -\frac{1}{k-1} \frac{d\left(1 + \frac{k-1}{2}M^2\right)}{1 + \frac{k-1}{2}M^2} - \frac{ds}{R} \qquad (5.12)$$

In an adiabatic flow process of a perfect gas, the velocity may be found by considering the definition of Mach number

$$V = Ma = M\sqrt{kg_0 RT} \qquad (5.13)$$

$$dV = \sqrt{kg_0 RT}\, dM + \sqrt{kg_0 R}\, M\, d\sqrt{T} \qquad (5.14)$$

Dividing equation (5.14) by (5.13),

$$\frac{dV}{V} = \frac{dM}{M} + \frac{d\sqrt{T}}{\sqrt{T}} = \frac{dM}{M} + \frac{1}{2}\frac{dT}{T} \qquad (5.15)$$

Substituting for dT/T from equation (5.4),

$$\frac{dV}{V} = \frac{dM}{M} - \frac{1}{2} \frac{d\left(1 + \frac{k-1}{2}M^2\right)}{1 + \frac{k-1}{2}M^2} \qquad (5.16)$$

It is frequently necessary to analyze the adiabatic flow of a fluid through a changing cross sectional area. The area change is obtained from the continuity equation.

$$\frac{dA}{A} = -\frac{d\rho}{\rho} - \frac{dV}{V} \tag{5.17}$$

Then from equations (5.12) and (5.16):

$$\frac{dA}{A} = \frac{k+1}{2(k-1)} \frac{d\left(1 + \dfrac{k-1}{2}M^2\right)}{1 + \dfrac{k-1}{2}M^2} + \frac{ds}{R} - \frac{dM}{M} \tag{5.18}$$

Finally, the impulse function is

$$I = pA(1 + kM^2) \tag{5.19}$$

Differentiating and dividing by I,

$$\frac{dI}{I} = \frac{dp}{p} + \frac{dA}{A} + \frac{d(1 + kM^2)}{1 + kM^2} \tag{5.20}$$

or using equations (4.18) and (4.7),

$$\frac{dI}{I} = -\frac{1}{2} \frac{d\left(1 + \dfrac{k-1}{2}M^2\right)}{1 + \dfrac{k-1}{2}M^2} - \frac{dM}{M} + \frac{d(1 + kM^2)}{1 + kM^2} \tag{5.21}$$

It is interesting to note the effect of entropy increase on the change in fluid properties expressed in the above equations. For two adiabatic processes with the same limits on Mach number:

(*a*) From equation (5.4): the temperature change is the same, regardless of any entropy increase.

(*b*) From equation (5.7): the final pressure must always be lower (for both expansions and compressions) in the process with the greater entropy increase.

(*c*) From equation (5.10): the stagnation pressure decreases a larger amount in the process with the greater entropy increase.

(*d*) From equation (5.12): the final density must always be lower (for both expansions and compressions) in the process with the greater entropy increase.

(*e*) From equation (5.16): the velocity increase for an expansion, or decrease for a compression, is independent of the entropy increase.

(f) From equation (5.18): the area must always be larger, (in both subsonic and supersonic flow) to permit passage of the same quantity of flow for the case with the greater entropy increase.

(g) From equation (5.21): the change in the impulse function is independent of the entropy increase.

Note that in each equation in which the entropy increase is a factor, integration of the equation will yield a multiplying term with the entropy change as an exponential. For the case of isentropic flow, the factor involved with entropy becomes unity, and the ideal case is thus easily evaluated.

5.3 Effects of area variation

Consider now the isentropic ($ds = 0$) flow of any fluid through a passage of varying cross section. Since the entropy of the fluid is constant in this case, the stagnation state is fixed at a single point for all possible static state points. This process becomes a special case of that shown in Figure 5.1 and discussed in the previous section. Figure 5.2 shows the isentropic flow process and is presented for easy reference to this section.

From the Bernoulli equation (3.37), for the special case of isentropic flow:

$$dp = -\frac{\rho V\,dV}{g_0} = -\frac{\rho V^2}{g_0}\frac{dV}{V} \tag{5.22}$$

Using the continuity equation to eliminate the relative velocity change, from equation (5.17), we get

$$\frac{dV}{V} = -\frac{dp}{\rho} - \frac{dA}{A} \tag{5.23}$$

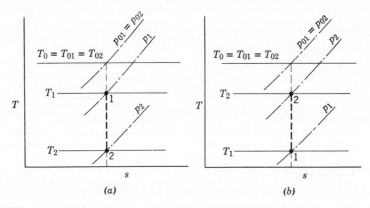

Fig. 5.2 Isentropic flow process. (a) Isentropic expansion. (b) Isentropic compression.

Then

$$dp = \frac{\rho V^2}{g_0}\left[\frac{d\rho}{\rho} + \frac{dA}{A}\right] \tag{5.24}$$

An examination of equation (5.24) shows that if the density change is small the pressure goes up as the area goes up, and vice versa. This is the usually expected action in incompressible fluid flow. However, it must be noted that the pressure increase is also a function of the square of the velocity. As the velocity becomes large, the pressure change for a given area may become so large that for compressible fluids the corresponding density change can no longer be considered small.

As shown in Chapter 3, the acoustic velocity in any fluid,

$$a^2 = g_0\left(\frac{\partial p}{\partial \rho}\right)_s \tag{5.25}$$

For an isentropic process, the density change may then be expressed in terms of the pressure change and the acoustic velocity.

$$d\rho = \frac{g_0}{a^2}\,dp \tag{5.26}$$

Substituting equation (5.26) into (5.24), an expression for pressure and area changes is obtained.

$$dp = \frac{V^2}{a^2}\,dp + \frac{\rho V^2}{g_0}\frac{dA}{A} \tag{5.27}$$

or

$$(1 - M^2)\,dp = \frac{\rho V^2}{g_0}\frac{dA}{A} \tag{5.28}$$

$$dp = \frac{\rho V^2}{g_0}\left(\frac{1}{1 - M^2}\right)\frac{dA}{A} \tag{5.29}$$

The density change may be found from equation (5.26)

$$d\rho = \frac{g_0}{a^2}\,dp = \rho M^2\left(\frac{1}{1 - M^2}\right)\frac{dA}{A} \tag{5.30}$$

Dividing by ρ gives the relative density change

$$\frac{d\rho}{\rho} = \frac{M^2}{1 - M^2}\frac{dA}{A} \tag{5.31}$$

Using the continuity equation, $\dfrac{dV}{V} = \dfrac{d\rho}{\rho} - \dfrac{dA}{A}$, relative velocity change may be expressed as a function of area change and Mach number as

$$\frac{dV}{V} = -\frac{M^2}{1 - M^2}\frac{dA}{A} - \frac{dA}{A} = \frac{1}{1 - M^2}\frac{dA}{A} \tag{5.32}$$

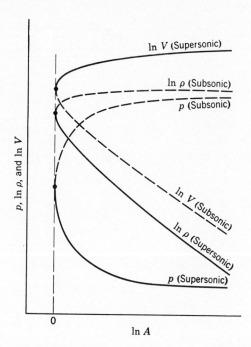

Fig. 5.3 Pressure, density, and velocity variation in isentropic flow.

The three equations (5.29), (5.31), and (5.32) express the variation with area of, respectively, pressure, density, and velocity. They are repeated for easy reference in the following discussion, and shown schematically in Figure 5.3.

$$dp = \frac{\rho V^2}{g_0} \frac{1}{1 - M^2} \frac{dA}{A} \qquad (5.29)$$

$$\frac{d\rho}{\rho} = \frac{M^2}{1 - M^2} \frac{dA}{A} \qquad (5.31)$$

$$\frac{dV}{V} = -\frac{1}{1 - M^2} \frac{dA}{A} \qquad (5.32)$$

For subsonic flow, ($M < 1$), Figure 5.3 shows:
1. The pressure increases with an area increase.
2. The density increases with an area increase.
3. The velocity decreases with an area increase.

For supersonic flow, ($M > 1$), Figure 5.3 shows:
1. The pressure decreases with an area increase.
2. The density decreases with an area increase.
3. The velocity increases with an area increase.

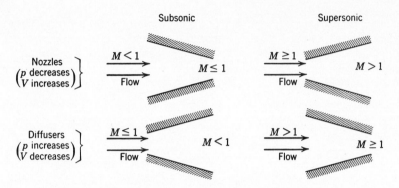

Fig. 5.4 Effects of area change in subsonic and supersonic flow.

For flow at *sonic* speeds, ($M = 1$), the three equations show:

1. $\dfrac{dA}{dp} = 0 = \dfrac{dA}{d\rho} = \dfrac{dA}{dV}$; thus the area may be either a maximum or a minimum. Figure 5.3 shows that at $M = 1$, it must be a minimum.

2. As the sonic condition is approached (from either side) the pressure changes (and also density changes) become very large for even a small area change.

3. Combining (5.31) and (5.32),

$$\frac{d\rho}{\rho} = -M^2 \frac{dV}{V} \tag{5.33}$$

Thus near sonic velocities the change in density and the change in velocity will compensate.

The use of the three equations in the design of nozzles and diffusers will be apparent if we consider the purpose of each device. A nozzle is a device in which we hope to gain a velocity increase at the expense of pressure (pressure decrease). To accomplish this, in subsonic flow the nozzle area must decrease, and in supersonic flow the area must increase.

A diffuser is a device in which we hope to gain a pressure increase at the expense of velocity (velocity decrease). This may be accomplished in subsonic flow by making the diffuser diverge, and in supersonic flow by making the diffuser converge. (See Figure 5.4.)

5.4 Reference states

As has already been seen, it is frequently convenient to express the value of a property in terms of the corresponding stagnation property. Thus it is common to refer to p/p_0 or T/T_0. Such ratios may be easily obtained from the definition of a stagnation state.

It is frequently more convenient to refer to the value of a property in terms of the value of the corresponding property at conditions where the Mach number is unity. Such a state is indicated by the use of the asterisk, such as p^*, T^*, ρ^*, etc. The dimensionless ratios such as p/p^* may be easily obtained for the case of isentropic flow by integrating the equations in section 5.2. For example, with $ds = 0$, equation (5.7) integrates to:

$$\frac{p}{p^*} = \left(\frac{1 + \dfrac{k-1}{2}}{1 + \dfrac{k-1}{2} M^2} \right)^{k/(k-1)} = \left[\frac{k+1}{2\left(1 + \dfrac{k-1}{2} M^2\right)} \right]^{k/(k-1)} \tag{5.34}$$

Similarly, in the case of area, equation (5.18) may be integrated and the ratio A/A^* obtained. A^* is the cross-sectional area of the duct or stream tube that would be required for isentropic acceleration (or deceleration) to conditions for unity Mach number. The methods of obtaining the quantities, A/A^*, V/V^*, and I/I^*, and the convenience of their use will be apparent in the following section.

It should be pointed out that whenever the entropy changes, the value of A^* changes. Equation (5.18) may be used to obtain a ratio A^*_2/A^*_1 by letting both limits of integration in M become unity. Then the lower limit on area, A_1, becomes the area required for flow with $M_1 = 1$, or by definition this is A^*_1. Similarly the upper limit, A_2, becomes A^*_2 and equation (5.18) integrates to:

$$\ln \frac{A^*_2}{A^*_1} = \frac{k+1}{2(k-1)} \ln \left(\frac{1 + \dfrac{k-1}{2}}{1 + \dfrac{k-1}{2}} \right) + \frac{s_2 - s_1}{R} - \ln \left(\frac{1}{1} \right) \tag{5.35}$$

or,

$$\frac{A^*_2}{A^*_1} = e^{(s_2 - s_1)/R} \tag{5.36}$$

A comparable equation is obtained by integrating equation (5.10). This yields:

$$\frac{p_{02}}{p_{01}} = e^{-[(s_2 - s_1)/R]} \tag{5.37}$$

$$\frac{p_{02}}{p_{01}} = \frac{A^*_1}{A^*_2} = e^{-[(s_2 - s_1)/R]} \tag{5.38}$$

Then it is evident that either the stagnation pressure ratio or the ratio of A^*'s may be used to evaluate the entropy change.

As a dimensionless ratio, the Mach number is an extremely valuable quantity. However, it has a disadvantage because it is not a function of the velocity alone; it depends on the state of the fluid, particularly its temperature. A second disadvantage is that the Mach number may become extremely large. It is, therefore, sometimes convenient to use a dimensionless velocity ratio defined to be the flow velocity divided by the acoustic velocity at the state where fluid velocity and sonic velocity are equal.

That is,

$$M^* = \frac{V}{a^*} = \frac{V}{V^*} \tag{5.39}$$

$$M^{*2} = \frac{V^2}{a^{*2}}\left(\frac{a^2}{a^2}\right) = M^2 \frac{a^2}{a^{*2}} \tag{5.40}$$

The ratio V/V^* may be found by integrating equation (5.16), which yields:

$$\frac{V}{V^*} = \frac{M}{(1)}\left(\frac{1 + \dfrac{k-1}{2}M^2}{1 + \dfrac{k-1}{2}}\right)^{-\frac{1}{2}}$$

$$M^* = \frac{V}{V^*} = \frac{M\sqrt{\dfrac{k+1}{2}}}{\sqrt{1 + \dfrac{k-1}{2}M^2}} \tag{5.41}$$

Solving for M:

$$M^{*2} = \frac{\left(\dfrac{k+1}{2}\right)M^2}{1 + \dfrac{k-1}{2}M^2}$$

$$M^{*2} + \frac{k-1}{2}M^2 M^{*2} - \frac{k+1}{2}M^2 = 0 \tag{5.42}$$

$$\left(1 - \frac{k-1}{k+1}M^{*2}\right)M^2 = \frac{2}{k+1}M^{*2}$$

$$M = \frac{M^*\sqrt{\dfrac{2}{k+1}}}{\sqrt{1 - \dfrac{k-1}{k+1}M^{*2}}} \tag{5.43}$$

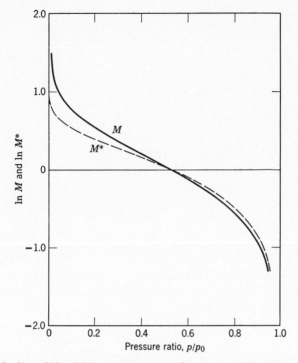

Fig. 5.5 Plot of M and M^* vs. pressure ratio for isentropic flow ($k = 1.4$).

From equations (5.41) and (5.43) it is seen that M^* is not only a simple function of flow velocity, but is related to M in such a way that when

$$M < 1, \qquad M^* < 1$$
$$M > 1, \qquad M^* > 1$$
$$M = 1, \qquad M^* = 1$$
$$M = 0, \qquad M^* = 0$$
$$M \rightarrow \infty, \qquad M^* = (k + 1)/(k - 1)$$

Figure 5.5 shows a plot of M and M^* as a function of p/p_0 for isentropic flow. Note that M^* does not become infinite as p/p_0 becomes very small. Also, M^* is dependent on the temperature at the sonic state and not the static temperature of the fluid.

5.5 Tables for isentropic flow

The relations developed in section 5.2 are all valid for adiabatic flows regardless of whether the flow is isentropic or nonisentropic. The usual procedure is to estimate the change in a given property on the basis of isentropic flow and then apply a corrective factor. These corrective factors may be in the form of exponential entropy increase factors—$\exp \dfrac{\Delta s}{R}$ (as would be obtained by direct integration of equations in section 5.2) or in the form of efficiencies, or even as stagnation pressure losses. Section 5.8 will explain these factors in more detail.

After integrating the differential equations of section 5.2, the arithmetic calculations required to evaluate the properties are extremely tedious. It is convenient, therefore, to make use of some reference state and tabulate a suitable dimensionless ratio for each property.

Integrating equation (5.4) between the limits T and T_0 corresponding to M and $M = 0$, the ratio T/T_0 may be shown to be

$$\frac{T}{T_0} = \frac{1}{1 + \dfrac{k-1}{2} M^2} \tag{5.44}$$

Similarly, integrating equations (5.6) and (5.12) for the case $ds = 0$:

$$\frac{p}{p_0} = \left(1 + \frac{k-1}{2} M^2\right)^{-[k/(k-1)]} \tag{5.45}$$

$$\frac{\rho}{\rho_0} = \left(1 + \frac{k-1}{2} M^2\right)^{-[1/(k-1)]} \tag{5.46}$$

From equation (5.41)

$$M^* = \frac{V}{V^*} = M\left(\frac{\dfrac{k+1}{2}}{1 + \dfrac{k-1}{2} M^2}\right)^{1/2} \tag{5.47}$$

The following are obtained by integrating equations (5.18) and (5.21) between appropriate limits for the case of isentropic flow.

$$\frac{A}{A^*} = \frac{1}{M}\left(\frac{1 + \dfrac{k-1}{2} M^2}{\dfrac{k+1}{2}}\right)^{(k+1)/2(k-1)} \tag{5.48}$$

$$\frac{I}{I^*} = \frac{1 + kM^2}{M\sqrt{2(k+1)}\sqrt{1 + \dfrac{k-1}{2} M^2}} \tag{5.49}$$

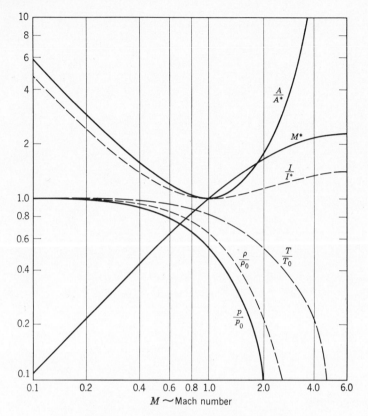

Fig. 5.6 Isentropic flow functions ($k = 1.4$).

Combining equations (5.45) and (5.48):

$$\frac{A}{A^*}\frac{p}{p_0} = \frac{\left(\dfrac{k+1}{2}\right)^{-[(k+1)/2(k-1)]}}{M\sqrt{1+\dfrac{k-1}{2}M^2}} \tag{5.50}$$

Each of these ratios, equations (5.44) through (5.50), are given in Table A.2 of the Appendix for Mach numbers varying from 0 to 10 and for k's of 1.4, 1.0, 1.1, 1.2, 1.3, and 1.67. The same information may be presented in graphical form as in Figure 5.6 which is prepared for $k = 1.4$. A similar presentation is necessary for other values of k, and in general the tabular form is preferred in making engineering calculations.

Illustrative example

Find the mass rate of flow, the area of the test section, and the fluid properties at the throat and test section in a supersonic wind tunnel designed for $M = 2.5$ and having a throat section of 1 sq ft. The air supply is at 15 psia and 70°F and has a negligible velocity (assume $k = 1.4$).

First, determining the stagnation properties:

$$p_0 = 15 \text{ psia}$$
$$T_0 = 70°\text{F} = 530°\text{R}$$
$$\rho_0 = p_0/RT_0 = \frac{15 \times 144}{53.34 \times 530} = 0.0765 \text{ lb}_m/\text{ft}^3$$

At the throat $M = 1$, and from the isentropic flow table for $k = 1.4$:

$p/p_0 = 0.528$; therefore, $p^* = 0.528 (15) = 7.91$ psia
$T/T_0 = 0.833$; therefore, $T^* = 0.833 (530) = 441°$R
$\rho/\rho_0 = 0.634$; therefore, $\rho^* = 0.634 (0.0765) = 0.0485 \text{ lb}_m/\text{ft}^3$

At the test section $M = 2.5$, and again from the table:

$p/p_0 = 0.0585$; therefore, $p = 0.0585 (15) = 0.88$ psia
$T/T_0 = 0.444$; therefore, $T = 0.444 (530) = 235°$R
$\rho/\rho_0 = 0.1317$; therefore, $\rho = 0.1317 (0.0765) = 0.01006 \text{ lb}_m/\text{ft}^3$
$A/A^* = 2.6367$; therefore, $A = 2.6367 (1) = 2.6367$ sq ft

The velocity at the throat is:

$$V^* = Ma^* = \sqrt{(32.2)(1.4)(53.34)(441)} = 1030 \text{ ft/sec}$$

At the test section:

$$V = Ma = 2.5 \sqrt{(32.2)(1.4)(53.34)(2.35)} = 1885 \text{ ft/sec}$$

The mass flow $w = \rho^*A^*V^* = (\rho A V)_{\text{test section}}$
$w = \rho^*A^*V^* = (0.0485) (1) (1030) = 50 \text{ lb}_m/\text{sec}$

As a check:

$w = (\rho A V)_{\text{test section}} = (0.01006) (2.6367) (1885) = 50 \text{ lb}_m/\text{sec}$

5.6 Mass flow and choking in isentropic flow

It was seen in section 5.3 that the cross-sectional area of the flow passage must change in accordance with certain equations. The area may not be varied at will without introducing the possibility of changing the upstream (inlet) conditions or the mass rate of flow, or both.

The mass rate of flow for a given set of inlet conditions can be found from the continuity equation

$$\frac{dw}{w} = \frac{d\rho}{\rho} + \frac{dA}{A} + \frac{dV}{V}$$

The mass flow per unit area is, then,

$$\frac{w}{A} = \rho V = \frac{pM}{\sqrt{RT/kg_0}} = \frac{p_0}{\sqrt{RT_0/kg_0}} M \left(\frac{p}{p_0}\right)\left(\frac{T_0}{T}\right)^{1/2} \qquad (5.51)$$

Then in terms of Mach number and stagnation conditions, this is

$$\frac{w}{A} = \frac{p_0}{\sqrt{RT_0/kg_0}} \frac{M}{\left(1 + \dfrac{k-1}{2} M^2\right)^{(k+1)/2(k-1)}} \qquad (5.52)$$

Notice that, for a given Mach number, the flow is proportional to the stagnation pressure and inversely proportional to the square root of the stagnation temperature. If the results of a given experimental test are to be made more general, it is better to determine the flow variable $\dfrac{w\sqrt{T_0}}{Ap_0}\sqrt{R/g_0}$. Then the data is applicable to conditions at different pressure and temperature levels (and even for different gases).

The quantity $\dfrac{w\sqrt{T_0}}{Ap_0}\sqrt{R/g_0}$ is the *isentropic flow function* which can be written:

$$f_w = \frac{w\sqrt{T_0}}{Ap_0}\sqrt{R/g_0} = \frac{\sqrt{k}M}{\left(1 + \dfrac{k-1}{2} M^2\right)^{(k+1)/2(k-1)}} \qquad (5.53)$$

It is evident that the mass flow per unit area can easily be found since the right-hand side of equation (5.53) is a function only of Mach number for a perfect gas. Even for the case of real gases, if a good estimate is available on the specific heat ratio and the gas constant, the function $\dfrac{w\sqrt{T_0}}{Ap_0}\sqrt{R/g_0}$ proves most valuable in relating the mass flow per unit area of streams with different stagnation pressures and temperatures.

The problem of determining the local Mach number for a given mass flow with a known stagnation state is a common type for which data calculated from equation (5.53) is valuable. Since equation (5.53) is dimensionless and a function only of Mach number, values for f_w may be calculated just as the other isentropic functions developed in section 5.3. The values of the isentropic flow function are tabulated for k's of 1.0, 1.1, 1.2, 1.3, 1.4, and 1.67 for Mach numbers from 0 to 10 in Table A.2 in the Appendix.

To illustrate the utility of the isentropic flow function, consider the following example:

Air flowing in a duct has a stagnation temperature of 1000°R and a stagnation pressure of 100 psia. How large must the cross-sectional area be at the point where the pressure is 25.7 psia in order to allow 3 lb/sec to pass in isentropic flow (assume $k = 1.4$).   At 25.7 psia, $p/p_0 = 0.257$, and from Table 1 in the Appendix, $M = 1.54$.

For $M = 1.54$

$$f_w = 0.5686$$

and

$$\frac{w}{A} = 0.5686 \frac{p_0}{\sqrt{T_0}} \sqrt{g_0/R}$$

or

$$A = \frac{w}{0.5686 p_0} \sqrt{\frac{RT_0}{g_0}} = \frac{3\sqrt{53.34 \times 1000}}{0.5686 \times 100 \times 144\sqrt{32.2}}$$

$$= 0.0149 \text{ sq ft} = 2.15 \text{ sq in.}$$

To find the conditions for maximum mass flow through a given area (in isentropic flow), the isentropic flow function must be differentiated and set equal to zero.

$$\frac{d}{dM}\left(\frac{w\sqrt{T_0}}{Ap_0} \sqrt{\frac{R}{g_0}}\right)$$

$$= \sqrt{k}\left[\frac{\left(1 + \frac{k-1}{2} M^2\right)^{[(k+1)/2(k-1)]} - \frac{k+1}{2} \times M^2\left(1 + \frac{k-1}{2} M^2\right)^{[(k+1)/2(k-1)]-1}}{\left(1 + \frac{k-1}{2} M^2\right)^{(k+1)/(k-1)}}\right] = 0$$

$$(5.54)$$

Then

$$1 - \frac{k+1}{2}\left(\frac{M^2}{1 + \frac{k-1}{2} M^2}\right) = 0 \qquad (5.55)$$

and solving for M^2,

$$M^2 = 1 \qquad (5.56)$$

Thus the maximum flow per unit area occurs at the section where the Mach number is unity.

The isentropic flow function is then

$$\left(\frac{w\sqrt{T_0}}{Ap_0} \sqrt{\frac{R}{g_0}}\right)_{max} = \frac{w}{A^*} \frac{\sqrt{T_0}}{p_0} \sqrt{\frac{R}{g_0}} = \sqrt{k}\left(\frac{2}{k+1}\right)^{(k+1)/2(k-1)} \qquad (5.57)$$

From this the maximum flow through a given section can be computed, and the pressure which will give this condition of maximum flow may be

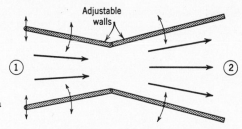

Fig. 5.7 Isentropic flow through a varying area duct.

calculated by considering equation (5.45) and employing the condition $M = 1$.

$$\left(\frac{p}{p_0}\right)_{\text{critical}} = \left[1 + \frac{k-1}{2}(1)\right]^{-k/(k-1)}$$

$$\left(\frac{p}{p_0}\right)_{\text{critical}} = \left(\frac{2}{k+1}\right)^{k/(k-1)} \tag{5.58}$$

Consider the flow in a duct as at section 1 in Figure 5.7. At section 1, the fluid has the values $M_1, p_1, T_1, \rho_1,$ and the area is A_1. From the continuity equation the mass rate of flow is $w = \rho_1 A_1 V_1$. At section 2 in the duct downstream from section 1, consider the area A_2 to be variable so that A_2/A_1 may be varied from very small to very large values. Integrating equation (5.18) for isentropic flow between station 1 and station 2,

$$\frac{A_2}{A_1} = \frac{M_1}{M_2}\left(\frac{1 + \dfrac{k-1}{2}M_2^{\,2}}{1 + \dfrac{k-1}{2}M_1^{\,2}}\right)^{(k+1)/2(k-1)} \tag{5.59}$$

For a given area ratio, A_2/A_1, and for a given value of M_1, M_2 may best be found by a trial and error solution of equation (5.60) for which the right-hand side may be evaluated numerically.

$$\frac{\left(1 + \dfrac{k-1}{2}M_2^{\,2}\right)^{(k+1)/(k-1)}}{M_2^{\,2}} = \left(\frac{A_2}{A_1}\right)^2 \frac{\left(1 + \dfrac{k-1}{2}M_1^{\,2}\right)^{(k+1)/(k-1)}}{M_1^{\,2}} \tag{5.60}$$

However, it is not always possible to obtain a value for M_2 which satisfies equation (5.60), for indeed a solution is impossible for certain combinations of M_1 and A_2/A_1.

When a solution is possible, there are always two values for M_2 which satisfy the equation. One solution is supersonic and the other is subsonic. For solutions which correspond to a subsonic flow at station 1 and a supersonic flow at station 2, and for those corresponding to a supersonic flow at station 1 and a subsonic flow at station 2, there must be a minimum section (throat) somewhere between station 1 and station 2. This is evident from the considerations of section 5.3.

For example, if the area ratio, A_2/A_1, is 0.8, and the value for Mach number at station 1 is 0.4, then (assuming $k = 1.4$):

$$\frac{(1 + 0.2M_2{}^2)^6}{M_2{}^2} = (0.64)\frac{(1.032)^6}{0.16} = 4.832$$

Solving by trial and error, with

$$M_2 = 0.55; \qquad \frac{(1 + 0.0605)^6}{0.3025} = \frac{1.422}{0.3025} = 4.70$$

$$M_2 = 0.53; \qquad \frac{(1 + 0.05618)^6}{0.2809} = \frac{1.388}{0.2809} = 4.94$$

$$M_2 = 0.54; \qquad \frac{(1 + 0.05832)^6}{0.2916} = \frac{1.405}{0.2916} = 4.83$$

and also, with

$$M_2 = 1.62; \qquad \frac{(1 + 0.52488)^6}{2.6244} = 4.80$$

$$M_2 = 1.63; \qquad \frac{(1 + 0.53138)^6}{2.6569} = 4.86$$

Thus M_2 will approximately equal 0.54 if there is no throat between station 1 and station 2, and may have either of the approximate values 0.54 or 1.63 if there is a throat between station 1 and station 2.

More important, for a given area ratio there is a corresponding maximum subsonic value for M_1. The function $\dfrac{\left(1 + \dfrac{k-1}{2}M_2{}^2\right)^{(k+1)/(k-1)}}{M_2{}^2}$ has a minimum value when $M_2 = 1$. This is shown by differentiating and setting equal to zero:

$$\frac{d}{dM_2}\left[\frac{\left(1 + \dfrac{k-1}{2}M_2{}^2\right)^{(k+1)/(k-1)}}{M_2{}^2}\right]$$

$$= \frac{(k+1)\left(1 + \dfrac{k-1}{2}M_2{}^2\right)^{2/(k-1)}M_2{}^3 - 2M_2\left(1 + \dfrac{k-1}{2}M_2{}^2\right)^{(k+1)/(k-1)}}{M_2{}^4} = 0$$

or

$$(k+1)M_2^2\left(1 + \frac{k-1}{2}M_2^2\right)^{2/(k-1)} - 2\left(1 + \frac{k-1}{2}M_2^2\right)^{(k+1)/(k-1)} = 0$$

from which $M_2 = 1$. Therefore, the function $\dfrac{\left(1 + \dfrac{k-1}{2}M_1^2\right)^{(k+1)/(k-1)}}{M_1^2}$ can never be less than

$$\left(\frac{A_1}{A_2}\right)^2\left(1 + \frac{k-1}{2}\right)^{(k+1)/(k-1)}$$

For example, with $A_2/A_1 = 0.8$,

$$\frac{\left(1 + \dfrac{k-1}{2}M_1^2\right)^{(k+1)/(k-1)}}{M_1^2} \leq 1.5625\left(1 + \frac{k-1}{2}\right)^{(k+1)/(k-1)}$$

and for $k = 1.4$

$$\frac{(1 + 0.2M_1^2)^6}{M_1^2} \leq 1.5625(1.2)^6 = 4.66$$

For

$$M_1 = 0.54; \quad \frac{\left(1 + \dfrac{k-1}{2}M_1^2\right)^6}{M_1^2} = \frac{(1.0583)^6}{0.2915} = 4.83$$

$$M_1 = 0.55; \quad \frac{\left(1 + \dfrac{k-1}{2}M_1^2\right)^6}{M_1^2} = \frac{(1.0605)^6}{0.3025} = 4.71$$

$$M_1 = 0.56; \quad \frac{\left(1 + \dfrac{k-1}{2}M_1^2\right)^6}{M_1^2} = \frac{(1.06272)^6}{0.3136} = 4.60$$

And thus it is shown that the maximum value for M_1 with an area ratio $A_2/A_1 = 0.8$ is about 0.555. If the initial M_1 is more than 0.555, the area reduction at station 2 will cause the conditions upstream (at point 1) to change and the Mach number to be reduced to a value at or below 0.555. Thus the mass flow rate is reduced. Such a flow is said to be "choked."

As the area A_2 is reduced there must be a corresponding decrease in back pressure p_2 as required for isentropic flow. The maximum M_1 (which also gives the maximum mass rate of flow) occurs when $M_2 = 1$. Thus a choked flow is one which has the fluid flowing with the acoustic velocity at the section of minimum flow area.

5.7 Thrust in isentropic flow

In an isentropic flow, as in any flow situation, the thrust which is developed by the fluid may be evaluated by using the impulse function, as explained in Chapter 4. Particularly in working with exhaust nozzles in propulsive devices, it was found in Chapter 4 that the thrust function had certain advantages in comparing experimental data.

It is now possible to apply isentropic conditions to a flow pattern and determine the ideal thrust which would result by expanding the fluid to a certain lower pressure. If the quantity $\dfrac{F}{w\sqrt{T_0}}\sqrt{\dfrac{g_0}{R}}$ can be evaluated for an ideal flow, then for a certain thrust, F, to result, a limit on the product $w\sqrt{T_0}$ is fixed. Thus, if F is to be a given number of pounds and T_0 cannot exceed a certain fixed temperature, the mass flow could be determined, which would provide the required thrust for isentropic flow. From equation (4.6)

$$\frac{F}{w\sqrt{T_0}}\sqrt{\frac{g_0}{R}} = \frac{I_2}{w\sqrt{T_0}}\sqrt{\frac{g_0}{R}} - \frac{I_1}{w\sqrt{T_0}}\sqrt{\frac{g_0}{R}} \tag{5.61}$$

and for isentropic flow, defining an isentropic impulse function, f_I

$$\frac{F}{w\sqrt{T_0}}\sqrt{\frac{g_0}{R}} = \frac{1 + kM_2^2}{M_2\left[k\left(1 + \dfrac{k-1}{2}M_2^2\right)\right]^{\frac{1}{2}}} - \frac{1 + kM_1^2}{M_1\left[k\left(1 + \dfrac{k-1}{2}M_1^2\right)\right]^{\frac{1}{2}}}$$

$$= f_{I2} - f_{I1} \tag{5.62}$$

where

$$f_I = \frac{1 + kM^2}{M\left[k\left(1 + \dfrac{k-1}{2}M^2\right)\right]^{\frac{1}{2}}} \tag{5.63}$$

The isentropic impulse function is (a) a dimensionless quantity, and (b) a function of Mach number only, and hence can be calculated just as the other isentropic functions developed in section 5.5. This function is tabulated in the Appendix for Mach numbers from 0 to 10, and for the usual values of k.

Example of use of the isentropic impulse function

A certain jet airplane is flying at a Mach number of 0.8 in an atmosphere where the temperature is 450°R. In the power plant sufficient fuel is added to increase the stagnation temperature to 2000°R, and the gases leave the exhaust nozzle with a Mach number of 1.1. Assuming all processes to be isentropic with the exception of the heating, find the thrust produced for each pound per second of air flow through the power plant (assume the mass of fuel to be small relative to the mass of air):

$$\frac{F}{w} = \frac{I_2}{w} - \frac{I_1}{w} = (f_{I2}\sqrt{T_{02}} - f_{I1}\sqrt{T_{01}})\sqrt{\frac{R}{g_0}}$$

For $k = 1.4$:

$$f_{I_2} = 1.8573$$

$$f_{I_1} = 1.8859$$

$$\frac{F}{w} = [1.8573(44.8) - 1.8859(21.2)]\sqrt{\frac{53.3}{32.2}}$$

$$= 55.5 \text{ lb}_f \text{ sec/lb}_m$$

5.8 Losses in adiabatic flow

In any no-work adiabatic flow in which there is friction or drag there must be some resulting increase in entropy. An entropy increase in a moving fluid will cause a reduction in the stagnation pressure of the fluid. Figure 5.8 shows this on a temperature entropy diagram. The ratio of stagnation pressures for an adiabatic flow was given in equation (5.37)

$$\frac{p_{02}}{p_{01}} = e^{(s_1 - s_2)/R} \tag{5.64}$$

Equations (5.7), (5.12), and (5.18) all have a term involving the entropy change. With an entropy increase, (*a*) the pressure ratio (final pressure divided by the initial pressure) must be less than the ideal ratio; (*b*) the density ratio must be less than the ideal ratio; and (*c*) the area ratio must be more than the ideal ratio.

While these other properties experience a change from their ideal values whenever there is an entropy increase, they are all also functions of Mach numbers. Thus it remains for the stagnation pressure ratio to give the best

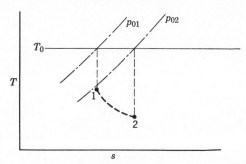

Fig. 5.8 Stagnation pressure loss with entropy increase.

indication of entropy increase and flow losses. The relative loss in stagnation pressure is related to entropy as follows:

$$\frac{p_{01} - p_{02}}{p_{01}} = 1 - \frac{p_{02}}{p_{01}} = 1 - e^{(s_1 - s_2)/R} \tag{5.65}$$

$\Delta p_0/p_{01}$ is frequently a very convenient measure of loss. It must have some relation to the various flow efficiencies, as will be seen in the following paragraphs.

It is usual to define an adiabatic nozzle efficiency as the actual increase in kinetic energy of the fluid divided by the ideal increase for the same pressure drop. For an adiabatic nozzle this must be equivalent to the actual enthalpy drop divided by the ideal enthalpy drop. That is,

$$\eta_n = \frac{\Delta h_{\text{actual}}}{\Delta h_{\text{ideal}}} \tag{5.66}$$

or, for the case with negligible inlet velocity,

$$\eta_n = \frac{(h_0 - h_2)_{\text{actual}}}{(h_0 - h_2)_{\text{ideal}}} \tag{5.67}$$

From this definition it is possible to express the nozzle efficiency in terms of the actual Mach number leaving the nozzle and the ideal Mach number leaving the nozzle.

If the efficiency of a nozzle is known, the entrance and exit states can be located on a Mollier chart, and thus the loss (or entropy increase) is readily determined.

Similarly, diffuser efficiency may be defined as the actual static pressure rise divided by the dynamic pressure loss (or ideal static pressure rise for the same kinetic energy decrease):

$$\eta_d = \frac{\Delta p_{\text{actual}}}{\Delta p_{\text{ideal}}} = \frac{p_2 - p_1}{(\rho_1 V_1^2 - \rho_2 V_2^2)/2g_0} \tag{5.68}$$

Note that $\Delta p_{\text{ideal}} = \Delta p_{\text{actual}} + \Delta p_{\text{loss}}$

$$\Delta p_{\text{ideal}} = (p_{2\,\text{actual}} - p_1) + (p_{2\,\text{ideal}} - p_{2\,\text{actual}})$$

Since $h_{2\,\text{actual}} = h_{2\,\text{ideal}}$ (for an adiabatic process with the same kinetic energy decrease), for a process from the ideal point to the actual point (see Figure 5.9):

$$ds = \frac{dh - \dfrac{1}{\rho} dp}{T} = -\frac{R\,dp}{p}$$

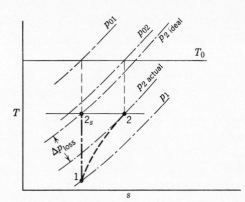

Fig. 5.9 Ts diagram for diffusion process.

Similarly at the stagnation points:

$$ds_0 = \frac{dh_0 - \frac{1}{\rho_0}dp_0}{T_0} = -\frac{R\,dp_0}{p_0}$$

Then, since $ds = ds_0$

$$\frac{p_{2\text{ actual}}}{p_{2\text{ ideal}}} = \frac{p_{02}}{p_{01}} \tag{5.69}$$

and because $p_{2\text{ ideal}} \approx p_{01}$, for most diffusers,

$$p_{2\text{ ideal}} - p_{2\text{ actual}} \approx p_{01} - p_{02} \tag{5.70}$$

Then a suitable, and frequently used, definition for diffuser efficiency is:

$$\eta_d = \frac{\Delta p}{\Delta p + \Delta p_0} \tag{5.71}$$

This expression may be related to entropy increase through use of equation (5.37).

Another nozzle performance characteristic, velocity coefficient, is frequently used. Velocity coefficient is usually defined as the actual velocity divided by the ideal velocity.

$$C_V = \frac{\text{Actual velocity}}{\text{Ideal velocity}} = \frac{V_{2\text{ actual}}}{V_{2\text{ ideal}}} \tag{5.72}$$

It may be shown that this is the square root of the nozzle efficiency as given in equation 5.67 (see problem 5.22). Hence $\eta_n = C_V^2$ as in most elementary thermodynamics courses.

One other performance characteristic is frequently used in discussing

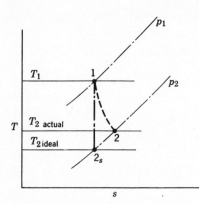

Fig. 5.10 Adiabatic flow expansion process.

adiabatic flow (particularly in nozzles). This is the flow or discharge co-efficient. It is defined as:

$$C_w = \frac{\text{Actual flow}}{\text{Ideal flow}} = \frac{w}{w_i} \tag{5.73}$$

The ratio C_V/C_w provides some interesting results.

$$\frac{C_V}{C_w} = \frac{V_{2\,\text{actual}}/V_{2\,\text{ideal}}}{(\rho_2 A_2 V_2)_{\text{actual}}/(\rho_2 A_2 V_2)_{\text{ideal}}} = \frac{\rho_{2\,\text{ideal}}}{\rho_{2\,\text{actual}}} \tag{5.74}$$

In the case of flow through a nozzle (or any other adiabatic flow expansion process), the entropy increase also can be evaluated from the ratio of ideal density to actual density. Since the pressure at the end of the ideal process is the same as the pressure at the end of the actual process (see Figure 5.10), the properties at point 2 actual and point 2 ideal may be related as follows:

$$ds = c_p \frac{dT}{T} - \frac{dp}{\rho T} = c_p \frac{dT}{T}$$

but for a perfect gas,

$$\frac{d\rho}{\rho} = \frac{dp}{p} - \frac{dT}{T}$$

or since $dp = 0$,

$$ds = -\frac{kR}{k-1} \frac{d\rho}{\rho}$$

$$\left(\frac{\rho_{2\,\text{ideal}}}{\rho_{2\,\text{actual}}}\right)^{k/(k-1)} = e^{\Delta s/R} \tag{5.75}$$

Where $\Delta s = s_{2\,\text{actual}} - s_{2\,\text{ideal}}$, which is the same as the entropy increase during the actual adiabatic expansion process.

Now, combining equations (5.74) and (5.75), the relation between the ratio of the coefficients and the entropy increase is found to be:

$$e^{\Delta s/R} = \left(\frac{C_V}{C_w}\right)^{k/(k-1)} = \left(\frac{\rho_{2\,\text{ideal}}}{\rho_{2\,\text{actual}}}\right)^{k/(k-1)} \tag{5.76}$$

From this relation, equation (5.76), it is evident that for an adiabatic flow, C_V must be always larger than C_w. In addition, it is evident that the actual density must be smaller than the ideal density. (This is also evident from Figure 5.10; since at point 2 actual the temperature is higher than at 2 ideal, the reverse must be true for the densities.)

Equation (5.76) may also provide an interesting way to measure the entropy increase in an adiabatic flow, if the velocity coefficient and the flow coefficient can each be determined experimentally with a reasonable degree of accuracy.

Problems

5.1 Products of combustion leave the nozzle of a rocket engine with a Mach number of 4. The pressure at this point is 10 psia. The specific heat ratio is 1.3. What is the nozzle inlet stagnation pressure for isentropic flow? What is the ratio of static to stagnation temperature?

5.2 Air flows isentropically through a circular tube of 5-in. radius with a Mach number of 0.4. Downstream the tube is smaller, having only a 4-in. radius. What is the Mach number at this section?

5.3 Air with a Mach number of 3.0 flows through a pipe with an area of 25 sq in. The pressure is 14.7 psia and the temperature is 40°F. Find the stagnation pressure, the stagnation temperature, the mass flow per unit area, the minimum area which will give this mass flow (this is sometimes called critical area), and the velocity where the area is 20 sq in.

5.4 Air flows with a subsonic velocity through a pipe having an area of 25 sq in. The air pressure is 14.7 psia and the temperature is 40°F. What is the maximum velocity at this section, if downstream the flow is choked by passing through a section of 6-sq in. area?

5.5 A certain diffuser has an area ratio of 2:1. What is the per cent pressure rise, if the inlet Mach number varies as below?
(a) 0.1
(b) 0.5
(c) 2.5
Assume isentropic flow with $k = 1.4$.

5.6 An ideal (isentropic) diffuser has air entering it with a Mach number of 0.7. The area ratio of this diffuser is 2.0. Inlet conditions are $p = 50$ psia and $T = 140°F$.
(a) Find the stagnation pressure at the inlet section.
(b) Find the stagnation temperature at the inlet section.
(c) Find the exit Mach number.
(d) Find the exit pressure.
(e) Find the exit temperature.
(f) Find the exit velocity.

5.7 Air flows through a duct area of 1 sq ft at a velocity of 700 ft/sec. The temperature is 140°F and the pressure is 50 psia. Find the area of the minimum section downstream which will assure that this flow is "choked."

5.8 Air is expanded from 100 psia and 540°F through a nozzle to pressure of 20 psia. The exit Mach number is found to be 1.6.
(a) Find the efficiency of this nozzle.
(b) Find the ratio of the inlet stagnation pressure to exit stagnation pressure.

5.9 Air is supplied to a converging-diverging nozzle at low velocity at 100 psia and 540°F. This nozzle discharges at atmospheric pressure and the flow is ideal adiabatic. For a rate of 1 lb/sec, calculate the exit Mach number, the throat pressure, the throat and exit areas, and the throat and exit velocities.

5.10 Air is supplied through a nozzle with an exit area of 10 sq in. A tank supplies the air at 75 psia and 340°F, and the discharge pressure is 50 psia. Assuming no loss, determine the discharge temperature, the discharge velocity and Mach number, and the mass flow.

5.11 Find the mass of air flow per second through 1 sq in. of area, if the air is supplied from a tank with a pressure of 100 psia and a temperature of 600°R and the Mach number varies as below.
(a) 0.5
(b) 0.8
(c) 1.0
(d) 1.5
(e) 2.0

5.12 In a certain model test in which low temperature ($T_0 = 530°R$, and $p_0 = 35$ psia) air is used, it is found that the flow is 50 lb/sec. Estimate the mass flow that occurs in the prototype which has three times the cross-sectional area at each point and which employs air at $T_0 = 800°R$ and $p_0 = 25$ psia.

5.13 Estimate how much gas flow is required to produce 1000 lb of thrust in a rocket engine which produces gases with a gas constant of 40 ft $lb_f/lb_m R$ and a stagnation temperature at 2000°R, if the gases leave the rocket exhaust nozzle at a Mach number of 2.0. What must be the nozzle exit area to pass this quantity of gas, if the pressure at the nozzle exit is 10 psia?

5.14 In a certain flow of air, it is found that the Mach number must be 0.9 at the section where the area is 1 sq ft in order to pass the proper amount of air. What is the impulse function, I, at this point? Assume $p_0 = 30$ psia.

5.15 Work problem 5.10 with the nozzle being 85% efficient.

5.16 Steam enters a certain nozzle at 700 psia and 700°F. The velocity leaving the nozzle is 2000 ft/sec and the nozzle efficiency is 90%. Find the entropy increase between the inlet and discharge states.

5.17 A diffuser having an area ratio of 0.5 has an inlet Mach number of 0.6 and an exit Mach number of 0.3. Find the ratio of inlet stagnation pressure to exit stagnation pressure. Find the entropy increase. Assume the fluid to be air.

5.18 Air is supplied through a nozzle with an exit area of 10 sq in. A tank supplies the air at 75 psia and 340°F and the discharge pressure is 50 psia. Assuming $C_V = 0.90$, find the discharge temperature, the discharge velocity and Mach number, the mass flow, and the entropy increase.

5.19 A certain diffuser has an area ratio of 1.5 to 1. The initial Mach number is 0.7. Find the ratio of the final pressure to the initial pressure if:
(a) The diffuser is 100% efficient.
(b) The diffuser is 90% efficient.
Assume $k = 1.4$.

5.20 A diffuser is designed to operate with an inlet Mach number of 0.7 and a discharge Mach number of 0.3. Find the inlet to discharge area ratio if:
(a) The diffuser is 100% efficient.
(b) The diffuser is 90% efficient.

5.21 Develop an expression for the efficiency of a nozzle in terms of the actual exit Mach number and the ideal exit Mach number.

5.22 Starting with the basic definition of velocity coefficient for a nozzle, develop an expression for nozzle velocity coefficient in terms of actual exit Mach number and ideal exit Mach number, and show that this is the square root of the nozzle efficiency.

5.23 Start with the fundamental definition of flow coefficient for a nozzle and show that

$$C_w = \frac{M_2}{M_{2i}} \left(\frac{1 + \dfrac{k-1}{2} M_{2i}^2}{1 + \dfrac{k-1}{2} M_2^2} \right)^{\frac{k+1}{2(k-1)}} e^{-(\Delta s/R)}$$

where M_2 is the actual exit Mach number
M_{2i} is the ideal exit Mach number

5.24 Show that

$$C_V C_w = \frac{M_2^2}{M_{2i}^2}$$

where M_2 is the actual exit Mach number
M_{2i} is the ideal exit Mach number

5.25 Show that the entropy increase in an adiabatic process may be related to the ideal and actual Mach numbers after the process as follows:

$$e^{\Delta s/R} = \left(\frac{1 + \dfrac{k-1}{2} M_{2i}^2}{1 + \dfrac{k-1}{2} M_2^2} \right)^{\frac{k}{k-1}}$$

References

1. A. H. Shapiro: *The Dynamics and Thermodynamics of Compressible Fluid Flow*, Vol. I, Ronald Press, New York, 1953.
2. Newman A. Hall: *Thermodynamics of Fluid Flow*, Prentice-Hall, Englewood Cliffs, N.J., 1951.
3. C. W. Smith: *Aircraft Gas Turbines*, John Wiley and Sons, New York, 1956.

6

adiabatic flow in constant-area ducts

Introduction—Fanno lines

In the previous chapter, an adiabatic flow was analyzed on the basis of isentropic flow with appropriate efficiencies or coefficients to account for the irreversibility in the flow. This plan is customary in the case of nozzles and diffusers. In the important case of constant-area flow, where friction is the chief factor bringing about changes in the fluid properties, it is possible to express the properties directly as a function of that friction.

In this chapter, the discussion will be limited to flow situations in which there is constant area, no work, and no heat transfer to or from the fluid transmission line. In short transmission lines where no attempt is made to provide heating or cooling, the flow may be considered to be experiencing no heat transfer and the procedures of this chapter will provide satisfactory calculation techniques. This is particularly true in some of the ducting between parts of an aircraft propulsion engine. Also, the flow in ducts associated with some high-vacuum work may be considered to be adiabatic with a satisfactory accuracy resulting.

For adiabatic, constant area, no work flow, the steady flow energy equation (2.22) gives

$$dh + \frac{dV^2}{2g_0} = 0 \qquad (6.1)$$

and since $A = $ constant, continuity shows

$$\frac{w}{A} = \rho V = \text{constant} \qquad (6.2)$$

Differentiating the square of equation (6.2),

$$dV^2 = -2\left(\frac{w}{A}\right)^2 \frac{d\rho}{\rho^3} \qquad (6.3)$$

and substituting in equation (6.1) for dV^2,

$$dh - \left(\frac{w}{A}\right)^2 \frac{d\rho}{g_0\rho^3} = 0 \qquad (6.4)$$

Equation (6.4) is the equation which describes constant area, adiabatic flow. This describes a family of curves, or Fanno lines as they are called, and the shape of these curves may be seen by integrating equation (6.4)

$$h - h_0 + \frac{1}{2g_0}\left(\frac{w}{A}\right)^2\left(\frac{1}{\rho^2} - \frac{1}{\rho_0^2}\right) = 0 \qquad (6.5)$$

or

$$h = h_0 - \frac{(w/A)^2}{2g_0}\left(\frac{1}{\rho^2} - \frac{1}{\rho_0^2}\right)$$

This equation gives the picture of Fanno line variations on an h versus $1/\rho$ diagram as shown in Figure 6.1.

To understand more completely the variation of state along a Fanno line, employ the relation from thermodynamics,

$$dh = T\,ds + \frac{dp}{\rho} \qquad (6.6)$$

Substituting for dh as given in equation (6.6) into the fundamental relation for constant-area, adiabatic flow (i.e., equation 6.4) gives,

$$\rho T\,ds + dp - \left(\frac{w}{A}\right)^2 \frac{d\rho}{g_0\rho^2} = 0 \qquad (6.7)$$

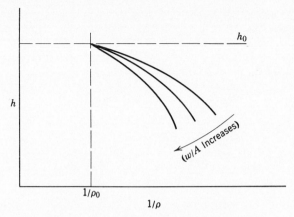

Fig. 6.1 Fanno lines on $h - (1/\rho)$ diagram.

For the point on the Fanno line where the entropy is a maximum, $ds = 0$;

$$\frac{dp}{d\rho} = \left(\frac{w}{A}\right)^2 \frac{1}{g_0 \rho^2}$$

or

$$g_0 \left(\frac{\partial p}{\partial \rho}\right)_s = \frac{(w/A)^2}{\rho^2} = V^2 \tag{6.8}$$

That is, for the point of maximum entropy on a Fanno line

$$a^2 = V^2 \tag{6.9}$$

It is desirable to be able to visualize the variations in the fluid properties along a Fanno line on an h–s or a T–s diagram. If the fluid is a pure substance for which the equation of state is known, then it is possible to eliminate two of the four variables (p, ρ, T, and s) from equation (6.7) and have an equation in only the two desired variables. In effect this is done in the following section for the case of a perfect gas; for example, evaluating T/T_1 from equation (6.12) and plotting versus $(s - s_1)/R$ evaluated from equation (6.17), for various values of Mach number, results in a curve of the general shape shown in Figure 6.2.

It was just shown, equation (6.9), that the maximum entropy must occur at a Mach number of 1.0. For adiabatic flow, the second law of thermodynamics requires that the entropy increase. This means that from either side, subsonic or supersonic, the state approaches the condition for sonic velocity. The upper part of the Fanno curve approaches the h_0 line asymptotically, indicating that at very low velocities the entropy may increase as a result of friction with the enthalpy remaining constant. This is the usual procedure of considering flow with friction equivalent to a throttling process ($h_1 = h_2$).

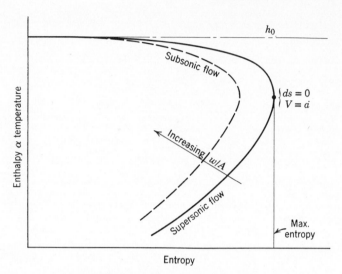

Fig. 6.2 Typical Fanno line for gases.

At points on the upper portion of the curve, the flow is subsonic; and as the entropy increases, the Mach number becomes closer to unity. At a maximum value of entropy, the Mach number reaches the limiting value, $M = 1$. At points on the lower portion of the curve, the flow is supersonic; and as the entropy increases, the Mach number is reduced and again reaches the limiting value of unity for the condition of maximum entropy. Since the entropy can never decrease (second law of thermodynamics), for adiabatic constant-area conditions a subsonic flow can never become supersonic; and in the absence of a discontinuity, a supersonic flow can never become subsonic.

6.2 Fanno relations for perfect gases

Obtaining an expression for the variation in fluid properties along the length of a constant-area duct is possible by analytical procedures for a perfect gas. Many gases are sufficiently close in behavior to make these analytical relations useful. In other cases, the expressions are helpful in drawing general conclusions which would otherwise be impossible.

By definition of stagnation state:

$$T = \frac{T_0}{1 + \dfrac{k-1}{2} M^2}$$

$$dT_0 = d\left[T\left(1 + \frac{k-1}{2} M^2\right)\right]$$

(6.10)

For adiabatic flow, $dT_0 = 0$, then performing the differentiation on the right-hand side of equation (6.10),

$$\frac{dT}{T} = - \frac{d\left(1 + \frac{k-1}{2} M^2\right)}{\left(1 + \frac{k-1}{2} M^2\right)} \tag{6.11}$$

or in integrated form,

$$\frac{T}{T_1} = \frac{1 + \frac{k-1}{2} M_1^{\,2}}{1 + \frac{k-1}{2} M^2} \tag{6.12}$$

For the condition of a Fanno line, $w/A = $ constant, and the equation of continuity,

$$\frac{dp}{p} + \frac{dM}{M} - \frac{1}{2} \frac{dT}{T} = 0 \tag{6.13}$$

Then the pressure variation along a Fanno line is described by

$$\frac{dp}{p} = \frac{1}{2} \frac{dT}{T} - \frac{dM}{M} \tag{6.14}$$

and substituting from equation (6.11),

$$\frac{dp}{p} = - \frac{1}{2} \frac{d\left(1 + \frac{k-1}{2} M^2\right)}{1 + \frac{k-1}{2} M^2} - \frac{dM}{M} \tag{6.15}$$

or

$$\frac{p}{p_1} = \frac{M_1}{M} \left(\frac{1 + \frac{k-1}{2} M_1^{\,2}}{1 + \frac{k-1}{2} M^2}\right)^{1/2} \tag{6.16}$$

For the entropy change,

$$\frac{ds}{R} = \frac{k}{k-1} \frac{dT}{T} - \frac{dp}{\rho RT}$$

$$= - \frac{(k+1)}{2(k-1)} \frac{d\left(1 + \frac{k-1}{2} M^2\right)}{1 + \frac{k-1}{2} M^2} + \frac{dM}{M} \tag{6.17}$$

The density change is easily found by using the perfect gas equation of state and equations (6.12) and (6.16)

$$\frac{\rho}{\rho_1} = \frac{p}{T}\frac{T_1}{p_1} = \frac{M_1}{M}\left(\frac{1 + \dfrac{k-1}{2}M^2}{1 + \dfrac{k-1}{2}M_1^2}\right)^{\frac{1}{2}} \tag{6.18}$$

Similarly

$$\frac{I}{I_1} = \frac{pA(1 + kM^2)}{p_1A(1 + kM_1^2)} = \frac{M_1}{M}\left(\frac{1 + kM^2}{1 + kM_1^2}\right)$$

$$\left(\frac{1 + \dfrac{k-1}{2}M_1^2}{1 + \dfrac{k-1}{2}M^2}\right)^{\frac{1}{2}} \tag{6.19}$$

And finally the stagnation pressure ratio can be obtained,

$$\frac{p_0}{p_{01}} = e^{-[(s-s_1)/R]} = \frac{M_1}{M}\left(\frac{1 + \dfrac{k-1}{2}M^2}{1 + \dfrac{k-1}{2}M_1^2}\right)^{(k+1)/2(k-1)} \tag{6.20}$$

6.3 The nature of the loss

As suggested in the previous two sections, friction may cause an entropy increase in the case of an adiabatic flow in a constant-area duct. Friction is not the only physical factor which will give an entropy increase in such a flow. It will be seen that internal drag losses can have a similar effect, and in each case it is desirable to have some rather direct method for evaluating the effect in terms of Mach number.

Considering the momentum equation in terms of Mach number, equation (3.46):

$$\frac{dp}{p} + \frac{k}{2}dM^2 + \frac{k}{2}M^2\frac{dT}{T} + \frac{k}{2}M^2\left(f\frac{dx}{D} + dC_D\right) = 0 \tag{6.21}$$

it is evident that the fluid properties undergo change because of the effects of the friction term, $f\dfrac{dx}{D}$, and the drag term, dC_D. To evaluate each, let the other be zero and determine the corresponding changes in the fluid properties.

For example, if all the entropy increase is due to friction, as in the case of a fluid moving at a high speed in a straight duct, then $dC_D = 0$, and equation (6.21) becomes

$$\frac{dp}{p} + \frac{k}{2} dM^2 + \frac{k}{2} M^2 \frac{dT}{T} + \frac{kM^2}{2} f \frac{dx}{D} = 0 \qquad (6.22)$$

Dividing by $kM^2/2$;

$$\frac{2dp}{kpM^2} + \frac{dM^2}{M^2} + \frac{dT}{T} + f \frac{dx}{D} = 0 \qquad (6.23)$$

It is desirable to eliminate the terms involving pressure and temperature before integrating. This is particularly true for the first term where both pressure and Mach number are variables.

Substituting for dp/p from equation (6.15) and for dT/T from equation (6.11), equation (6.23) becomes

$$-\frac{1}{kM^2} \frac{d\left(1 + \frac{k-1}{2} M^2\right)}{1 + \frac{k-1}{2} M^2} - \frac{2dM}{kM^3} + \frac{dM^2}{M^2} - \frac{d\left(1 + \frac{k-1}{2} M^2\right)}{1 + \frac{k-1}{2} M^2}$$

$$+ f \frac{dx}{D} = 0 \qquad (6.24)$$

Each of these terms is readily integrable except the first. Noting that,

$$-\frac{d\left(1 + \frac{k-1}{2} M^2\right)}{kM^2\left(1 + \frac{k-1}{2} M^2\right)} = -\frac{(k-1)\, dM^2}{2kM^2\left(1 + \frac{k-1}{2} M^2\right)}$$

$$= \frac{(k-1)\left(\dfrac{k-1}{2}\right) dM^2}{2k\left(1 + \dfrac{k-1}{2} M^2\right)} - \frac{k-1}{2k} \frac{dM^2}{M^2} \qquad (6.25)$$

Replacing the first term in equation (6.24) with its equivalent, as given in equation (6.25), and rearranging

$$f \frac{dx}{D} = \frac{k+1}{2k} \frac{d\left(1 + \dfrac{k-1}{2} M^2\right)}{1 + \dfrac{k-1}{2} M^2} + \frac{2dM}{kM^3} - \frac{k+1}{2k} \frac{dM^2}{M^2} \qquad (6.26)$$

Integrating

$$f\frac{x - x_1}{D} = \frac{1}{k}\left(\frac{1}{M_1{}^2} - \frac{1}{M^2}\right) + \frac{k + 1}{2k}\ln\frac{M_1{}^2}{M^2}\left(\frac{1 + \dfrac{k - 1}{2}M^2}{1 + \dfrac{k - 1}{2}M_1{}^2}\right) \qquad (6.27)$$

Thus for a given M_1 there is a maximum length which will allow such a flow to exist. This is true because no entropy increase (or length addition) is possible beyond that required for $M = 1$. This length is given by

$$f\frac{L_{\max}}{D} = \frac{1}{k}\left(\frac{1}{M_1{}^2} - 1\right) + \frac{k + 1}{2k}\ln\left(\frac{\dfrac{k + 1}{2}M_1{}^2}{1 + \dfrac{k - 1}{2}M_1{}^2}\right) \qquad (6.28)$$

A similar analysis is possible for the case of an entropy increase due to internal drag losses. In this case $f = 0$, and equation (6.21) becomes:

$$\frac{dp}{p} + \frac{k}{2}dM^2 + \frac{k}{2}M^2\frac{dT}{T} + \frac{kM^2}{2}dC_D = 0 \qquad (6.29)$$

In this equation it is again desirable to express the loss in terms of the Mach number. For the condition of continuity, $w/A = $ constant, just as in equation (6.13),

$$\frac{dp}{p} + \frac{dM}{M} = \frac{1}{2}\frac{dT}{T} \qquad (6.30)$$

Using equation (6.30) to eliminate dT/T in equation (6.29),

$$(1 + kM^2)\frac{dp}{p} + k\,dM^2 + \frac{kM^2}{2}dC_D = 0 \qquad (6.31)$$

$$dp + k\,d(pM^2) + \frac{kp_1M_1{}^2}{2}dC_D = 0 \qquad (6.32)$$

where the subscripts in the coefficient of the dC_D term indicate that the drag loss is evaluated in terms of the flow parameters just upstream from the flow interruption.

Integrating

$$p(1 + kM^2) - p_1(1 + kM_1{}^2) = -\frac{kp_1M_1{}^2}{2}C_D \qquad (6.33)$$

$$\frac{p}{p_1} = \frac{1 + kM_1{}^2 - \dfrac{kM_1{}^2C_D}{2}}{1 + kM^2} \qquad (6.34)$$

Equation (6.16) also gives an expression for p/p_1 which is valid for this condition. Equating the two,

$$1 + kM_1^2 - \frac{kM_1^2}{2} C_D = \frac{M_1}{M}(1 + kM^2)\left(\frac{1 + \frac{k-1}{2}M_1^2}{1 + \frac{k-1}{2}M^2}\right)^{\frac{1}{2}} \tag{6.25}$$

or solving for C_D,

$$C_D = \frac{2}{kM_1^2} + 2 - \frac{2(1 + kM^2)}{kMM_1}\left(\frac{1 + \frac{k-1}{2}M_1^2}{1 + \frac{k-1}{2}M^2}\right)^{\frac{1}{2}} \tag{6.36}$$

Note that for the case where $M_1 = M$ (that is, flow with constant Mach number),

$$C_D = \frac{2 + 2kM^2 - 2 - 2kM^2}{kM^2} = 0 \tag{6.37}$$

Thus, in order for the Mach number to be a constant in constant-area adiabatic flow with $f = 0$, the drag coefficient C_D must also equal 0.

For either a given drag coefficient or a known friction length, equation (6.36) or equation (6.28) must be solved for Mach number by trial and error.

From the equations in this section it may be shown that for $C_D \neq 0$ or $f\frac{L}{D} \neq 0$, M must increase in subsonic flow and decrease in supersonic flow.

Using this fact in connection with equations (6.11), (6.15), and (6.18) of the previous section, it is evident that the following table can be established to summarize the various changes:

	Equation	Subsonic	Supersonic
Temperature	(6.11)	decreases	increases
Pressure	(6.15)	decreases	increases
Density	(6.18)	decreases	increases
Velocity	(6.18)	increases	decreases

6.4 Reference states

As in the case of isentropic flow, it is more convenient to use the information of section 6.2 from a table of dimensionless ratios. In the preparation of such tabular data it is necessary again to employ certain references states in the computation of the several dimensionless ratios.

The stagnation state is one possible reference state, but more convenient and more useful is the state along the Fanno line where the Mach number is unity. Such a state is marked with an asterisk, i.e., p^*, T^*, etc. This is a different state from that used in the isentropic table where the fluid was accelerated to condition $M = 1.0$ with the entropy being held constant. In this case the entropy certainly is not constant. Confusion should not result from this notation if one is careful in noting the table which is being used.

6.5 Fanno tables

Just as in the case of isentropic flow, it is easier to calculate the dimensionless ratios for various Mach numbers and tabulate them for future reference, rather than calculate each case separately as needed. The temperature dimensionless ratio is found from equation (6.12)

$$\frac{T}{T^*} = \frac{\dfrac{k+1}{2}}{1 + \dfrac{k-1}{2} M^2} \tag{6.38}$$

Similarly from other equations already presented,

$$\frac{p}{p^*} = \frac{1}{M}\left(\frac{\dfrac{k+1}{2}}{1 + \dfrac{k-1}{2} M^2}\right)^{\frac{1}{2}} \tag{6.39}$$

$$\frac{\rho}{\rho^*} = \frac{V^*}{V} = \frac{1}{M}\left(\frac{1 + \dfrac{k-1}{2} M^2}{\dfrac{k+1}{2}}\right)^{\frac{1}{2}} \tag{6.40}$$

$$\frac{I}{I^*} = \frac{1 + kM^2}{M\sqrt{2(k+1)\left(1 + \dfrac{k-1}{2} M^2\right)}} \tag{6.41}$$

$$\frac{p_0}{p_0^*} = \frac{1}{M}\left(\frac{1 + \dfrac{k-1}{2} M^2}{\dfrac{k+1}{2}}\right)^{k+1/[2(k-1)]} \tag{6.42}$$

and finally,

$$f\frac{x^* - x}{D} = \frac{1}{k}\left(\frac{1}{M} - 1\right) + \frac{k+1}{2k} \ln\left(\frac{\dfrac{k+1}{2} M^2}{1 + \dfrac{k-1}{2} M^2}\right) \tag{6.43}$$

These ratios are tabulated in Table A.3 of the Appendix for Mach numbers from 0 to 10 and for k's of 1.4, 1.0, 1.1, 1.2, 1.3, and 1.67.

6.6 Choking resulting from friction or drag

In a given flow the question always arises as to what happens when the duct is made longer than $f\dfrac{x^* - x}{D}$. Do the laws of constant area adiabatic flow break down? (The entropy cannot go beyond the maximum value on that Fanno line.) Yet adding more length, and hence more friction, must result in some entropy change. If the flow is subsonic, it is a requirement that the Mach number at the maximum length cannot exceed unity. If it is unity then the added length will serve to decrease the Mach number at all points upstream and the mass flow will be decreased.

This condition is evident from Figure 6.2. If the maximum entropy is forced to increase then there must be a shift to a new Fanno line with a smaller mass flow, w/A. Under such conditions we may speak of "choked flow" as a result of friction.

It is interesting to consider the variation of maximum duct friction length for a given Mach number. Figure 6.3 shows the variation in the maximum length–diameter ratio with initial Mach number for a friction factor of 0.01.

Figure 6.3 shows that the frictional effects are very serious at higher Mach

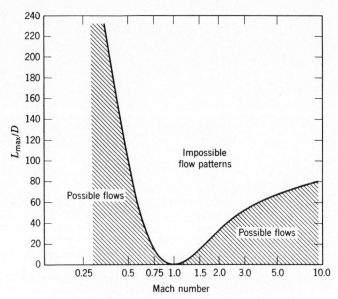

Fig. 6.3 Maximum length-diameter ratio for $f = 0.01$.

numbers. For supersonic flow, no matter how great the initial Mach number becomes, with $f = 0.01$, the total length cannot exceed 82 diameters. Any length longer than this prohibits supersonic flow.

Note that for subsonic flow if the length is increased, the initial Mach number has a lower maximum value. For example, if the L/D is 100, the Mach number must be about 0.5 or less. If the L/D is made larger, the Mach number must become smaller and the mass flow must be reduced.

Only points on the curve, or in the shaded area under the curve are possible. For points on the curve the flow is choked and the Mach number at the end of the duct must be 1.0. In the shaded areas under the curve, the Mach number at the end of the duct must be more than or less than unity, depending on whether the flow was initially supersonic or subsonic.

Problems

6.1 Air is flowing in an insulated duct with Mach number 0.25. At a section downstream the entropy is greater (as a result of friction) by an amount of 0.03 Btu/lb °R. What is the Mach number at this section? Initially the air is at 100 psia and 140°F. What is the velocity at the downstream section? What is the pressure?

6.2 Air, flowing in an insulated constant-area duct, experiences an increase of Mach number from 0.2 to 0.6 as a result of friction. The initial pressure and temperature are 20 psia and 70°F, respectively. What is the final pressure? What is the final velocity?

6.3 Air is flowing in an insulated duct with a velocity of 500 ft/sec. The temperature and pressure are 540°F and 200 psia, respectively.
  (a) Find the temperature in this duct where the pressure has dropped to 150 psia as a result of friction.
  (b) If the duct has a diameter of 6 in. and if the friction factor is 0.02, find the distance between the two points.
  (c) Find the velocity where the pressure is 150 psia.

6.4 Air flows in an insulated 6-in. duct at the rate of 1000 lb/min. The temperature is 540°F at the point where the pressure is 60 psia. What is the Mach number at a point where the pressure is 50 psia?

6.5 Find the ratio of stagnation pressure at the two points in problem 6.4. What is the entropy increase?

6.6 Assume a friction factor of 0.02 and find the distance between the two points in problem 6.4.

6.7 What is the temperature at the second point in problem 6.4?

6.8 Show that for a perfect gas flowing in an insulated duct the pressure at the choking condition is

$$p^* = \frac{w}{A} \sqrt{R/kg_0} \sqrt{2T_0/(k + 1)}$$

6.9 Air flows through a duct of area 1 sq ft. At the inlet the pressure is 15 psia and the temperature is 80°F. The mass flow is 25 lb/sec and the exhaust pressure is low enough to assure "choked" flow.

(*a*) What is the inlet Mach number?

(*b*) What is the pressure at the exit section?

(*c*) What is the temperature at the exit section?

(*d*) What is the Mach number at the point in the duct where the pressure is 10 psia?

(*e*) How much thrust is exerted by the fluid on this duct in the axial direction between the inlet and the point where the pressure is 10 psia?

6.10 A certain orifice having a drag coefficient of 1.0, is placed in an air flow where the upstream Mach number is 0.5. What is the downstream Mach number? What is the ratio of stagnation pressures? What is the entropy increase?

References

1. N. A. Hall: *Thermodynamics of Fluid Flow*, Prentice-Hall, Englewood Cliffs, N. J., 1951.
2. A. H. Shapiro: *The Dynamics and Thermodynamics of Compressible Fluid Flow*, Vol. I, Ronald Press, New York, 1953.

7

normal shock

7.1 Occurrence of shocks

With certain fixed boundary conditions on a given steady flow, it is not always possible for the various fluid properties to vary in a smooth and continuous manner. For example, a supersonic flow in a duct in which the discharge pressure is too high to allow the continuation of supersonic flow will experience a discontinuity which is called a shock wave. The fluid undergoes a change of all its physical quantities across the shock wave, and in particular the discontinuity in the pressure makes it possible for the fluid to have the proper discharge pressure. Such variations (across a shock wave) are not isentropic even in flows which might otherwise be isentropic.

An attempt to understand the physical nature of the shock has been made by the use of schlieren photographs of flows in ducts and around projectiles. These photographs show that the discontinuity in fluid properties is very sharp. There is evidence that a normal shock is of the order of 10^{-5} in. in thickness. The shock is so thin that it is extremely difficult to obtain data on the heat transfer and viscous phenomena which occur in the interior of a shock wave. Fortunately it is usually sufficient to determine the variation (net change) in fluid properties across the shock wave. The major portion of this chapter is devoted to explaining how such variations can be determined.

7.2 Fundamental equations for normal shock

Consider a control volume as in Figure 7.1, specified so as to include the normal shock and a small quantity of fluid on each side of the discontinuity.

A normal shock is essentially adiabatic and since no external work is done, energy considerations give one basic equation for the selected control volume.

$$dh + \frac{dV^2}{2g_0} = dh_0 = 0 \qquad (7.1)$$

The continuity equation (since the flow area must be the same on both sides of the discontinuity) gives a second equation.

$$\frac{w}{A} = \rho V = \text{Constant} \qquad (7.2)$$

The momentum equation may be written for the control volume of Figure 7.1, thus giving a third basic equation.

$$dp + \rho V \frac{dV}{g_0} = 0 \qquad (7.3)$$

Dividing equation (7.3) by ρV and integrating (with $\rho V = $ constant):

$$\frac{p_x}{\rho_x V_x} - \frac{p_y}{\rho_y V_y} + \frac{V_x - V_y}{g_0} = 0 \qquad (7.4)$$

The three fundamental equations, (7.1), (7.2), (7.3), are expressed in terms of four variables, p, ρ, V, and T. Therefore, one more relationship is

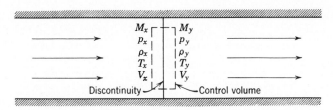

Fig. 7.1 Control volume, including a normal discontinuity.

required before the fluid properties on one side of the shock can be expressed in terms of the properties on the other side. Such a suitable relationship is the equation of state of the fluid. The solution of a set of equations with four variables is not necessarily easy to accomplish. Frequently methods involving approximations are required, but for a perfect gas, the equation of state is such that exact solutions are possible.

7.3 Normal shock equations for a perfect gas

When considering a perfect gas, equation (7.1) may better be expressed in terms of temperature, with $kR/(k-1)$ substituted for the constant pressure specific heat capacity.

$$\frac{2kRg_0}{k-1} dT + dV^2 = \frac{2kRg_0}{k-1} dT_0 \tag{7.5}$$

$$\frac{2}{k-1} da^2 + dV^2 = \frac{2kRg_0}{k-1} dT_0 \tag{7.6}$$

or

$$\frac{2}{k-1} a_x^2 + V_x^2 = \frac{2}{k-1} a_y^2 + V_y^2 = \frac{2kRg_0}{k-1} T_0 \tag{7.7}$$

Multiplying equation (7.4) by kg_0:

$$kg_0 \frac{p_x}{\rho_x} \frac{1}{V_x} - \frac{kg_0 p_y}{\rho_y} \frac{1}{V_y} + k(V_x - V_y) = 0 \tag{7.8}$$

Combining equations (7.7) and (7.8),

$$\frac{1}{V_x}\left(kg_0 R T_0 - \frac{k-1}{2} V_x^2\right) - \frac{1}{V_y}\left(kg_0 R T_0 - \frac{k-1}{2} V_y^2\right)$$
$$+ k(V_x - V_y) = 0$$

or

$$\frac{kg_0 R T_0 (V_y - V_x)}{V_x V_y} + \frac{k+1}{2}(V_x - V_y) = 0 \tag{7.9}$$

Since $V_x \neq V_y$,

$$V_x V_y = \frac{2T_0}{k+1}(kg_0 R) = T^*(kg_0 R) = a^{*2} \tag{7.10}$$

This is the Prandtl relation (or Meyer relation).

Recalling that a^* is the acoustic velocity corresponding to the state where the fluid is moving with sonic velocity, it is evident that if V_x is more than a^*, then V_y must be less than a^*. Obviously the solution, $V_x = V_y = a^*$, is valid mathematically, but is trivial in this case since there is then no

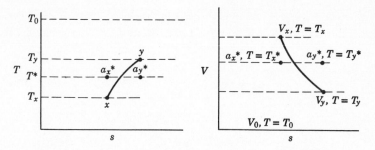

Fig. 7.2 Temperature and velocity changes across a normal shock.

discontinuity. (See Figure 7.2.) In terms of the speed ratio M^* (see equation 5.39),

$$M_x^* = \frac{1}{M_y^*} \tag{7.11}$$

M_x^* is more than unity when and only when M_x is more than unity and is less than unity only when M_x is less than unity. Similar relations hold for M_y^* relative to M_y, and hence the changes across a normal shock must be from subsonic to supersonic, or from supersonic to subsonic. It will be pointed out later (section 7.5) in this chapter that only the case of supersonic to subsonic is possible as a consequence of the second law of thermodynamics.

The proper relationship between the Mach numbers before and after the shock is not as simple as the relationship of the speed ratio in equation (7.11). In order to obtain the relationship between the Mach numbers, consider equation (7.10) with $V_x = M_x \sqrt{kg_0 RT_x}$ and $V_y = M_y \sqrt{kg_0 RT_y}$.

$$M_x M_y \sqrt{T_x T_y} = \frac{2}{k+1} T_0 \tag{7.12}$$

$$M_x{}^2 M_y{}^2 = \left(\frac{2}{k+1}\right)\left(1 + \frac{k-1}{2} M_x{}^2\right)\left(1 + \frac{k-1}{2} M_y{}^2\right) \tag{7.13}$$

and solving for M_y in terms of M_x:

$$M_y{}^2 = \frac{M_x{}^2 + \dfrac{2}{k-1}}{\dfrac{2k}{k-1} M_x{}^2 - 1} \tag{7.14}$$

This equation expresses the Mach number on the downstream side of the discontinuity in terms of the Mach number on the upstream side. If a normal shock exists in a fluid moving with a certain Mach number M_x, the Mach number following the shock must be as given by equation (7.14), regardless of other flow variables or fluid properties.

7.4 Tables for normal shock

As in the flow situations described in Chapters 5 and 6, it is often convenient to have the relations governing normal shock tabulated for easy reference rather than to solve the system of equations for each given problem. Equation (7.14) is most valuable in writing the basic equations in a form for easy tabulation.

For perfect gases the energy equation applied to the conditions of a normal shock yields:

$$T_y\left(1 + \frac{k-1}{2} M_y{}^2\right) = T_x\left(1 + \frac{k-1}{2} M_x{}^2\right) \tag{7.15}$$

Using equation (7.14), this ratio T_y/T_x is easily written in a form for tabulation as a function of M_x.

$$\frac{T_y}{T_x} = \frac{\left(1 + \dfrac{k-1}{2} M_x{}^2\right)\left(\dfrac{2k}{k-1} M_x{}^2 - 1\right)}{\dfrac{(k+1)^2}{2(k-1)} M_x{}^2} \tag{7.16}$$

It is evident that this ratio can easily be tabulated for various values of Mach number ahead of the shock, M_x.

The momentum equation applied to the steady state conditions of a normal shock gives

$$p_y(1 + kM_y{}^2) = p_x(1 + kM_x{}^2) \tag{7.17}$$

Again using the equation for Mach number following the shock as a function of Mach number ahead of the shock, the ratio of the static pressures on the two sides of the shock may be expressed in a form for easy tabulation,

$$\frac{p_y}{p_x} = \frac{1 + kM_x{}^2}{1 + kM_y{}^2} = \frac{2k}{k+1} M_x{}^2 - \frac{k-1}{k+1} \tag{7.18}$$

From the equation of state for a perfect gas,

$$\frac{\rho_y}{\rho_x} = \frac{p_y T_x}{p_x T_y} \tag{7.19}$$

and from the condition of continuity applied to the flow on the two sides of the normal shock,

$$\frac{V_x}{V_y} = \frac{\rho_y}{\rho_x} = \frac{k+1}{2}\left(\frac{M_x{}^2}{1 + \dfrac{k-1}{2} M_x{}^2}\right) \tag{7.20}$$

A measure of the irreversibility in a shock wave may be obtained by considering p_{0y}/p_{0x}.

$$\frac{p_{0y}}{p_{0x}} = \left(\frac{p_{0y}}{p_y}\right)\left(\frac{p_y}{p_x}\right)\left(\frac{p_x}{p_{0x}}\right) \tag{7.21}$$

Expressing the pressure ratios on the right side of equation (7.21) in terms of M_x and M_y and then replacing M_y by the appropriate function of M_x (equation 7.14),

$$\frac{p_{0y}}{p_{0x}} = \left(\frac{\dfrac{k+1}{2}M_x^2}{1 + \dfrac{k-1}{2}M_x^2}\right)^{k/(k-1)} \left(\frac{2kM_x^2}{k+1} - \frac{k-1}{k+1}\right)^{1/(1-k)} \tag{7.22}$$

Finally, it is desirable to have an expression for p_{0y}/p_x. This, along with the pressure ratios already worked out, makes it possible, by simple combinations, to obtain any ratio of pressures or stagnation pressures.

$$\frac{p_{0y}}{p_x} = \frac{p_{0y}}{p_y}\frac{p_y}{p_x} = \left[1 + \frac{k-1}{2}\left(\frac{M_x^2 + \dfrac{2}{k-1}}{\dfrac{2k}{k-1}M_x^2 - 1}\right)\right]^{k/(k-1)} \left(\frac{2kM_x^2}{k+1} - \frac{k-1}{k+1}\right) \tag{7.23}$$

$$\frac{p_{0y}}{p_x} = \left(\frac{k+1}{2}M_x^2\right)^{k/(k-1)}\left(\frac{2kM_x^2}{k+1} - \frac{k-1}{k+1}\right)^{1/(1-k)} \tag{7.24}$$

The value for M_y, the ratios $\dfrac{p_y}{p_x}, \dfrac{T_y}{T_x}, \dfrac{\rho_y}{\rho_x}, \dfrac{p_{0y}}{p_{0x}}$, and $\dfrac{p_{0y}}{p_x}$ can be tabulated in a normal shock table just as certain information was conveniently tabulated in isentropic tables and Fanno tables. Equations (7.14), (7.16), (7.18), (7.20), (7.22), and (7.24) are convenient in the preparation of such a table. These tabulated values may be found in Table A.4 of the Appendix for Mach numbers varying from 0 to 10 and for k's of 1.4, 1.0, 1.1, 1.2, 1.3, and 1.67.

7.5 Impossibility of shock from subsonic to supersonic flow

On the basis of equation (7.14), a solution to the mathematics is obtained for the case of M_x less than unity with the resulting M_y being greater than unity. Although mathematically possible, this situation is physically impossible, as shown by the following considerations:

$$ds = \frac{c_p\,dT}{T} - \frac{1}{\rho T}\,dp \tag{7.25}$$

Integrating for a perfect gas,

$$s_y - s_x = R \ln \frac{p_x}{p_y}\left(\frac{T_y}{T_x}\right)^{k/(k-1)} \tag{7.26}$$

For adiabatic conditions, i.e., $T_{0x} = T_{0y}$, the entropy increase may be expressed in terms of the stagnation pressure.

$$s_y - s_x = R \ln \frac{p_{0x}}{p_{0y}} \tag{7.27}$$

Using equation (7.22) for p_{0y}/p_{0x},

$$\frac{s_y - s_x}{R} = \frac{k}{k-1} \ln \left[\frac{2 + (k-1)M_x^2}{(k+1)M_x^2}\right] + \frac{1}{k-1} \ln \left[\frac{2kM_x^2 - (k-1)}{k+1}\right] \tag{7.28}$$

Thus the entropy increase across a normal shock discontinuity is expressed in terms of the ratio of the specific heat capacities, k, and the Mach number on the upstream side of the shock. Since the flow is adiabatic, and because the entropy cannot decrease in adiabatic flow, M_x must have a value which makes the right-hand side of equation (7.28) positive.

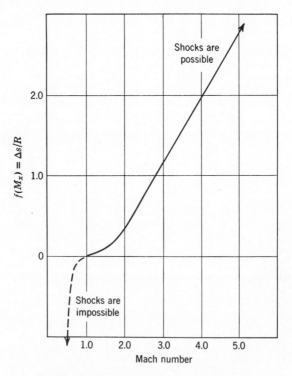

Fig. 7.3 Entropy change across a normal shock.

It is now in order to investigate the function

$$f(M_x) = \frac{k}{k-1} \ln \left[\frac{2 + (k-1)M_x^2}{(k+1)M_x^2} \right] + \frac{1}{k-1} \ln \left[\frac{2kM_x^2 - (k-1)}{k+1} \right]$$

(7.29)

By expanding the logarithm in a series for the case of M_x near unity, it is shown that $f(M_x)$ is approximately proportional to $(M_x - 1)^3$ which is positive only when $M_x > 1.0$. A more direct approach (at least for most undergraduate engineering students) might be to plot equation (7.29) by calculating $f(M_x)$ for various values of M_x. Figure 7.3 shows such a plot and it is now evident that for $f(M_x)$ to be positive, M_x must be greater than 1.0. Hence, if the second law of thermodynamics is to be obeyed, then only normal shocks from supersonic speeds to subsonic speeds are possible.

7.6 Shock strength

It is evident that the discontinuities which may exist in the fluid properties as the shock front is crossed may be relatively large or they may be rather small. In Figure 7.1, M_x may be considerably greater than unity and hence p_y/p_x, and T_x/T_y are relatively large. This notion of large or small discontinuities leads directly to the notion that a shock wave may be "strong" or "weak." While these relative terms are useful, it is frequently desirable to have some characteristic of the shock which expresses "strength" on an absolute scale.

Various parameters can be used to measure shock strength. Simply the upstream Mach number would provide such information, since the larger M_x, the larger the discontinuities in the fluid properties. Since a shock wave is usually thought of as being a large scale pressure wave, it has become customary to use the *pressure jump* as a measure of shock strength. Thus the shock strength may be defined to be $\dfrac{p_y - p_x}{p_x}$. Writing

$$\frac{p_y - p_x}{p_x} = \frac{p_y}{p_x} - 1$$

and using equation (7.18) as the expression for pressure ratio across the shock,

$$\frac{p_y - p_x}{p_x} = \frac{2kM_x^2}{k+1} - \frac{k-1}{k+1} - 1 = \frac{2k}{k+1}(M_x^2 - 1) \qquad (7.30)$$

While the ratio $\Delta p/p_x$ is usually taken as the definition of shock strength it is very often more convenient to work with the pressure ratio p_y/p_x in the mathematical manipulations. For example, the Rankine-Hugoniot relations express the density ratio and the temperature ratio on the two sides of a normal shock wave as functions of the pressure ratio p_y/p_x. The proof of these equations will be left for a student exercise.

$$\frac{\rho_y}{\rho_x} = \frac{V_x}{V_y} = \frac{1 + \dfrac{k+1}{k-1}\dfrac{p_y}{p_x}}{\dfrac{k+1}{k-1} + \dfrac{p_y}{p_x}} \tag{7.31}$$

$$\frac{T_y}{T_x} = \frac{p_y}{p_x}\left(\frac{\rho_x}{\rho_y}\right) = \frac{p_y}{p_x}\left[\frac{\dfrac{k+1}{k-1} + \dfrac{p_y}{p_x}}{1 + \dfrac{k+1}{k-1}\dfrac{p_y}{p_x}}\right] \tag{7.32}$$

For weak shocks, i.e., $\Delta p/p_x \ll 1$, the above equations can be used to show that

$$\frac{\Delta\rho}{\rho_x} \approx \frac{1}{k}\frac{\Delta p}{p_x}$$

$$\frac{\Delta T}{T_x} \approx \frac{k-1}{k}\frac{\Delta p}{p_x}$$

Also, for strong shocks, i.e., p_y/p_x very large, equations (7.31) and (7.32) show that:

$$\frac{\rho_y}{\rho_x} \text{ approaches } \frac{k+1}{k-1}$$

$$\frac{T_y}{T_x} \text{ approaches } \frac{k-1}{k+1}\frac{p_y}{p_x}$$

7.7 Shocks in a converging-diverging nozzle

In isentropic flow (Chapter 4) in a converging-diverging nozzle with Mach number of unity at the throat section, the fluid may continue to expand with the velocity becoming supersonic, or it may diffuse to a higher pressure with a subsonic velocity. Which one of the two possibilities the fluid follows depends on the pressure at the entrance and exit sections.

Consider an experiment in which a flow from a tank at p_0 and T_0 passes through a convergent-divergent nozzle to a region where the pressure may be lowered gradually to permit a study of the flow pattern with various pressure ratios. Figure 7.4 shows this arrangement.

Initially the pressure, p_E and p_0 are equal and there is no flow. As the pressure, p_E, is reduced to a value such as p_{E1}, the flow begins and will be maintained completely as subsonic. The pressure at the throat section

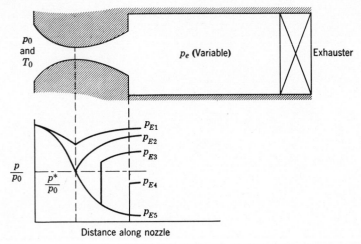

Fig. 7.4 Performance of converging-diverging nozzle for different pressure ratios.

will be less than the exit pressure. Hence, the converging section acts as a nozzle with the fluid expanding but not reaching a Mach number of unity, and the diverging section acts as a diffuser with the Mach number decreasing as the pressure increases. The flow in this situation is similar to that through a venturi and the mass rate of flow changes with changes in exhaust pressure.

As the pressure, p_E, is reduced further, the Mach number in the converging section will increase. When the pressure ratio becomes p_{E2}/p_0 the ratio of the throat pressure to inlet stagnation pressure becomes p^*/p_0, and the Mach number at the throat becomes unity. The pressure ratio required for this condition, p_{E2}/p_0, is determined by the nozzle area ratio, and for nozzles with small frictional losses may be close to unity. The converging section continues to act as a nozzle and expands the fluid to a pressure given by p^*/p_0, and to a Mach number of unity. Recall from Chapter 5, $\dfrac{p^*}{p_0} = \left(\dfrac{2}{k+1}\right)^{k/k-1}$. The diverging section diffuses the fluid so that subsonic flow is found throughout (except at the precise minimum section where $M = 1$).

When the pressure is lowered below p_{E2}/p_0, such as p_{E3}/p_0, a normal shock appears downstream from the throat, and the diverging section of the nozzle is divided into supersonic and subsonic portions. With this pressure ratio the variations in the converging section are identical with those for the ratio p_{E2}/p_0. The pressure at the throat section is given by the ratio p^*/p_0 and the Mach number there is unity. The diverging section acts as a supersonic nozzle for a portion of its length and then a normal shock wave reduces the flow to subsonic with the remaining length acting as a subsonic diffuser. The smaller the ratio p_{E3}/p_0 becomes, the greater the distance from the throat to the shock location (the closer the shock becomes to the nozzle exit section). The mass flow rate is independent of the pressure ratio in this case, since the conditions at the throat section are fixed for all ratios smaller than p_{E2}/p_0 and this fixes the mass flow rate.

Lowering the exhaust pressure still more acts to move the shock wave to the nozzle exit section. This condition is shown in Figure 7.4 for the case where the exhaust pressure is p_{E4}. In general the remarks of the preceding paragraph describing flow for a ratio p_{E3}/p_0 apply here. This may be considered a special case where the shock is located at the nozzle exit.

Further lowering of the exhaust pressure (with pressure ratios between p_{E4}/p_0 and p_{E5}/p_0, causes the shock to move outside the nozzle. The flow in the diverging section is completely supersonic and the compression waves outside the nozzle involve oblique shocks which will be discussed later.

When the pressure ratio becomes p_{E5}/p_0, the flow may proceed smoothly out of the nozzle exit section. This is the design condition for the nozzle under supersonic operation. The entire diverging section contains smooth supersonic flow.

As the exhaust pressure drops still further, there is no change in the flow pattern within the nozzle. However, the pressure at the nozzle exit is higher than the surroundings so expansion waves occur outside the nozzle.

Summarizing: (1) For nozzle pressure ratios more than p_{E2}/p_0, there is a completely different pressure-distance curve for each value of p_E/p_0. (2) For nozzle pressure ratios less than p_{E2}/p_0, the pressure-distance curve is completely fixed in the converging section, and is fixed in the diverging section until the shock location is reached. Thereafter, the curve is unique for each pressure ratio. (3) The mass flow rate is a function of the pressure ratio only for the case of p_E/p_0 greater than p_{E2}/p_0. For other pressure ratios the mass flow rate is independent of the pressure and may be computed from throat conditions where $M = 1$.

The changes in flow patterns through converging-diverging nozzles have been completely and carefully studied using schlieren photography. Such results substantiate the above ideas.

Example problem

A converging-diverging nozzle is designed for a pressure ratio of 0.120 ($p_E/p_0 = 0.12$). (a) Find the exhaust pressure which will locate the plane of the shock at the exit section. (b) Find the location of the shock when the pressure ratio is 0.60. (Assume that the nozzle has uniform divergence in its diverging section and that $k = 1.4$.)

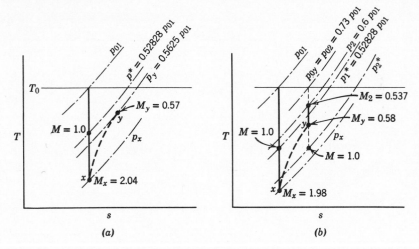

Fig. 7.5 Temperature entropy diagrams for normal shocks in nozzles. (a) Shock at nozzle exit. (b) Shock with nozzle pressure ratio = 0.6.

Solution. (a) Refer to Figure 7.5(a). From the isentropic tables, the ideal exit Mach number (just ahead of the exit shock) is

$$M_2 = M_x = 2.04$$

$$\frac{p_x}{p_0} = 0.120$$

From the shock tables for $M_x = 2.04$,

$$M_y = 0.57068$$

$$\frac{p_y}{p_x} = 4.6886$$

Therefore, the exhaust pressure for a shock at the exit is:

$$p_y = 4.6886 p_x = (4.6886)(0.120 p_0) = 0.5625 p_0$$

(b) Refer to Figure 7.5(b). For adiabatic flow

$$\frac{p_2}{p_{01}} = \frac{p_2}{p_{02}}\frac{p_{02}}{p_{01}} = \left(1 + \frac{k-1}{2}M_2^2\right)^{k/(1-k)} e^{-(\Delta s/R)} \qquad (7.33)$$

The divergence ratio for adiabatic flow, from the integration of equation (5.18), is

$$\frac{A_2}{A_1^*} = \frac{1}{M_2}\left(\frac{1 + \dfrac{k-1}{2}M_2^2}{\dfrac{k+1}{2}}\right)^{\frac{k+1}{2(k-1)}} e^{\Delta s/R} \qquad (7.34)$$

Then multiplying (7.33) by (7.34)

$$\frac{p_2}{p_{01}}\frac{A_2}{A_1{}^*} = \frac{1}{M_2}\left(\frac{2}{k+1}\right)^{(k+1)/2(k-1)}\left(1 + \frac{k-1}{2}M_2{}^2\right)^{-\frac{1}{2}} \quad (7.35)$$

This equation is tabulated in the isentropic tables, but may be used here since the loss across the shock has been made to drop out. From the isentropic tables, for design conditions,

$$\frac{A_2}{A_1{}^*} = 1.7452$$

Therefore

$$\frac{p_2}{p_{01}}\frac{A_2}{A_1{}^*} = (0.6)(1.7452) = 1.04712$$

Since

$$p_{01}A_1{}^* = p_{02}A_2{}^*,$$

$$\frac{p_2 A_2}{p_{02}A_2{}^*} = 1.04712$$

Then from the isentropic tables:

$$M_2 = 0.537$$

and

$$\frac{p_2}{p_{02}} = \frac{p_2}{p_{0y}} = 0.8218$$

$$\frac{p_{0y}}{p_{0x}} = \frac{p_2/p_{0x}}{p_2/p_{0y}} = \frac{0.6}{0.8218} = 0.730$$

From the shock tables, the Mach number ahead of the shock:

$$M_x = 1.98$$

and

$$M_y = 0.5808$$

The area ratio for isentropic flow from the throat to the shock location

$$\frac{A_x}{A_1{}^*} = 1.6597$$

Since the radius at each point is proportional to the distance from the throat

$$\frac{r_L}{r^*} = \sqrt{1.7452} = 1.32$$

$$\frac{r_x}{r^*} = \sqrt{1.6597} = 1.288$$

$$\frac{r_x - r^*}{r_L - r^*} = \frac{x}{L}; \quad x = \frac{0.288}{0.32}L = 0.9L$$

Problems

7.1 It is frequently valuable to be able to express the Mach number ahead of a normal shock wave in terms of the pressure ratio across the shock. Show that

$$M_x = \left(\frac{k-1}{2k} + \frac{k+1}{2k} \frac{p_y}{p_x} \right)^{\frac{1}{2}}$$

7.2 Prove the validity of the Rankin-Hugoniot relations [equations (7.31) and (7.32)] for normal shocks.

7.3 Show that the Mach number behind a normal shock wave is given by

$$M_y = \left(\frac{\dfrac{k+1}{2k} + \dfrac{k-1}{2k} \dfrac{p_y}{p_x}}{\dfrac{p_y}{p_x}} \right)^{\frac{1}{2}}$$

7.4 The Mach number preceding a normal shock in air is 2.20. Find the percentage increase in density through this shock. What is the temperature ratio across this shock? What is the entropy increase through this shock?

7.5 Air flows through a 6-in. duct with a velocity of 2500 ft/sec. The temperature is 540°F and the pressure is 5 psia. Because the pressure downstream is too high to allow continued flow at this high a velocity, a shock discontinuity results. Find the pressure, temperature, density, and velocity downstream from the shock.

7.6 Show that the velocity following a stationary normal shock wave is

$$V_y = a_y \left(\frac{k+1}{2k} + \frac{k-1}{2k} \frac{p_y}{p_x} \right) \left(\frac{\dfrac{2k}{k+1}}{\dfrac{k-1}{k+1} + \dfrac{p_y}{p_x}} \right)^{\frac{1}{2}}$$

7.7 Show that for strong shocks the expression for V_y as given in problem 7.6 may be written

$$V_y \approx \frac{(k-1)a_y}{\sqrt{2k(k+1)}} \left(\frac{p_y}{p_x} \right)^{\frac{1}{2}}$$

and that for very weak shocks, $V_y \approx a_y$ as should be expected.

7.8 The air ahead of a normal shock wave is moving with a Mach number of 4.0, has a temperature of 80°F, and a pressure of 14 psia. What is the pressure behind the shock? What is the velocity and what is the stagnation temperature behind the shock?

7.9 Air flows through a converging-diverging nozzle which was designed to operate at an ideal ratio of stagnation to exhaust pressure of 8.0. Find the pressure ratio (exhaust pressure to inlet stagnation pressure) which locates a shock wave at the nozzle exit section.

7.10 In a certain converging-diverging nozzle with an exit area 20 times the throat area, under certain conditions there is found to be a normal shock wave standing in the diverging section at the point where the area is 1.5 times the throat area. Assuming the fluid to be air ($k = 1.4$), find the pressure ratio across this nozzle (pressure at nozzle exit divided by inlet stagnation pressure).

7.11 An air nozzle is designed for a Mach number of 2.5. The inlet stagnation pressure is 100 psia. Find how much the change in exhaust pressure must be to move the shock wave from the throat to the exit section.

7.12 A certain nozzle is designed for an exit Mach number of 2.0 when used with air. The diverging section diverges uniformly. Find the location of the shock wave when the ratio of exhaust pressure to inlet stagnation pressure is 0.7. Express the location as a fraction of the length of the diverging section.

7.13 A diffuser having an inlet Mach number of 1.5 diverges uniformly to an area 1.5 times the inlet area. The exit Mach number under certain conditions is 0.4. Assume the fluid is air and find:
(a) The shock location.
(b) The entropy increase across the shock.
(c) The diffuser efficiency.

7.14 A certain converging-diverging nozzle for air is designed on the basis of isentropic flow exit Mach number of 2.0. When this nozzle exhausts to a pressure above the design value, a normal discontinuity appears in the nozzle. Find the pressure ratio which will locate the discontinuity at a point halfway down the diverging section of the nozzle. Assume the nozzle is uniformly diverging in the diverging section.

7.15 Find the efficiency of the nozzle in problem 7.14. What is the entropy increase across the shock?

7.16 Air with a Mach number of 2.5 enters a converging duct with an area ratio $A_2/A_1 = 0.5$. Under certain conditions a normal shock results at the point where $A/A_1 = 0.6$. For this condition, find the exit Mach number and the pressure ratio across this duct.

References

1. A. H. Shapiro: *The Dynamics and Thermodynamics of Compressible Fluid Flow*, Vol. I, Ronald Press, New York, 1953.
2. N. A. Hall: *Thermodynamics of Fluid Flow*, Prentice-Hall, Englewood Cliffs, N.J. 1951.
3. H. W. Liepmann and A. Roshko: *Elements of Gasdynamics*, John Wiley and Sons, New York, 1957.
4. D. G. Shepherd: *Principles of Turbomachinery*, Macmillan, New York, 1956.
5. A. B. Cambel and B. H. Jennings: *Gas Dynamics*, McGraw-Hill, New York, 1958.

8

flow with heating or cooling

8.1 Introduction to heat-exchange systems

Whenever fluid flows through a heat exchanger, the stagnation enthalpy (and hence the stagnation temperature) is changed. The flow is not adiabatic and those equations of Chapters 5, 6, and 7 which depend on the condition of adiabatic flow do not apply. In the early portions of this chapter attention is given to flows in which friction may be neglected. Then in section 8.5, the special case of heat transfer and friction effects resulting in isothermal flow is discussed. In section 8.6, techniques for estimating the results of more general processes involving both heat transfer and friction are presented.

In general, all heat exchangers involve some fluid friction. The frictional effects per unit length are small compared with the heating or cooling effects when there is a large temperature difference between the duct and the moving fluid. Then the assumption

131

of a simple heating (no friction, constant area, constant mass flow rate) process is a good one and the equations developed in sections 2 through 4 of this chapter will give satisfactory results.

Similarly, in combustion chambers, the fuel–air ratio is so small that the effects caused by change in chemical composition and changes in mass are small compared with the effects of changes in the stagnation enthalpy. The assumption of a simple heating process is then a good one.

8.2 Fundamental equations for simple heating or simple cooling—the Rayleigh line

Under conditions of steady flow through constant cross-sectional area, with no friction and no drag losses, the steady-flow momentum equation (2.33) may be written (for no gravity forces) as

$$dp + \frac{\rho V \, dV}{g_0} = 0 \tag{8.1}$$

The continuity condition for steady flow, equation (2.11), gives (for constant area)

$$\rho V = \frac{w}{A} = \text{Constant}$$

By using this condition in equation (8.1),

$$dp + \frac{w}{A} \frac{dV}{g_0} = d\left(p + \frac{wV}{Ag_0}\right) = 0 \tag{8.2}$$

Recalling the definition of the impulse function, equation (4.5), the fundamental equation for all simple heating or simple cooling processes is obtained.

$$d\left(p + \frac{wV}{Ag_0}\right) = d\left(\frac{I}{A}\right) = 0 \tag{8.3}$$

or

$$\frac{I}{A} = \text{Constant} \tag{8.4}$$

In order to visualize the changes dictated by simple heating and simple cooling processes, it is helpful to plot this equation on thermodynamic diagrams. For example, a form suitable for plotting on a pressure-volume diagram is obtained by replacing V in equation (8.3) by its equivalent, $\left(\frac{w}{A}\right)\left(\frac{1}{\rho}\right)$. Then

$$d\left[p + \left(\frac{w}{A}\right)^2 \frac{1}{g_0}\left(\frac{1}{\rho}\right)\right] = 0 \tag{8.5}$$

or integrating,

$$p + \left(\frac{w}{A}\right)^2 \frac{1}{g_0}\left(\frac{1}{\rho}\right) = \text{Constant} = \frac{I}{A} \tag{8.6}$$

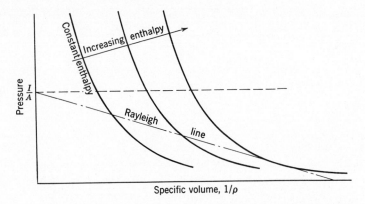

Fig. 8.1 Rayleigh line on a pressure-specific volume diagram.

Plotting this equation on a p versus $\dfrac{1}{\rho}$ diagram, a straight line results. This line has a slope of $-\left(\dfrac{w}{A}\right)^2\dfrac{1}{g_0}$, and an intercept on the p-axis of $\dfrac{I}{A}$. (See Figure 8.1.) This line is called a Rayleigh line.

Since the slope of the Rayleigh line is $-\left(\dfrac{w}{A}\right)^2\dfrac{1}{g_0}$, it is determined by the mass velocity. The larger the mass velocity, w/A, the greater the rate of pressure drop becomes for a certain enthalpy change.

As a simple heating process in subsonic flow progresses, the point representing the fluid state moves along the Rayleigh line toward the right and in general toward an increase in enthalpy. If the heating proceeds long enough, the enthalpy will reach a maximum value. This occurs when the enthalpy curve, because of its natural curvature, becomes tangent to the Rayleigh line. At this point the enthalpy is the maximum which the fluid can attain. Further heating is possible, but this causes the density to drop so rapidly that the velocity must increase at a much more rapid rate. The rate of kinetic energy increase equals or exceeds the rate of energy addition, and thus the static enthalpy cannot increase, and may decrease, as the fluid is accelerated. This condition is represented in Figure 8.1.

Performing the differentiation indicated in equation (8.5) the following results:

$$dp - \left(\frac{w}{A}\right)^2\frac{1}{g_0\rho^2}\,d\rho = 0 \tag{8.7}$$

or

$$g_0\frac{dp}{d\rho} = \left(\frac{w}{A}\right)^2\frac{1}{\rho^2} = V^2 \tag{8.8}$$

At any point on the p versus $1/\rho$ diagram the absolute value of the slope of an isothermal line is always less than that of an isentropic line. This is evident because, for a perfect gas:

$$\left[\frac{\partial p}{\partial(1/\rho)}\right]_T = -\frac{p}{(1/\rho)}$$

and

$$\left[\frac{\partial p}{\partial(1/\rho)}\right]_s = -k\frac{p}{(1/\rho)}$$

Both families of curves (isothermals and isentropics) become more nearly horizontal as the value for $1/\rho$ becomes larger and the pressure smaller. Hence there is also a point on the Rayleigh line where the isentropic curve is tangent and this tangency must occur to the right of the point where the isothermal or line of constant enthalpy is tangent. Thus a point of maximum entropy along a Rayleigh line is defined. If the entropy curve is tangent, then the differential $dp/d\rho$, describing the change along the Rayleigh line, is also valid for constant entropy. Consequently, at the point of maximum entropy on a Rayleigh line

$$\frac{dp}{d\rho} = \left(\frac{\partial p}{\partial \rho}\right)_s \tag{8.9}$$

and then at this point

$$V^2 = g_0 \frac{dp}{d\rho} = g_0\left(\frac{\partial p}{\partial \rho}\right)_s = a^2 \tag{8.10}$$

The fact that this point is also the condition for maximum stagnation enthalpy is shown by considering the following development. Differentiating equation (2.47) to find the condition for a maximum,

$$dh_0 = dh + \frac{V\,dV}{g_0} = 0 \tag{8.11}$$

From the Rayleigh line equation in the form of (8.1)

$$\frac{V\,dV}{g_0} = -\frac{dp}{\rho} \tag{8.12}$$

However, from the relation

$$T\,ds = dh - \frac{dp}{\rho}$$

it is evident that for the condition $ds = 0$ (maximum entropy on the Rayleigh line),

$$dh = \frac{dp}{\rho} = -\frac{V\,dV}{g_0} \tag{8.13}$$

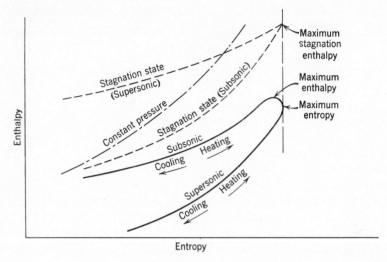

Fig. 8.2   Rayleigh line on enthalpy-entropy diagram.

and this is the condition for maximum stagnation enthalpy (equation 8.11). Thus the stagnation enthalpy is a maximum at the same point where the entropy is a maximum. An attempt to increase the stagnation enthalpy still farther by heating will change the upstream conditions.

The foregoing equations suggest the possibility of drawing a Rayleigh line on an enthalpy versus entropy diagram to show clearly the points of maximum entropy and maximum enthalpy. Any two independent properties determine the state of a perfect gas, so equation (8.5) may be written in terms of enthalpy and entropy rather than pressure and specific volume. By following such procedures and plotting the results, a diagram similar to Figure 8.2 is obtained.

The upper branch of the Rayleigh curve in Figure 8.2 (corresponding to the line in Figure 8.1 to the left of the maximum entropy point) describes the changes in subsonic flow. As the fluid is heated, the entropy increases, and a point representing the fluid properties moves to the right (Mach number increases) until the maximum entropy is reached. Cooling results in a movement to the left, with a decrease in entropy and Mach number. Since there is no friction or internal drag allowed in a simple heating or simple cooling process, the internal entropy change is zero. Thus the entropy change is positive for heating and negative for cooling processes.

The supersonic portion of the Rayleigh line indicates that as heating occurs (entropy increases), the Mach number will decrease, approaching unity as a limit. As cooling occurs, the entropy must decrease and the Mach number will increase.

Figure 8.2 also shows the variation of stagnation enthalpy during a simple heating or cooling process. Note that the stagnation enthalpy is a maximum at the point of maximum entropy. Stagnation enthalpy *always* increases with heating along a Rayleigh line and decreases with cooling.

The amount of heat addition at either subsonic or supersonic speeds cannot be greater than that which will make the exit Mach number unity. Further addition of heat will choke the flow—that is, the initial flow conditions will be changed to allow for the specified amount of heat input.

8.3 Rayleigh equations for a perfect gas

In the previous chapters, the equation of state of a perfect gas was applied with the fundamental equations governing that type of flow. In each case it was then possible to obtain equations in terms of Mach number and mean specific heat ratio. For the case of simple heating or simple cooling, the same procedure is convenient. Any inaccuracies resulting from the perfect gas assumption will ordinarily be small and the problem is simplified to such an extent that this is an extremely desirable procedure.

Expressing equation (8.3) in terms of Mach number instead of velocity,

$$d\left(\frac{I}{A}\right) = d[p(1 + kM^2)] = 0 \tag{8.14}$$

and integrating between two state points in the flow,

$$p_2(1 + kM_2^2) = p_1(1 + kM_1^2) \tag{8.15}$$

or

$$\frac{p_2}{p_1} = \frac{1 + kM_1^2}{1 + kM_2^2} \tag{8.16}$$

In differential form, the steady flow continuity condition, equation (3.37), may be written

$$\frac{dp}{p} + \frac{dA}{A} + \frac{dM}{M} - \frac{1}{2}\frac{dT}{T} = 0 \tag{8.17}$$

and for constant area flow (as along a Rayleigh line),

$$\frac{dT}{T} = 2\frac{dp}{p} + 2\frac{dM}{M} \tag{8.18}$$

Thus

$$\frac{T_2}{T_1} = \left(\frac{p_2M_2}{p_1M_1}\right)^2 = \frac{M_2^2}{M_1^2}\left(\frac{1 + kM_1^2}{1 + kM_2^2}\right)^2 \tag{8.19}$$

By the definition of stagnation state,

$$T_0 = T\left(1 + \frac{k-1}{2}M^2\right) \tag{8.20}$$

Therefore,

$$\frac{T_{02}}{T_{01}} = \frac{T_2\left(1 + \dfrac{k-1}{2}M_2{}^2\right)}{T_1\left(1 + \dfrac{k-1}{2}M_1{}^2\right)} = \frac{M_2{}^2(1 + kM_1{}^2)^2\left(1 + \dfrac{k-1}{2}M_2{}^2\right)}{M_1{}^2(1 + kM_2{}^2)^2\left(1 + \dfrac{k-1}{2}M_1{}^2\right)} \tag{8.21}$$

Also by the definition of stagnation state,

$$p_0 = p\left(\frac{T_0}{T}\right)^{k/(k-1)} \tag{8.22}$$

Then

$$\frac{p_{02}}{p_{01}} = \frac{1 + kM_1{}^2}{1 + kM_2{}^2}\left(\frac{1 + \dfrac{k-1}{2}M_2{}^2}{1 + \dfrac{k-1}{2}M_1{}^2}\right)^{k/(k-1)} \tag{8.23}$$

For constant area steady flow, the density variation and velocity variation are inversely equal

$$\frac{\rho_2}{\rho_1} = \frac{V_1}{V_2} = \left(\frac{p_2}{T_2}\right)\left(\frac{T_1}{p_1}\right) = \frac{M_1{}^2}{M_2{}^2}\left(\frac{1 + kM_2{}^2}{1 + kM_1{}^2}\right) \tag{8.24}$$

The entropy increase along a Rayleigh line may be computed by using the fundamental equation

$$ds = \frac{dh - \dfrac{1}{\rho}dp}{T} \tag{8.25}$$

Employing the expressions for a perfect gas and integrating

$$\frac{s_2 - s_1}{R} = \ln\left(\frac{T_2}{T_1}\right)^{k/(k-1)} - \ln\frac{p_2}{p_1} \tag{8.26}$$

Thus

$$\frac{s_2 - s_1}{R} = \ln\left[\frac{M_2(1 + kM_1{}^2)}{M_1(1 + kM_2{}^2)}\right]^{2k/(k-1)}\left(\frac{1 + kM_2{}^2}{1 + kM_1{}^2}\right)$$

$$= \ln\left(\frac{M_2}{M_1}\right)^{2k/(k-1)}\left(\frac{1 + kM_1{}^2}{1 + kM_2{}^2}\right)^{(k+1)/(k-1)} \tag{8.27}$$

A simple heating or cooling problem is generally solved by taking the known initial conditions and the known heat transfer per pound and computing the final stagnation temperature. From the steady flow energy equation, with no external work as along a Rayleigh line,

$$\delta Q = dh_0 \tag{8.28}$$

Integrating with constant specific heat capacity, the heat transferred per pound of gas is found to be

$$Q = c_p(T_{02} - T_{01}) \tag{8.29}$$

After the resulting stagnation temperature is found, a value for M_2 is found to satisfy equation (8.21). The values for the other properties after the heat transfer are then easily determined from the above equations.

8.4 Reference state and Rayleigh tables

Just as in the case of isentropic flow and constant-area flow with friction, it is necessary to employ a suitable reference state in discussing the changes in fluid properties. As before, the best point for this purpose is the point of maximum entropy. Here the Mach number is unity, so the asterisk symbol is usually used. In dealing with simple heating and simple cooling processes, the asterisk designation refers to the point on a Rayleigh line which represents Mach number of unity. Confusion should not result from the use of this symbol for the reference state in Rayleigh flow, if care is taken to be sure of the type of flow.

Using the reference state, the properties may be presented in tabular form by employing the following relations which are obtained directly from equations (8.16), (8.19), (8.21), (8.23), and (8.24)

$$\frac{p}{p^*} = \frac{k+1}{1+kM^2} \tag{8.30}$$

$$\frac{T}{T^*} = \frac{M^2(k+1)^2}{(1+kM^2)^2} \tag{8.31}$$

$$\frac{T_0}{T_0^*} = \frac{2(k+1)M^2\left(1 + \frac{k-1}{2}M^2\right)}{(1+kM^2)^2} \tag{8.32}$$

$$\frac{p_0}{p_0^*} = \frac{k+1}{1+kM^2}\left(\frac{1 + \frac{k-1}{2}M^2}{\frac{k+1}{2}}\right)^{k/(k-1)} \tag{8.33}$$

$$\frac{\rho^*}{\rho} = \frac{V}{V^*} = \frac{(k+1)M^2}{1+kM^2} \tag{8.34}$$

These ratios are tabulated in Table A.5 of the Appendix for Mach numbers from 0 to 10 and for k's of 1.4, 1.0, 1.1, 1.2, 1.3, and 1.67.

As an example of the use of Rayleigh tables, consider the following simple problem. In a certain combustion chamber, the air enters with a Mach number of 0.25. Sufficient heat is added that the ratio $T_{02}/T_{01} = 3.5$. Find the Mach number of the combustion products (assume air-fuel ratio high enough that this is very largely air) leaving the combustion chamber, and find the percentage of loss in pressure.

Solution. At

$$M_1 = 0.25, \qquad \frac{T_{01}}{T_0^*} = 0.2568$$

$$\frac{T_{02}}{T_0^*} = \frac{T_{02}}{T_{01}} \frac{T_{01}}{T_0^*} = (3.5)(0.2568) = 0.9$$

$$M_2 = 0.688$$

$$\frac{p_2}{p^*} = 1.4429, \qquad \frac{p_1}{p^*} = 2.2069$$

$$\frac{\Delta p}{p_1} = \frac{2.2069 - 1.4429}{2.2069} = 34.6\%$$

8.5 Isothermal flows in long ducts

In the transport of gases over very long distances in pipe lines, the friction may not be neglected because it results in sizeable pressure changes. In a long duct there is generally sufficient opportunity for heat transfer to assure that the gas flowing in the duct is always at or very near the temperature of the surroundings. While the Mach numbers are usually low, the great pressure changes make the assumption of constant density very poor.

As the pressure drops, heat must be added if the temperature is to remain constant. It will be shown that in isothermal flow the Mach number must always approach $\sqrt{1/k}$. The isothermal process is shown in Figure 8.3.

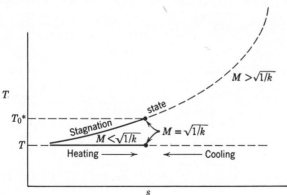

Fig. 8.3 Isothermal flow in ducts.

For isothermal flow, the equation of state for a perfect gas is

$$\frac{dp}{p} - \frac{d\rho}{\rho} = 0 \tag{8.35}$$

Combining this with the condition for continuity,

$$\frac{d\rho}{\rho} + \frac{dV}{V} = 0 \tag{8.36}$$

yields,

$$\frac{dp}{p} = \frac{d\rho}{\rho} = -\frac{dV}{V} \tag{8.37}$$

The steady-flow momentum equation is employed in much the same manner as in the simple heating process (except considering the friction term),

$$dp + \frac{\rho V^2}{2g_0}\left(f\frac{dx}{D}\right) + \frac{\rho V\, dV}{g_0} = 0 \tag{8.38}$$

Dividing by p and eliminating the velocity by using Mach number yields,

$$(1 - kM^2)\frac{dp}{p} + \frac{kM^2}{2}f\frac{dx}{D} = 0 \tag{8.39}$$

Then

$$\frac{dp}{p} = \frac{d\rho}{\rho} = -\frac{dV}{V} = -\frac{kM^2}{2(1 - kM^2)}f\frac{dx}{D} \tag{8.40}$$

Equation (8.40) shows that as the length of duct increases, the pressure will decrease for values of $M < \sqrt{1/k}$, and the pressure will increase for $M > \sqrt{1/k}$. Increasing the pressure requires moving toward the left in Figure 8.3. Since $f(dx/D)$ must always be positive, this means that for flow with $M < \sqrt{1/k}$ the point describing the state of the gas moves to the right (toward $M = \sqrt{1/k}$), and for flow with $M > \sqrt{1/k}$ the point moves to the left (again toward $M = \sqrt{1/k}$). Thus, regardless of the initial Mach number, in isothermal flow in ducts, the Mach number must approach $\sqrt{1/k}$.

In order for the flow to remain isothermal with Mach numbers more than $\sqrt{1/k}$, the stagnation temperature must decrease. This means that the gas must be cooled by the surroundings rather than heated as intuition suggests, but this condition also satisfies physical reasoning when it is considered that the pressure is steadily increasing, and unless cooling occurs the temperature cannot remain constant.

For isothermal flows, the entropy change is rather easily determined from the *static* pressure ratio. This may be shown by considerations from the equation

$$T\,ds = c_p\,dT - \frac{dp}{\rho}$$

which for $T = $ constant yields

$$\Delta s = -R \ln \frac{p_2}{p_1} = R \ln \frac{p_1}{p_2} \tag{8.41}$$

(Note the contrast here to the equation for evaluating entropy change in adiabatic flows in terms of the *stagnation* pressure ratio.)

The change in stagnation temperature can be found from the basic equation defining stagnation state.

$$T_0 = T\left(1 + \frac{k-1}{2}M^2\right)$$

Differentiating logarithmically, $(dT = 0)$,

$$\frac{dT_0}{T_0} = \frac{\left(\dfrac{k-1}{2}\right)dM^2}{1 + \dfrac{k-1}{2}M^2} \tag{8.42}$$

Defining the state where $M = \sqrt{1/k}$ as the reference state, again denoted with the asterisk, the stagnation temperature may be written

$$\left(\frac{T_0}{T_0{}^*}\right)_{\text{isoth}} = \frac{2k}{3k-1}\left(1 + \frac{k-1}{2}M^2\right) \tag{8.43}$$

Values for $(T_0/T_0{}^*)_{\text{isoth}}$ are tabulated in the table of Rayleigh functions in the Appendix. Care should be taken not to confuse $(T_0/T_0{}^*)$ along the Rayleigh line with $(T_0/T_0{}^*)_{\text{isoth}}$ which is valid only for isothermal flows.

As pointed out in the previous sections, the amount of heating or cooling depends on the stagnation temperature change. This is given by the familiar expression

$$Q = c_p(T_{02} - T_{01}) \tag{8.44}$$

It is evident from equation (8.40) that as the Mach number approaches $\sqrt{1/k}$, the fluid properties change rapidly with length. In isothermal flow, a great velocity change means a large Mach number change and, as a result, the heat transfer must be quite large per unit of duct length in order to maintain the isothermal conditions. This means heat transfer must be done intentionally and not merely as the result of the duct passing through an isothermal atmosphere.

8.6 Heating or cooling with friction

Actually it is impossible to find simple heating and simple cooling processes in fluid flow. Heat transfer cannot be had without some friction. Friction can be assumed to be negligible only in cases where the temperature difference between the walls of the duct and bulk of the moving fluid is quite large. Of course, the larger the potential for heat transfer—the difference between wall and fluid temperatures—the greater the accuracy in the results when the frictionless case is assumed.

One approach to the case of heating or cooling with friction is to lump each phenomenon separately. That is, the analysis may consist of first taking a simple heating or cooling process until the resulting stagnation temperature is reached, and then taking a constant-area adiabatic flow until the proper friction length has been added.

In cases where both the heat transfer and frictional effects are large and of near equal size, an accurate analysis requires the simultaneous consideration of both phenomena. For steady flow, from momentum considerations,

$$\frac{dp}{p} + \frac{kM^2}{2} f \frac{dx}{D} + kM^2 \frac{dM}{M} + \frac{kM^2}{2} \frac{dT}{T} = 0 \qquad (8.45)$$

and from energy considerations,

$$\frac{\delta Q}{c_p T} = \left(1 + \frac{k-1}{2} M^2\right) \frac{dT}{T} + \frac{k-1}{2} M^2 \frac{dM^2}{M^2} \qquad (8.46)$$

These two fundamental equations, along with the continuity condition for a gas in constant area, steady flow,

$$\frac{dp}{p} + \frac{dM}{M} - \frac{1}{2} \frac{dT}{T} = 0 \qquad (8.47)$$

enable one to obtain an expression for the change in Mach number in terms of the friction length and the heat transfer parameter.

Eliminating dp/p in equation (8.45) with the use of (8.47), and dT/T with the use of (8.46),

$$\left[1 - kM^2 + \frac{(1 + kM^2)(k-1)M^2}{2\left(1 + \frac{k-1}{2} M^2\right)} \right] \frac{dM}{M}$$

$$= \frac{k}{2} M^2 \frac{f\,dx}{D} + \frac{1 + kM^2}{2\left(1 + \frac{k-1}{2} M^2\right)} \frac{\delta Q}{c_p T} \qquad (8.48)$$

and simplifying,

$$\frac{dM^2}{M^2} = \frac{\left(1 + \frac{k-1}{2}M^2\right)(kM^2)f\frac{dx}{D} + (1 + kM^2)\frac{\delta Q}{c_p T}}{1 - M^2} \quad (8.49)$$

The heat transfer per unit mass along a length of duct, dx, is

$$\delta Q = \frac{h_c(T_w - T_0)\pi D\, dx}{\rho \frac{\pi}{4} D^2 V} = \frac{4h_c(T_w - T_0)}{\rho V}\frac{dx}{D} \quad (8.50)$$

where h_c is the heat transfer coefficient

T_w is the temperature of the duct walls

T_0 is the fluid stagnation temperature and the increment $(T_w - T_0)$ is taken to be the temperature difference immediately adjacent to the walls.

Employing the Reynolds analogy between friction and heat transfer which has been shown to be valid for fluid flow where $c_p\mu/k$ is approximately unity,

$$h_c = \frac{\rho V c_p f}{8} \quad (8.51)$$

and substituting equations (8.50) and (8.51) for the heat transfer in equation (8.49), the expression for Mach number variation under these conditions results.

$$dM^2 = \frac{M^2\left(1 + \frac{k-1}{2}M^2\right)}{1 - M^2}\left[kM^2 + \left(\frac{1 + kM^2}{2}\right)\left(\frac{T_w - T_0}{T_0}\right)\right]f\frac{dx}{D} \quad (8.52)$$

Equation (8.52) shows that for adiabatic flow, i.e., $T_w = T_0$, the Mach number will increase in subsonic flow and decrease in supersonic flow as along a Fanno line. In subsonic flow heat addition, i.e., $T_w > T_0$, will cause the Mach number to increase more rapidly than the adiabatic case, while cooling will cause it to tend to decrease thus countering the effect of friction in the adiabatic case. In supersonic flow it is evident that the opposite will result just as was the case along a Rayleigh line. Furthermore, equation (8.52) provides an indication of the relative size of the effects of friction and heat transfer. If the term kM^2 is much larger than $\left(\frac{1 + kM^2}{2}\right)\left(\frac{T_w - T_0}{T_0}\right)$, then friction is more important than heat transfer, and conversely. This provides an indication of the magnitude of the error involved in the assumption of a simple heating or cooling process, and also the error involved in assuming the heat transfer to be negligible when friction is involved in the flow.

Problems

8.1 Air is moving in a constant area duct with a temperature of $-60°F$ and a pressure of 7.5 psia. The velocity is 500 ft/sec. Find:

(a) The stagnation temperature.

(b) The maximum stagnation temperature after fuel is injected and burned in this air stream.

(c) The temperature corresponding to the maximum stagnation temperature.

(d) The pressure corresponding to the maximum stagnation temperature.

(e) The stagnation pressure corresponding to the maximum stagnation temperature.

8.2 In a certain combustion chamber of a jet, the air enters with a velocity of 300 ft/sec, a temperature of 140°F, and a pressure of 50 psia. If 200 Btu/lb of air are added through the combustion process, find (assuming $c_p = 0.24$ Btu/lb°R, $k = 1.4$):

(a) The stagnation temperature after combustion.

(b) The Mach number after combustion.

(c) The temperature after combustion.

(d) The pressure after combustion.

(e) The velocity after combustion.

8.3 Air is flowing in a constant-area, frictionless duct with a Mach number of 1.5. The stagnation temperature and stagnation pressure are, respectively, 1000°R and 100 psia. By a cooling process the stagnation temperature is cooled to 800°R. Find the Mach number after the cooling, and the pressure and temperature after cooling.

8.4 In a certain heat exchanger, the stagnation temperature of air is raised from 200°F to 800°F. If the inlet Mach number is 0.3, determine the final Mach number and the percentage of drop in pressure.

8.5 For a certain combustion chamber the ratio T_{02}/T_{01} is 4.0. The inlet pressure is 7.5 psia, the temperature is $-60°F$, and the mass velocity is 8 lb/sq ft sec. Find, for $k = 1.4$,

(a) The inlet and exit Mach numbers.

(b) The exit temperature.

(c) The exit pressure.

8.6 Air enters a straight pipe of uniform 6-in. diameter with a pressure of 30 psia, a temperature of 600°R, and a velocity of 200 ft/sec. The friction factor, f, for this pipe is 0.025 and in 100 ft of length sufficient heat is added to increase the stagnation temperature by 30%. Predict the resulting Mach number, temperature, and pressure.

8.7 What additional length of pipe is needed in problem 8.6, with the same friction factor and same rate of T_0 increase of 3% in each 10 ft, in order to choke the flow?

8.8 A flow of air at 500°R and Mach number 0.3, is heated in a duct with a wall temperature of 1500°R. Estimate the percentage of error involved in assuming this to be a simple heating process. Is this a reasonable assumption?

8.9 In a long duct of constant area, air is flowing with the temperature being held constant at 540°R. For an inlet Mach number of 0.20, find the amount of heat transfer required to increase the stagnation temperature by 10%. With an inlet pressure of 50 psia, find the exit pressure and the entropy change per pound of air.

References

1. A. H. Shapiro: *The Dynamics and Thermodynamics of Compressible Fluid Flow*, Vol. I, Ronald Press, New York, 1953.

2. N. A. Hall: *Thermodynamics of Fluid Flow*, Prentice-Hall, Englewood Cliffs, N.J., 1951.

3. B. L. Hicks, D. J. Montgomery, and R. H. Wasserman: The One-Dimensional Theory of Steady Compressible Fluid Flow in Ducts with Friction and Heat Addition, NACA TN 1336 July 1947.

4. W. H. McAdams: *Heat Transmission*, 2nd ed., McGraw-Hill, New York, 1942.

9

moving and oblique shock waves

9.1 Introduction

For conditions of equilibrium to exist in actual flows, it is not necessary for all discontinuities to be stationary normal shocks. In the more general case the discontinuity may be moving relative to the stationary observer. Even the relatively simple stationary normal shocks can be made to appear to be moving by merely causing the observer to move. If the coordinate reference frame is moving in a direction normal to the plane of the shock, what was a stationary normal shock wave will now appear as a propagating shock wave.

An analysis of a normal compression shock wave which is traveling at a constant speed is necessary to the careful consideration of the waves resulting from an explosion. The same physical pattern serves as a good approach to some of the problems involved in a pulse-jet (e.g., the V-1, buzz bomb) engine as well as in handling the phenomena in shock tubes.

In cases where the direction of a supersonic flow is changed sharply, the fluid may be compressed in such a manner that a shock front is formed—this shock being inclined (or oblique in contrast to being normal) to the flow direction. With these *oblique* shocks, the flow following the discontinuity need not be subsonic; it can be either subsonic or remain supersonic, depending on the angle of inclination of the shock and the initial Mach number. This situation will be evident in later discussions in this chapter.

9.2 Propagating normal shock waves

In contrast to the stationary or standing normal shocks which have been considered in Chapter 7, fluid discontinuities frequently move and the analysis of this physical pattern is the subject of this section. As suggested above, in a shock tube, a shock wave moves down the tube into an undisturbed fluid. In the case of an atmospheric disturbance, such as a bomb explosion, a pressure wave of considerable magnitude (shock wave) moves through the atmosphere until a state of equilibrium is again reached.

A shock tube is simply a chamber (usually long in one dimension compared with the other two) which is divided into two parts by a diaphragm. When the pressure on one side of the diaphragm is increased to a value considerably more than that on the other side, the shock tube is ready for "firing." Rupturing the diaphragm causes a pressure wave (shock wave if pressure differential is sizable) to move into the low pressure part of the shock tube.

In such a shock tube the shock is essentially a normal shock if the boundary layer near the walls is neglected, and in an explosion in the atmosphere the resulting shock wave is approximately normal after it has moved some distance from the source of the explosion.

Consider the same shock wave being analyzed in two ways. (See Figure 9.1.) In both approaches, a control volume which is fixed in space may be selected so as to include a portion of the fluid on each side of the shock at a given instant.

If the condition of Figure 9.1(a) is considered in a coordinate system

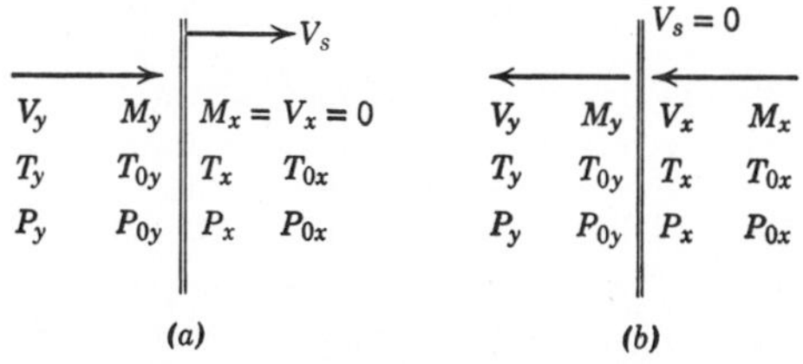

V_y	M_y	$M_x = V_x = 0$	V_y	M_y	V_x	M_x
T_y	T_{0y}	T_x	T_{0x}	T_y	T_{0y}	T_x	T_{0x}
P_y	P_{0y}	P_x	P_{0x}	P_y	P_{0y}	P_x	P_{0x}

$\longrightarrow V_s$ $V_s = 0$

(a)   (b)

Fig. 9.1   Moving vs. stationary shocks. (a) Moving shock wave. (b) Stationary shock wave.

which is moving to the right with a velocity just equal to V_s, then the condition of Figure 9.1(b) is obtained. The following relationships should be apparent:

(*a*) *Moving Shock Wave*

(*b*) *Stationary Shock Wave*

$$M_x = V_x = 0 \qquad\qquad M_x = \frac{V_x}{a_x}$$

$$p_x = p_{0x} \qquad\qquad p_{0x} = p_x\left(1 + \frac{k-1}{2} M_x^2\right)^{k/(k-1)}$$

$$T_x = T_{0x} \qquad\qquad T_{0x} = T_x\left(1 + \frac{k-1}{2} M_x^2\right) \qquad (9.1)$$

$$V_y = a_y M_y \qquad\qquad V_y = a_y M_y$$

$$T_{0y} = T_y\left(1 + \frac{k-1}{2} M_y^2\right) \qquad T_{0y} = T_y\left(1 + \frac{k-1}{2} M_y^2\right) = T_{0x}$$

$$p_{0y} = p_y\left(1 + \frac{k-1}{2} M_y^2\right)^{k/(k-1)} \qquad p_{0y} = p_y\left(1 + \frac{k-1}{2} M_y^2\right)^{k/(k-1)}$$

Changing the coordinate system from stationary to moving does not affect the static properties because these are really properties measured with the measuring device moving with the same velocity as the fluid. Hence for the same physical situation:

$$T_{y(a)} = T_{y(b)} \qquad T_{x(a)} = T_{x(b)}$$

$$p_{y(a)} = p_{y(b)} \qquad p_{x(a)} = p_{x(b)} \qquad (9.2)$$

The same is not true for the stagnation properties, however, since the stagnation properties depend upon the fluid velocity (which implies measurement with reference to some coordinate system).

Comparing the two control volumes of Figure 9.1, it is evident that the fluid velocity change across the shock is independent of whether or not the shock is moving into the fluid or not. That is, $(V_y - V_x)_a = (V_y - V_x)_b$. This must be true for continuity of mass to be satisfied. Since the two V_x's are different by an amount V_s, it is evident that the values for the differences in velocity squared are not equal. That is,

$$\left(\frac{V_y^2}{2g_0} - \frac{V_x^2}{2g_0}\right)_a \neq \left(\frac{V_y^2}{2g_0} - \frac{V_x^2}{2g_0}\right)_b$$

From energy considerations of the control volume of Figure 9.1(b) (for adiabatic conditions),

$$dh + \left(\frac{dV^2}{2g_0}\right)_{(b)} = -\delta W_{x(b)} = 0 \qquad (9.3)$$

The same procedure for Figure 9.1(a) yields

$$dh + \left(\frac{dV^2}{2g_0}\right)_{(a)} = -\delta W_{x(a)} \neq 0 \qquad (9.4)$$

Thus $dT_{0(a)} \neq 0$, even though $dT_{0(b)} = 0$.

The velocity of a moving shock wave as in Figure 9.1(a) must be the same as the velocity of the fluid moving into the shock when the coordinate system is moved with the velocity V_s. Hence,

$$V_s = V_{x(b)} = M_{x(b)} \, a_x \qquad (9.5)$$

Equation (7.18) may be solved for M_x and the result substituted in equation (9.5) to obtain,

$$V_s = a_x \left(\frac{k+1}{2k} \frac{p_y}{p_x} + \frac{k-1}{2k}\right)^{\frac{1}{2}} \qquad (9.6)$$

This expression is a very convenient one to use in estimating the velocity of a sizable pressure wave when the strength of the wave, i.e., p_y/p_x, is known.

As pointed out above, the *static* properties on the two sides of a normal shock wave are independent of whether the discontinuity is moving or stationary. Therefore, the Rankine-Hugoniot relations, equations (7.31) and (7.32), apply equally well to the situation of propagating shock waves as to stationary normal shocks. They are repeated here for convenience in calculating the density and temperature ratios.

$$\frac{\rho_y}{\rho_x} = \frac{1 + \dfrac{k+1}{k-1}\dfrac{p_y}{p_x}}{\dfrac{k+1}{k-1} + \dfrac{p_y}{p_x}} \qquad (7.31)$$

$$\frac{T_y}{T_x} = \frac{p_y}{p_x} \frac{\dfrac{k+1}{k-1} + \dfrac{p_y}{p_x}}{1 + \dfrac{k+1}{k-1}\dfrac{p_y}{p_x}}$$

Consider an example of how the change in the coordinate axes may be applied with the tables for normal stationary shock in order to analyze the physical conditions of a moving shock wave.

A normal shock wave moves down a shock tube with a velocity of 2500 ft/sec into undisturbed air at a pressure of 14.7 psia and a temperature of 520°R. Find the velocity, the pressure, the temperature, and the stagnation temperature after the shock wave passes an observation point in the shock tube.

Transferring the physical pattern from coordinate system (a) to coordinate system (b) and carrying out the analysis in the system (b) in which the shock is stationary:

$$V_s = 0, \ M_x = \frac{2500}{a_x} = \frac{2500}{(1.4 \times 32.2 \times 53.34 \times 520)^{\frac{1}{2}}} = 2.24$$

$$T_x = 520°R$$

and from the isentropic tables

$$\frac{T_x}{T_{0x}} = 0.49912, \qquad T_{0x} = \frac{520}{0.49912} = 1042°R$$

$$p_x = 14.7 \text{ psia}$$

From the normal shock tables in the Appendix,

$$M_y = 0.54182$$

$$\frac{p_y}{p_x} = 5.6872 \quad p_y = (14.7)(5.6872) = 83.5 \text{ psia}$$

$$\frac{T_y}{T_x} = 1.8924 \quad T_y = (520)(1.8924) = 985°R$$

$$V_y = M_y a_y = (0.54182)(1.4 \times 32.2 \times 53.34 \times 985)^{\frac{1}{2}} = 835 \text{ ft/sec}$$

Transferring back to the coordinate system (a) in which the reference plane is stationary and the shock wave is moving,

$$V_y = 2500 - 835 = +1665 \text{ ft/sec. (moving to the right)}$$

$$p_y = p_{y(b)} = 83.5 \text{ psia}$$

$$T_y = T_{y(b)} = 985°R$$

$$M_y = \frac{V_y}{a_y} = \frac{1665}{(1.4 \times 32.2 \times 53.34 \times 985)^{\frac{1}{2}}} = \frac{1665}{1540} = 1.08$$

$$\frac{T_y}{T_{0y}} = 0.81084 \quad T_{0y} = \frac{985}{0.81084} = 1213°R$$

Note that in system (a) $T_{0x} = T_x = 520°R$. Then it is evident that in this system $T_{0y} \neq T_{0x}$, and further that T_{0y} is not equal to $T_{0y(b)}$ or $T_{0x(b)}$.

9.3 Oblique shocks

Considerable insight into the phenomena of stationary oblique shock waves can be rather easily obtained by considering a moving coordinate system, just as was done in the discussion of propagating normal shock waves. This time, however, the coordinate system should be moved in a

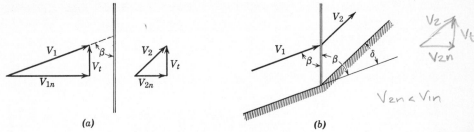

Fig. 9.2 Oblique shock wave.

direction parallel to the shock front with a velocity, V_t. Then the fluid approaches the shock with a velocity V_1 at an angle

$$\beta = \cos^{-1} \frac{V_t}{V_1}. \quad \text{(See Figure 9.2.)}$$

Since the velocity V_{2n} is different from the velocity V_{1n}, the angle that the resultant velocity vector V_2 makes with the shock must be different from the shock inclination, β. That is, the flow must be abruptly turned at the shock and angle of this turning is the deflection angle, δ. Since V_{2n} must always be less than V_{1n}, the inclination angle, which is made with the shock by the fluid following the shock, must be less than the initial inclination angle β. Thus the flow is always turned toward the shock.

It should be kept in mind that, as was the case when the coordinate system was moved in a direction perpendicular to the shock wave as in section 9.2, the movement of the coordinate system with a velocity, V_t, results in no change in the pressure, temperature, density, entropy, or acoustic velocity on either side of the shock. The Mach number, the velocity, the stagnation temperature, and the stagnation pressure on both sides of the shock are all functions of motion and, hence, depend in part on the motion of the coordinate reference plane relative to the shock front.

In a normal shock the flow must be supersonic ahead of the shock and subsonic after the shock. In Figure 9.2 this corresponds to V_{1n} being greater than a_1, and V_{2n} being less than a_2. Notice that V_2 may be either a subsonic velocity or a supersonic velocity, depending on the magnitude of V_t. If V_t is small, the angle β approaches $90°$ and the flow after the shock is likely to be subsonic. On the other hand, a large V_t indicates that β is relatively small and following the shock the flow may remain supersonic. The significance of this will be apparent in the following paragraphs.

Since the static properties are independent of the motion of the coordinate axes, the relations for the normal shock may be used if the M_x in the normal shock equations is replaced by its equivalent, the normal component of the velocity, V_{1n}, divided by a_1. From Figure 9.2, this equivalence is,

$$M_x = \frac{V_{1n}}{a_1} = \frac{V_1 \sin \beta}{a_1} = M_1 \sin \beta \tag{9.7}$$

Then the pressure ratio across an oblique shock may be written easily by referring to equation (7.18).

$$\frac{p_2}{p_1} = \frac{2k}{k+1} M_1{}^2 \sin^2 \beta - \frac{k-1}{k+1} \tag{9.8}$$

Similarly, the density ratio and the temperature ratio may be written from equations (7.20) and (7.16).

$$\frac{\rho_2}{\rho_1} = \frac{(k+1) M_1{}^2 \sin^2 \beta}{(k-1) M_1{}^2 \sin^2 \beta + 2} \tag{9.9}$$

$$\frac{T_2}{T_1} = \frac{a_2{}^2}{a_1{}^2} = \frac{[2 + (k-1)M_1{}^2 \sin^2 \beta][2kM_1{}^2 \sin^2 \beta - (k-1)]}{(k+1)^2 M_1{}^2 \sin^2 \beta} \tag{9.10}$$

In addition, since the static properties are unaffected by the relative motion of the coordinate system, the entropy change across an oblique shock must be the same as the entropy change across a normal shock in which the velocity of fluid approaching the shock is exactly the same as the normal component of velocity approaching the oblique shock. Since both the normal and oblique shocks discussed here are assumed adiabatic,

$$\frac{p_{02}}{p_{01}} = e^{(s_1 - s_2)/R} = e^{(s_x - s_y)/R} = \frac{p_{0y}}{p_{0x}} \tag{9.11}$$

and from equation (7.22), using the equivalence of equation (9.7), we obtain

$$\frac{p_{02}}{p_{01}} = \left(\frac{\dfrac{k+1}{2} M_1{}^2 \sin^2 \beta}{1 + \dfrac{k-1}{2} M_1{}^2 \sin^2 \beta} \right)^{k/(k-1)} \left(\frac{2kM_1{}^2 \sin^2 \beta}{k+1} - \frac{k-1}{k+1} \right)^{1/(1-k)} \tag{9.12}$$

Thus the entropy change across an oblique shock may be expressed as

$$\frac{s_2 - s_1}{R} = \frac{-k}{k-1} \ln \left(\frac{\dfrac{k+1}{2} M_1{}^2 \sin^2 \beta}{1 + \dfrac{k-1}{2} M_1{}^2 \sin^2 \beta} \right)$$

$$+ \frac{1}{k-1} \ln \left(\frac{2kM_1{}^2 \sin^2 \beta}{k+1} - \frac{k-1}{k+1} \right) \tag{9.13}$$

These basic equations relating the properties on the two sides of an oblique shock wave, equations (9.8), (9.9), (9.10), and (9.12), may be obtained by a more rigorous and more fundamental procedure. If a control surface is taken such that the sides of the control surface are streamlines and the ends are planes parallel to the oblique shock, the basic steady-state equations for continuity, momentum, and energy, in conjunction with the perfect gas relationship, will give these same results. It is then necessary, however, to consider two momentum equations, one in the direction parallel to the shock and one in the direction normal to the shock. These relations not only make it possible to find the ratios cited above but also the inclination angle, β, and the deflection angle, δ. The actual analysis as outlined will be left as an exercise for the student.

In Chapter 7, it was noted that a normal shock wave could exist only when $M_x > 1.0$. In the limit, if the shock was negligibly weak, $M_x = 1.0$. Following the same reasoning, an oblique shock must have an inclination angle, β, such that

$$\beta \geq \sin^{-1} \frac{1}{M_1}$$

At the other extreme, if β becomes as large as $\pi/2$, then the shock is no longer oblique, but normal. Hence,

$$\sin^{-1} \frac{1}{M_1} \leq \beta \leq \frac{\pi}{2} \tag{9.14}$$

9.4 The deflection angle

From the geometry of Figure 9.2 it is evident that:

$$\frac{V_{1n}}{\tan \beta} = \frac{V_{2n}}{\tan (\beta - \delta)} = V_t \tag{9.15}$$

With some rearrangement, and noting that $V_{2n}/V_{1n} = \rho_1/\rho_2$,

$$\frac{\tan (\beta - \delta)}{\tan \beta} = \frac{V_{2n}}{V_{1n}} = \frac{\rho_1}{\rho_2} = \frac{(k - 1)M_1^2 \sin^2 \beta + 2}{(k + 1)M_1^2 \sin^2 \beta} \tag{9.16}$$

Equation (9.16) may be solved for δ by using the trigonometric relation for the tangent of the difference of two angles. After some algebra

$$\delta = \tan^{-1}\left[\left(\frac{M_1^2 \sin^2 \beta - 1}{kM_1^2 + M_1^2 \cos 2\beta + 2}\right)(2 \cot \beta)\right] \tag{9.17}$$

Equation (9.17) may be analyzed by selecting values for inlet Mach number, M_1, and shock inclination angle, β, and plotting the resulting deflection angle δ. Figure 9.3 is such a plot and shows δ as a function of M_1 and β. Notice that for each value of inlet Mach number there is a definite maximum value of δ.

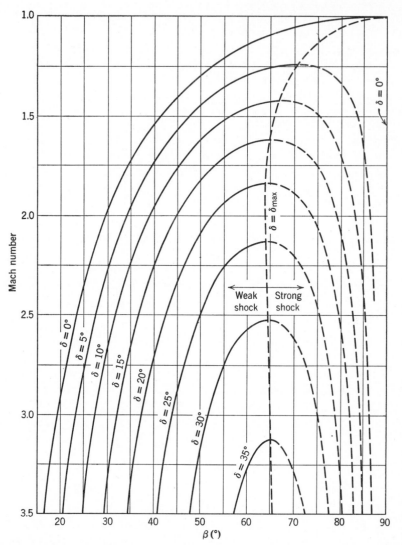

Fig. 9.3 Deflection angle, δ, as a function of inlet Mach number and shock inclination angle ($k = 1.4$).

From Figure 9.3 and from equation (9.17), it is evident that the value of δ becomes zero for both the limits previously established on β, i.e.,

$$\beta = \sin^{-1}\frac{1}{M_1}, \text{ and } \beta = \frac{\pi}{2}.$$

Figure 9.3 shows that for a given value of M_1 there are two values of shock inclination which will give the same deflection angle. For example, with an initial Mach number of 2.0, a shock wave with an inclination angle of 45° will result in a 15° deflection in the flow. With the same initial Mach number of 2.0, a shock wave with an inclination of 80° will also result in a 15° deflection. Both conditions satisfy the equations for oblique shock waves. In general one of the solutions will result in a subsonic M_2 and the other will result in a supersonic M_2. This possibility was pointed out in the previous section.

Oblique shocks with large inclination angles are stronger shocks than those with smaller angles. The stronger shocks are, in general, the ones in which the value of M_2 is less than unity and weaker ones have M_2 greater than unity. In the example above, the shock with an inclination of 80° will give a 15° deflection and a subsonic flow following the shock, while the shock with an inclination of 45° will give a 15° deflection and the flow will remain supersonic.

9.5 Mach lines

In section 9.3 it was pointed out that the inclination angle, β, had certain definite limits. Equation (9.14) expressed the limits on β, as

$$\sin^{-1}\frac{1}{M_1} \leq \beta \leq \frac{\pi}{2} \qquad (9.14)$$

Since the upper limit, $\beta = \pi/2$, leads to the condition for a normal shock which has been previously discussed at considerable length, it is now appropriate to investigate the lower limit, $\beta = \sin^{-1}\frac{1}{M_1}$. Notice that this is identical with the Mach angle, α, defined by equation (3.34). The Mach angle is simply a characteristic property of any supersonic flow such that

$$\alpha = \sin^{-1}\frac{1}{M} \qquad (3.34)$$

Thus the lower limit for the inclination angle, β, is the Mach angle, α.

If the condition for minimum shock inclination angle is substituted into equation (9.17), it is evident that the deflection angle, δ, must be zero. Hence with minimum inclination the shock causes no turning whatever in the flow.

Applying this same condition, i.e, $\beta = \alpha = \sin^{-1}\frac{1}{M}$, to equations (9.8), (9.9), (9.10) and (9.13), it is evident that there is no pressure change, no density change, no temperature change, and no entropy change across such an oblique shock. In other words, there is no discontinuity whatever in the fluid properties or in the flow direction, and hence no shock wave.

Actually, as the angle β approaches $\sin^{-1} \dfrac{1}{M}$, the shock becomes weaker and weaker. When $\beta = \alpha = \sin^{-1} \dfrac{1}{M}$, we have the condition for an infinitely weak shock.

These infinitely weak oblique shock waves may be drawn at any point in the flow since there is no change in any of the fluid properties. The *Mach lines*, as these are called, are frequently very helpful in analyzing the flow. As already pointed out in section 3.4, the Mach lines are straight as long as the flow is at a constant Mach number, and they are curved when the Mach number is varying.

9.6 Compression by turning in supersonic flow

An understanding of oblique shock waves makes it possible to study supersonic flows at corners. At a sharp concave corner, as illustrated in Figure 9.4(*a*), there will be an oblique shock wave which allows the flow to turn through the deflection angle, δ. For a given M_1 and δ, Figure 9.3 will give the required inclination angle of the oblique shock.

The shock wave must increase the pressure, density, and temperature of the fluid. The ratio of the values before and after the shock have already been established in terms of M_1 and β. After the oblique shock of Figure 9.4(*a*), the fluid is *compressed*, and this suggests that fluid in supersonic flow may be compressed by turning it through an oblique shock. Such a compression is nonisentropic, with the entropy increase being given by equation (9.13).

For a weak oblique shock wave, it can be shown that the entropy increase across the shock is proportional to the third power of the deflection angle, δ. That is,

$$\Delta s \alpha \delta^3 \tag{9.18}$$

If a given turn can be divided into a series of n smaller turns such that

$$\delta = n\Delta\phi \tag{9.19}$$

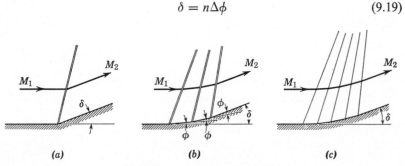

(a)   *(b)*   *(c)*

Fig. 9.4 Compression by turning.

then the entropy increase can be made to be much less. For the complete turn of Figure 9.4(b), the entropy increase is reduced since

$$\Delta s \propto n (\Delta \phi)^3 = \frac{\delta^3}{n^2} \tag{9.20}$$

In the limit as the number of small turns becomes extremely large, the condition of a smooth continuous curving of the flow is approached. In Figure 9.4(c) this condition is represented. The individual shocks have now become infinitely weak and they approach Mach lines. The total entropy change for the bending of the flow approaches zero, since n in equation (9.20) becomes excessively large. Hence in flow through a smooth and continuous curve, the compression is isentropic.

9.7 Prandtl-Meyer expansions

In contrast to the compressions which result in a supersonic flow at a concave corner, when the wall of the duct confining the fluid is bent away from the flow so that a convex corner is formed (see Figure 9.5), an expansion results.

In order for a turn of this type to occur through an oblique wave, as shown in Figure 9.5(b), it is necessary for the normal component of the velocity after the shock to be greater than the normal component of the velocity before the shock. Construction of a vector diagram according to the required restrictions makes this fact evident. The velocity, V_2, after the turn must be parallel to the wall, just as the velocity before the turn, V_1, had to be parallel to that wall. After drawing a line AA' perpendicular to the oblique shock, it is then possible to define the components of velocity parallel to and perpendicular to the shock. No matter how the shock is oriented, the normal component of the velocity after the shock must be greater than the normal component of the velocity before the shock. This was shown to be impossible in Chapter 7, since it leads to an entropy decrease in adiabatic flow.

Actually, as a supersonic flow turns a convex corner, a series of Mach lines emanate from the corner and diverge as the distance from the corner

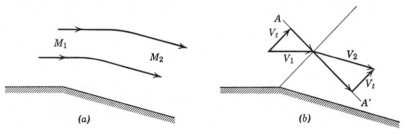

Fig. 9.5 Expansion by turning. (a) Convex corner. (b) Impossible velocity vectors.

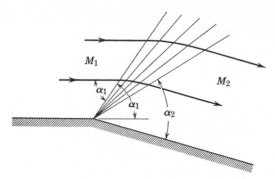

Fig. 9.6   Centered expansion wave (isentropic).

is increased. In much the same way as converging Mach lines produce increasing gradients in flow around a concave corner, the diverging Mach lines from a convex corner tend to decrease gradients. Figure 9.6 shows such a *centered expansion wave* which must be isentropic.

At all points along a particular Mach line in Figure 9.6 the flow parameters are constant. Thus all fluid properties vary as function of angular position with the first Mach line inclined at an angle α_1 with respect to the flow ahead of the corner and the terminal Mach line inclined at an angle α_2 with respect to the flow after the corner.

A centered wave, or a *Prandtl-Meyer expansion fan*, has the property that the angle of flow deflection at any point, δ, is a function only of Mach number at that point.

$$\delta = \omega(M) \tag{9.21}$$

It is now in order to evaluate this function.

Consider a single ray of a Prandtl-Meyer expansion fan as in Figure 9.7. From the velocity diagram of Figure 9.7(*b*), it is evident that

$$V \cos \alpha = (V + dV) \cos (\alpha - d\delta) \tag{9.22}$$

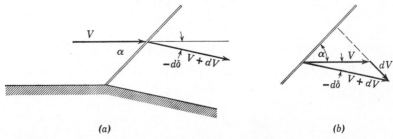

(*a*)   (*b*)

Fig. 9.7   Velocity change across single "ray" of Prandtl-Meyer expansion fan.

Expanding the cosine of the difference of two angles and employing the fact that $d\delta$ is very small, we may obtain

$$V \cos \alpha \approx (V + dV)(\cos \alpha + d\delta \sin \alpha) \tag{9.23}$$

If the product of two differentials is taken as negligible, i.e., $dV\, d\delta \sin \alpha \ll dV \cos \alpha$,

$$\frac{dV}{V} = -d\delta \tan \alpha = -\frac{d\delta}{\sqrt{M^2 - 1}} \tag{9.24}$$

The velocity, V, is given by

$$V = aM \tag{9.25}$$

Then,

$$\frac{dV}{V} = \frac{da}{a} + \frac{dM}{M} = \frac{1}{\left(1 + \dfrac{k-1}{2} M^2\right)} \frac{dM}{M} \tag{9.26}$$

Equation (9.24) may now be written in the form

$$-d\delta = \left(\frac{\sqrt{M^2 - 1}}{1 + \dfrac{k-1}{2} M^2}\right) \frac{dM}{M} \tag{9.27}$$

and the function $\omega(M)$ is defined as follows:

$$\omega(M) = -\delta + \text{Constant} = \int \frac{\sqrt{M^2 - 1}}{1 + \dfrac{k-1}{2} M^2} \frac{dM}{M} \tag{9.28}$$

When the tedious and lengthy (though straight-forward) integration is performed, the *Prandtl-Meyer function*, $\omega(M)$, is obtained.

$$\omega(M) = \sqrt{\frac{k+1}{k-1}} \tan^{-1} \sqrt{\frac{k-1}{k+1}(M^2 - 1)} - \tan^{-1} \sqrt{M^2 - 1} \tag{9.29}$$

It is evident that equation (9.29) is dimensionless, and hence $\omega(M)$, which is an angle, is given in radians. With the appropriate conversion constant, the angle can easily be expressed in degrees as is usually desirable for engineering computations. If the constant of integration is chosen so that $\delta = 0$, when $M = 1.0$, then a reference level is assigned for $\omega(M)$ such that $\omega(M) = 0$ when $M = 1.0$.

Figure 9.8 shows that for each value of Mach number there is a single value for ω, and conversely. ω is the maximum turning angle which may be attained for flow at the given Mach number without experiencing finite waves (oblique compression shocks).

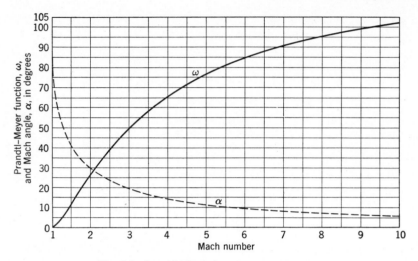

Fig. 9.8 Prandtl-Meyer function and Mach angle.

Problems

9.1 A normal shock wave moves down a shock tube with a Mach number of 3.0. The undisturbed air is at a temperature of 80°F and a pressure of 10 psia. What is the pressure behind the shock? What is the velocity, and what is the stagnation temperature behind the shock?

9.2 The pressure behind a normal shock wave moving into still atmosphere ($p = 14.7$ psia, $T = 70°F$) is 100 psia. (a) Find the speed with which the shock wave is moving into the atmosphere and the speed of the air behind the shock. (b) Find the entropy increase per pound of air across this shock wave.

9.3 A shock wave moves with a velocity of 2000 ft/sec into still air at 500°R. Find the stagnation temperature of the air behind the shock. What is the air velocity behind the shock?

9.4 An atomic bomb is exploded in the South Pacific and at some distance from the center of the explosion it is found that the blast wave is moving into the undisturbed atmosphere with a velocity of 100,000 ft/sec. Assume the still atmosphere to be at 14.7 psia and 80°F. Then (a) find the wind velocity striking an observer after the shock wave passes; (b) find the temperature and pressure after the shock wave passes, (c) find the stagnation temperature behind the shock, and (d) find the entropy increase per pound of air as the blast wave compresses it.

9.5 Show that, for a normal shock wave moving into a stationary medium, the shock velocity may be expressed in terms of the pressure ratio on the two sides of the shock by:

$$V_s = a_1 \left(\frac{k-1}{2k} + \frac{k+1}{2k} \frac{p_y}{p_x} \right)^{\frac{1}{2}}$$

9.6 Show that an acoustic wave in a medium behind a normal shock wave moves with a velocity greater than the shock wave, and hence catches up with the shock.

9.7 Show that the velocity behind a moving normal shock wave is given by:

$$V_y = \frac{a_x}{k}\left(\frac{p_y}{p_x} - 1\right)\left(\frac{\dfrac{2k}{k+1}}{\dfrac{p_y}{p_x} + \dfrac{k-1}{k+1}}\right)^{\!\frac{1}{2}}$$

and that for strong shocks this reduces to:

$$V_y \approx a_x\sqrt{\frac{2}{k(k+1)}}\sqrt{\frac{p_y}{p_x}}$$

9.8 Consider a control volume bounded by streamlines as a fluid passes through an oblique shock wave with the ends of the control volume consisting of planes parallel to the shock wave. Write the basic steady-state equations for continuity, momentum, and energy and, considering a perfect gas, develop the equations for an oblique shock. (*Hint*: There are now two momentum equations, one parallel to the shock, and one normal to it.)

9.9 In a supersonic flow at Mach 3, an oblique shock wave with an inclination angle of 30° is formed by turning a sharp corner. (*a*) What is the turning angle? (*b*) What is the compression effect of this corner, i.e., what is the ratio of pressure after the shock to pressure before the shock?

9.10 A supersonic flow of air at Mach number = 2.5 is compressed by turning a sharp corner of 15°. (*a*) What angles of shock inflection are possible? (*b*) Which gives the stronger shock? (*c*) Verify your answer to part (*b*) by computing the entropy change for each.

9.11 Show that for any oblique shock wave,

$$V_{1n}V_{2n} = a^{*2} - \frac{k-1}{k+1}V_t^2$$

9.12 A wedge with a total angle of 20° is inserted in a flow having a Mach number of 2.0. If the wedge is placed in the flow symmetrically, i.e., causing a flow deflection of 10° on each side, find the possible wave angles. If the wedge is placed so that the flow is deflected 5° on one side and 15° on the other, find the possible wave angles.

9.13 Use the normal shock tables to compute the pressure ratios, the density ratios, and the temperature ratios for the possible shocks in problem 9.10.

9.14 Use the normal shock tables to compute the pressure ratio for each of the possible shocks in problem 9.12.

9.15 What is the minimum Mach number which can give a shock inclination angle of (*a*) 20°, (*b*) 40°, (*c*) 65°?

9.16 Show that the maximum deflection with an (attached) oblique shock wave in a fluid flowing at Mach 2.0 is 23°. Verify this by differentiating equation (9.17).

9.17 Perform the integration indicated in equation (9.28) and verify equation (9.29).

References

1. A. H. Shapiro: *The Dynamics and Thermodynamics of Compressible Fluid Flow*, Vol. I, Ronald Press, New York, 1953.

2. H. W. Liepmann and A. Roshko: *Elements of Gasdynamics*, John Wiley and Sons, New York, 1957.

3. A. B. Cambel and B. H. Jennings: *Gas Dynamics*, McGraw-Hill, New York, 1958.

4. R. Courant and D. Friedrichs: *Supersonic Flow and Shock Waves*, Interscience Publishers, New York, 1948.

10

method of characteristics

10.1 Natural coordinate system

With the exception of Chapter 9, the material presented in this textbook has been idealized to one-dimensional flow. This makes it possible to solve many of the problems encountered in the design of passages such as nozzles and diffusers, and in the analysis of flow in propulsive devices. It has been found convenient to assume that all effects can be accounted for either by variations along the streamlines or by a variation in the flow area of the "stream-tube." These simplifications have always been possible by taking the x-direction along a streamline.

In this chapter a two-dimensional flow will be analyzed with the same pattern taken for the coordinate axes. One coordinate will be taken along the streamline just as in the one-dimensional flow case, and the other coordinate normal to the streamlines. This system which is shown in Figure 10.1 is called the *natural coordinate system.*

163

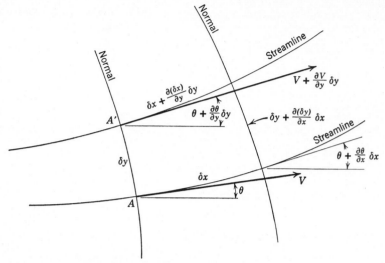

Fig. 10.1   Flow element in natural coordinates.

In the case of two-dimensional flow, it is proper to think of the flow as being of a unit depth such that at section AA' the flow area is (δy) (1) or just δy. In the case of steady flow, with no friction or drag losses, the continuity and momentum equations may be written from the equations in Chapter 2.

$$\frac{\partial}{\partial x}(\rho V\, \delta y) = 0 \tag{10.1}$$

$$\frac{\rho V}{g_0}\frac{\partial V}{\partial x} + \frac{\partial p}{\partial x} = 0 \qquad \text{(Momentum equation for the x-direction)} \tag{10.2}$$

$$F_y = -\frac{\partial p}{\partial y} \qquad \text{(Momentum equation for the y-direction)} \tag{10.3}$$

where F_y is the centrifugal force acting on a unit element of fluid moving along a streamline. It is evident that for one-dimensional flow, there can be no pressure gradient in the y-direction and hence no centrifugal force acting on the fluid. Conversely if there is a pressure gradient in the y-direction there must be a centrifugal force acting on the fluid element and hence the fluid must be moving along a streamline with a finite radius of curvature.

The centrifugal force acting on an elemental unit volume of the fluid is

$$F_y = \frac{\rho}{g_0}\frac{V^2}{R} \tag{10.4}$$

where R is the radius of curvature of the streamlines. From geometry, at any point along a streamline the radius of curvature is the same as $1 \Big/ \dfrac{\partial \theta}{\partial x}$, and hence equation (10.3) becomes

$$\frac{\rho V^2}{g_0} \frac{\partial \theta}{\partial x} = -\frac{\partial p}{\partial y} \tag{10.5}$$

Now the steady-flow energy equation along a streamline may be combined with the expression for entropy change such that

$$T \frac{\partial s}{\partial x} = \frac{\partial h}{\partial x} - \frac{1}{\rho} \frac{\partial p}{\partial x} = \frac{\partial h_0}{\partial x} - \frac{\partial V^2}{2g_0 \partial x} - \frac{1}{\rho} \frac{\partial p}{\partial x} \tag{10.6}$$

Noting that $\dfrac{\partial h_0}{\partial x} = 0$, i.e., constant stagnation enthalpy along a streamline, is proper for any adiabatic, no-work flow; and using equation (10.2) for $\dfrac{\partial p}{\partial x}$, it is evident that

$$\frac{\partial s}{\partial x} = 0 \tag{10.7}$$

Similarly,

$$T \frac{\partial s}{\partial y} = \frac{\partial h_0}{\partial y} - \frac{\partial V^2}{2g_0 \partial y} - \frac{1}{\rho} \frac{\partial p}{\partial y} \tag{10.8}$$

Using equation (10.5) for $\partial p/\partial y$, and noting that $\partial h_0/\partial y = 0$, for adiabatic conditions, the entropy change normal to a streamline is found.

$$T \frac{\partial s}{\partial y} = \frac{V}{g_0} \left(V \frac{\partial \theta}{\partial x} - \frac{\partial V}{\partial y} \right) \tag{10.9}$$

The quantity, $V \dfrac{\partial \theta}{\partial x} - \dfrac{\partial V}{\partial y}$, has been defined in fluid mechanics as the *vorticity*. The student should recall that the vorticity is the *circulation* per unit of area, and in *irrotational flow* the vorticity is zero.

Equation (10.7) shows that the entropy must be constant along a streamline, and equation (10.9) shows that the entropy must be constant normal to the streamlines in irrotational flow. The condition for an adiabatic flow to be *isentropic throughout* requires, (1) that there be no friction or drag, and hence $\partial s/\partial x = 0$, and (2) that the vorticity, $V(\partial \theta/\partial x) - (\partial V/\partial y)$, be zero, and hence $\partial s/\partial y = 0$.

10.2 Equations of motion for isentropic (irrotational) flow

For a fluid-flow pattern which is isentropic throughout, the equations describing the flow may be summarized from the previous section.

$$\frac{\partial}{\partial x}(\rho V \, \delta y) = 0 \tag{10.1}$$

$$\frac{\rho V}{g_0}\frac{\partial V}{\partial x} + \frac{\partial p}{\partial x} = 0 \tag{10.2}$$

$$V\frac{\partial \theta}{\partial x} - \frac{\partial V}{\partial y} = 0 \tag{10.10}$$

and

$$\frac{1}{p}\frac{\partial p}{\partial i} = \frac{k}{\rho}\frac{\partial \rho}{\partial i} \tag{10.11}$$

where i can be either of the natural coordinates, x or y. Equation (10.10) is the condition for vorticity equal to zero, and equation (10.11) is the isentropic relation which must be valid in both x and y directions.

Note that $\partial \delta y/\partial x$ in the expanded form of (10.1) may be expressed in terms of the angle θ.

From Figure 10.2 it is evident that,

$$\sin\frac{\partial \theta}{\partial y}\,\delta y = \frac{1}{\delta x}\frac{\partial(\delta y)}{\partial x}\,\delta x \tag{10.12}$$

In the limit as δx and $\delta y \to 0$, $\sin\dfrac{\partial \theta}{\partial y}\,\delta y \to \dfrac{\partial \theta}{\partial y}\,\delta y$, and

$$\frac{\partial \theta}{\partial y} = \frac{1}{\delta y}\frac{\partial(\delta y)}{\partial x} \tag{10.13}$$

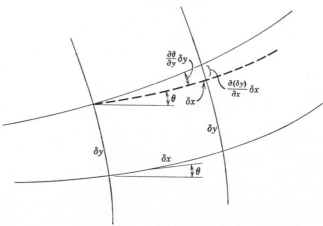

Fig. 10.2 Relation between δy and θ.

Equation (10.1) can now be expanded and the distance between adjacent streamlines can be eliminated.

$$\frac{1}{\rho}\frac{\partial \rho}{\partial x} + \frac{1}{V}\frac{\partial V}{\partial x} + \frac{\partial \theta}{\partial y} = 0 \tag{10.14}$$

Equations, (10.14), (10.2), (10.10), (10.11) form four independent equations with the variables p, ρ, V, θ. In this case the four equations with four variables can be reduced or simplified by combining the equations and eliminating variables. For example, equation (10.2) with the isentropic condition yields:

$$\frac{\partial p}{\partial x} = \frac{a^2}{g_0}\frac{\partial \rho}{\partial x} = -\frac{\rho V}{g_0}\frac{\partial V}{\partial x} \tag{10.15}$$

Now using equation (10.14) to eliminate ρ,

$$\frac{a^2}{V}\frac{\partial V}{\partial x} - V\frac{\partial V}{\partial x} + a^2\frac{\partial \theta}{\partial y} = 0 \tag{10.16}$$

$$(M^2 - 1)\frac{1}{V}\frac{\partial V}{\partial x} - \frac{\partial \theta}{\partial y} = 0 \tag{10.17}$$

Equations (10.17) and (10.10) are independent of pressure and density. Only the fluid velocity and direction are expressed as functions of position in the natural coordinate system. These *equations of motion* describe the flow of a fluid which is isentropic throughout.

Summarizing, in natural coordinates the equations of motion are:

$$V\frac{\partial \theta}{\partial x} - \frac{\partial V}{\partial y} = 0 \tag{10.10}$$

$$(M^2 - 1)\frac{1}{V}\frac{\partial V}{\partial x} - \frac{\partial \theta}{\partial y} = 0 \tag{10.17}$$

10.3 Characteristics

In one sense equations (10.10) and (10.17) are analogous to equations (3.20) and (3.22) which were developed for the acoustic wave. Of course, in Chapter 3, the equations were developed for one-dimensional flow which varied with time, i.e., unsteady flow. Equations (3.20) and (3.22) were made linear by the assumption of "small perturbations," and thus it was possible to find solutions by ordinary classical techniques.

The equations (10.10) and (10.17) appear nonlinear. In general the equations of motion fall into a class which the mathematician calls the elliptic type for subsonic flow, and into the hyperbolic type for supersonic flow. The discussion here will be centered on the technique of solution of the hyperbolic type, since the design of flow passages for supersonic flow presents a much more difficult problem for most engineers. The

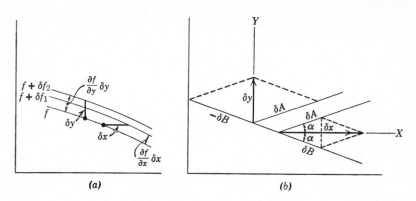

(a)   (b)

Fig. 10.3 Functional changes in Cartesian coordinates and in characteristics as a coordinate system. (a) Cartesian coordinates. (b) Characteristics as coordinates.

equations developed in the previous section for flow which is isentropic throughout are sometimes called quasi-linear since they are linear in the derivatives of the functions θ and V. At any rate the equations are subject to attack by the technique of changing the variables from the natural coordinate system to a coordinate system consisting of the left-running Mach lines and the right-running Mach lines. Hence, the equations of motion must now be rewritten with the coordinate axes (independent variables) being the characteristics.

It is more convenient to employ the relationship between velocity and the Prandtl-Meyer function before changing coordinates. From equation (9.24)

$$d\omega = -d\delta = \cot \alpha \, \frac{dV}{V} \tag{10.18}$$

The Prandtl-Meyer function is related to the velocity or Mach number in such a fundamental way that its use with the natural coordinates leads to an easy approach to the method of characteristics. Equations (10.10) and (10.18) may now be written:

$$\frac{\partial \theta}{\partial x} - \tan \alpha \frac{\partial \omega}{\partial y} = 0 \tag{10.19}$$

$$\frac{\partial \omega}{\partial x} - \tan \alpha \frac{\partial \theta}{\partial y} = 0 \tag{10.20}$$

In Figure 10.3 it is shown that a quantity expressed in terms of x and y may be expressed in terms of lengths along the characteristics, A and B. The change in any function f with respect to a small change in x with y

being kept constant may be evaluated in terms of changes along the characteristics as shown in Figure 10.3(b)

$$\delta f = \frac{\partial f}{\partial x}\,\delta x = \frac{\partial f}{\partial A}\,\delta A + \frac{\partial f}{\partial B}\,\delta B$$

or

$$\frac{\partial f}{\partial x} = \frac{\partial f}{\partial A}\frac{\delta A}{\delta x} + \frac{\partial f}{\partial B}\frac{\delta B}{\delta x}$$

and since $\cos\alpha = \dfrac{\delta x/2}{\delta A}$ (see Figure 10.3),

$$\frac{\partial f}{\partial x} = 2\sec\alpha\,\frac{\partial f}{\partial A} + 2\sec\alpha\,\frac{\partial f}{\partial B} \tag{10.21}$$

Similarly,

$$\frac{\partial f}{\partial y} = 2\csc\alpha\,\frac{\partial f}{\partial A} - 2\csc\alpha\,\frac{\partial f}{\partial B} \tag{10.22}$$

Before employing the identities of equations (10.21) and (10.22) to the equations of motion in natural coordinates, (10.19) and (10.20), it is convenient first to add and then to subtract the equations of motion. This gives:

$$\frac{\partial(\omega + \theta)}{\partial x} + \tan\alpha\,\frac{\partial(\omega + \theta)}{\partial y} = 0 \tag{10.23}$$

$$\frac{\partial(\omega - \theta)}{\partial x} + \tan\alpha\,\frac{\partial(\omega - \theta)}{\partial y} = 0 \tag{10.24}$$

Using the form of (10.21) and (10.22) for the changes in $\omega + \theta$ with respect to x and y, equation (10.23) becomes

$$2\sec\alpha\,\frac{\partial(\omega + \theta)}{\partial A} + 2\sec\alpha\,\frac{\partial(\omega + \theta)}{\partial B} - 2\tan\alpha\csc\alpha\,\frac{\partial(\omega + \theta)}{\partial A}$$
$$+ 2\tan\alpha\csc\alpha\,\frac{\partial(\omega + \theta)}{\partial B} = 0$$

$$4\sec\alpha\,\frac{\partial(\omega + \theta)}{\partial B} = 0 \tag{10.25}$$

Similarly equation (10.24) may be transformed to read

$$4\sec\alpha\,\frac{\partial(\omega - \theta)}{\partial A} = 0 \tag{10.26}$$

This shows that in a supersonic flow which is irrotational (isentropic throughout) the quantity $\omega + \theta$ must remain constant along a B characteristic (right-running), and the quantity $\omega - \theta$ must remain constant along an A characteristic (left-running). The use of these so-called Riemann invariants will be illustrated by the computational procedure outlined in the next sections.

10.4 Dependence and influence—networks for flow types

Since values of $\omega + \theta$ must remain constant on right-running characteristics and values of $\omega - \theta$ must be constant on left-running characteristics in plane isentropic flow, it follows that knowledge of the flow variables along a certain section or curve will determine the flow in a particular region downstream from the section. As an example of this statement consider a data curve with extremities A and B, as shown in Figure 10.4. On the right-running characteristic through A the quantity $\omega + \theta$ is constant, and on the left-running characteristic through B the quantity $\omega - \theta$ is constant. Hence at the intersection of these characteristics, say, point P in Figure 10.4, the values of ω_p and θ_p are fixed. Similarly, all points within the shaded area of Figure 10.4 have values for ω and θ which are fixed by the values of ω and θ along the data curve. For any point, such as P, there is a corresponding segment of the data curve which is known as the domain of dependence of the point.

In a similar way, it can be seen that each point on a given data curve has its influence felt in a particular region bounded by the characteristics through that point. Consider the shaded region bounded by characteristics in Figure 10.5 and the arbitrarily chosen point P within the shaded region. Along either the right-running characteristics or the left-running characteristics, the values of the flow parameters are influenced by the values at point C, since either $\omega + \theta$ or $\omega - \theta$ is a constant. In a similar way, any point along each of the characteristics for point C influences the flow properties along the characteristics of that point. Hence in Figure 10.5, the flow properties at the arbitrary point P are influenced by the properties at points D and E which, in turn, are influenced by the properties at C.

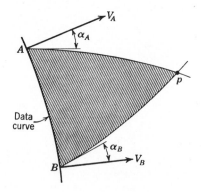

Fig. 10.4 Domain of dependence.

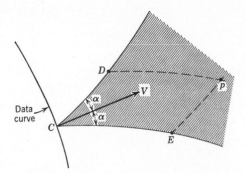

Fig. 10.5 Region of influence.

Similar reasoning can be applied to any point in the shaded region of Figure 10.5 and therefore this shaded region, i.e., the area between the characteristics through C, may be called the region of influence of point C.

In any *general flow*, the characteristics are curved and have values $(\omega + \theta)_1$, $(\omega + \theta)_2$, $(\omega + \theta)_3$, and $(\omega - \theta)_1$, $(\omega - \theta)_2$, $(\omega - \theta)_3$. Such a flow pattern is shown in Figure 10.6(*a*). The values of ω and θ at the

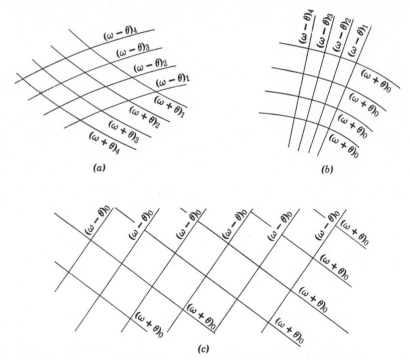

Fig. 10.6 Characteristic networks for three fundamental flow types (after Liepmann and Roshko). (*a*) General flow. (*b*) Simple flow or simple wave. (*c*) Uniform flow.

intersection of ith right-running characteristic and jth left-running characteristic may be found from:

$$\omega = \tfrac{1}{2}[(\omega + \theta)_i + (\omega - \theta)_j] \qquad (10.27)$$

and

$$\theta = \tfrac{1}{2}[(\omega + \theta)_i - (\omega - \theta)_j] \qquad (10.28)$$

The values for ω and θ at any point (and hence the other fluid properties) are easily determined from these equations, provided the domain of dependence has known data.

In a flow in which the value of either $(\omega + \theta)$ or $(\omega - \theta)$ is constant everywhere, the pattern is that of a *simple flow* or a *flow for a simple wave*. For example, if $(\omega + \theta)$ is constant at a value of $(\omega + \theta)_0$, the characteristic network is as shown in Figure 10.6(b). Then in crossing the left-running characteristics, the value of $(\omega - \theta)$ must change in a manner which keeps $(\omega + \theta)$ always constant. From equations (10.27) and (10.28), it is evident that the changes in ω and θ between two points in the network are

$$\delta\omega = \tfrac{1}{2}\delta(\omega - \theta)$$

and

$$\delta\theta = -\tfrac{1}{2}\delta(\omega - \theta)$$

or

$$\delta\omega = -\delta\theta \qquad (10.29)$$

A similar analysis shows that for $(\omega - \theta)$ always constant,

$$\delta\omega = \delta\theta \qquad (10.30)$$

It is suggested that the student compare this with the simple isentropic expansion, or compression waves, of the previous chapter. Note that if $(\omega + \theta)$ is everywhere the same, then the characteristics along which $(\omega - \theta)$ is a constant must be straight lines, and vice versa.

In a *uniform flow*, the values of $(\omega + \theta)$ and $(\omega - \theta)$ are both constant everywhere and both sets of characteristics are straight lines. Such a parallel network is shown in Figure 10.6(c).

10.5 Calculation procedures

Computing the solution to flow problems of supersonic passages by characteristics is relatively simple in theory, but it may become quite tedious if relatively precise results are desired. From information along a data curve, the values of ω and θ at some point, P, can be determined from equations (10.27) and (10.28). [See Figure 10.7(a).]

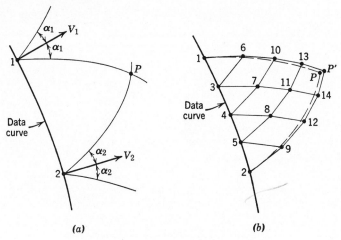

Fig. 10.7 Computation with characteristics.

Along the data curve both Mach number and direction are known (and hence also the Prandtl-Meyer function, ω). The values of ω and θ at point P are then, respectively,

$$\omega_p = \tfrac{1}{2}(\omega_1 + \omega_2) + \tfrac{1}{2}(\theta_1 - \theta_2) \qquad (10.31)$$

and

$$\theta_p = \tfrac{1}{2}(\omega_1 - \omega_2) + \tfrac{1}{2}(\theta_1 + \theta_2) \qquad (10.32)$$

These values for ω_p and θ_p are very easily obtained and from them the other flow parameters become known. It remains, however, to locate point P.

The characteristics through both 1 and 2 are curves and the degree of curvature depends on the changes in the flow as it moves downstream. These changes are initially unknown and must be determined by an approximate method. At point 1 the characteristic makes an angle α with the flow direction; but if the flow Mach number is changed as we progress downstream, the angle α changes (the characteristics are curved). The curved characteristics may be approximated by a series of straight lines, as shown in Figure 10.7(b).

The line 16 can be constructed at an angle α_1 with the flow direction through point 1, and the line 36 can be constructed at an angle α_3 with the flow direction through point 3. The intersection of these pseudo-characteristics locates point 6 which is an approximation to the location of the true point that is at the intersection of the true characteristics. As the mesh size is reduced, the location as indicated by the pseudo-characteristics and the true location becomes closer and closer. Hence the accuracy of the solution is increased.

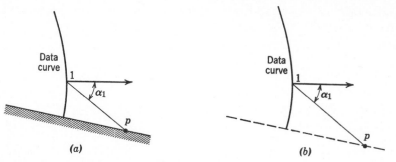

Fig. 10.8 Characteristic calculations at boundaries. (*a*) Solid boundary. (*b*) Free boundary.

By the methods suggested above, the values for ω and θ can be computed at points 6, 7, 8, and 9 and the locations of these points approximated by the intersection of the pseudo-characteristics. An imaginary, or calculated, data curve can be thought of as drawn through these points and the process repeated with the pseudo-characteristics leading to points 10, 11, and 12; then to 13 and 14; and finally to point P'. In this example the calculation procedure is such that the solution proceeds downstream; in general the solution proceeds outward from the data curve.

At interior points the values of ω_p and θ_p may be calculated from equations (10.31) and (10.32) and point P located as described above. For points in the flow which are located at the solid boundary containing the flow, this technique fails to supply an answer since both ω_2 and θ_2 are unknowns in (10.31) and (10.32). (See Figure 10.8.) At points on the solid boundary, however, the value of θ_p is known since the fluid follows the confining walls. From equation (10.32), with some rearranging:

$$(\omega_2 - \theta_2) = (\omega_1 + \theta_1) - 2\theta_p \qquad (10.33)$$

Then equation (10.31) may be written as

$$\omega_p = (\omega_1 + \theta_1) - \theta_p \qquad (10.34)$$

This same result is easily obtained by considering the fact that $(\omega + \theta)$ is constant on right-running characteristics. That is, $\omega_1 + \theta_1 = \omega_p + \theta_p$.

In the case of the free boundary, the pressure at point P is known initially and, since the flow is isentropic throughout, this is sufficient to determine the Mach number and ω at P. Only the angle θ_p (and, therefore, the boundary location) are unknown. Again $\omega_1 + \theta_1 = \omega_p + \theta_p$. That is,

$$\theta_p = (\omega_1 + \theta_1) - \omega_p \qquad (10.35)$$

The boundary is determined by making the mesh size small enough so that small velocity vectors along the free boundary determine the boundary shape.

10.6 Example of computation with method of characteristics

As an example of the use of the method of characteristics, consider the flow in a uniformly diverging channel.

In Figure 10.9, a flow enters radially with a Mach number of 1.108 along the arc abc, with the channel diverging with a half-angle of 10°. Find the relative area, i.e., A_2/A_1, where the Mach number is 1.554. Since the flow is symmetrical about a central axis, it is sufficient to construct the network for the upper half of the channel.

The example is solved by drawing characteristics for each 4°. At points a, b, c, the values for ω are found from the tables of Prandtl-Meyer functions at Mach 1.1 to be 1.5° and the θ's are, respectively, 10°, 6°, 2°. Table 10.1 is a convenient tabulation technique to use in conjunction with the construction of the characteristic network.

At point s the radius may be scaled and found to equal 1.20 of the radius

Table 10.1

Point	ω	θ	M	α	$\omega + \theta$	$\omega - \theta$
a	1.5	10	1.108	62.95	11.5	−8.5
b	1.5	6	1.108	62.95	7.5	−4.5
c	1.5	2	1.108	62.95	3.5	−0.5
d	3.5	8	1.198	53.11	11.5	−4.5
e	3.5	4	1.198	53.11	7.5	−0.5
f	3.5	0	1.198	53.11	3.5	+3.5
g	5.5	10	1.275	51.64	15.5	−4.5
h	5.5	6	1.275	51.64	11.5	−0.5
i	5.5	2	1.275	51.64	7.5	+3.5
j	7.5	8	1.348	47.90	15.5	−0.5
k	7.5	4	1.348	47.90	11.5	+3.5
l	7.5	0	1.348	47.90	7.5	+7.5
m	9.5	10	1.418	44.86	19.5	−0.5
n	9.5	6	1.418	44.86	15.5	+3.5
o	9.5	2	1.418	44.86	11.5	+7.5
p	11.5	8	1.486	42.29	19.5	+3.5
q	11.5	4	1.486	42.29	15.5	+7.5
r	11.5	0	1.486	42.29	11.5	+11.5
s	13.5	10	1.554			
t	13.5	6	1.554			
u	13.5	2	1.554			

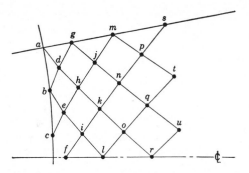

Fig. 10.9 Computation with method of characteristics.

at a. Thus the flow area for $M = 1.554$ must be about 1.20 of the area where $M = 1.108$. This answer is easier found for this simple case for one-dimensional flow from A/A^* for $M = 1.554$ divided by A/A^* for $M = 1.108$, or $1.2145/1.0093 = 1.205$. This example is used only to illustrate the method of characteristics technique. The procedure is more valuable in the design of passages which are not uniformly diverging, as will be discussed in the following section.

10.7 The design of supersonic nozzles

One of the most valuable applications of the method of characteristics is that of the design of a supersonic nozzle. Actually the technique is applicable to any supersonic flow which is being accelerated and in which the flow is to be *uniform* in both magnitude and direction. In a wind tunnel, for example, it is necessary to have the flow in the test section always parallel to the axis of the tunnel.

In a diverging supersonic passage, the flow may be made uniform by "contouring" the passage walls. A supersonic nozzle contour is obtained by turning the wall inward by the same number of degrees as the characteristic spacing at each intersection of the wall and a characteristic. For example, if a one-degree characteristic mesh is being used and the divergence half-angle is $10°$, then the wall angle is successively changed from $10°$ to $9°$, to $8°$, to $7°$, etc. When the nozzle walls are again parallel to the nozzle axis, the flow will be uniformly in the axial direction and with a constant Mach number. This is true, provided that the wall angle is changed gradually enough so that the oblique shocks which form are infinitesimally weak.

The smaller the mesh size in the characteristic network, the less the wall must be turned at each point, and hence the weaker the oblique shock which is formed. Depending on the application in a practical case, a two-degree mesh, or a one-degree mesh may be typical, but in some cases, particularly where digital computers are available fractional degree meshes have been used.

10.8 Weak waves as characteristics—field method

In a true characteristic network, the distribution of the flow properties is continuous. As described above, the value of $\omega + \theta$ or of $\omega - \theta$ is constant along a characteristic and thus, as the flow direction is changed continuously, ω (and therefore the Mach number) is also experiencing a continuous change. Only the location of successive points of intersection of the characteristics are left to some degree of approximation. This technique is sometimes referred to as the *lattice method* because the lattice points are located by construction of a lattice which approximates a true characteristic mesh.

At any boundary change or other flow disturbance, waves are formed, and if these waves are weak, they may be used in a manner similar to the characteristics. It should be remembered throughout such analyses that across a wave front, i.e., oblique shock or expansion wave, the flow properties are discontinuous. The Mach numbers on the two sides of a wave are different whereas across a characteristic the Mach number is continuous and may be constant.

In the region bounded by wave fronts, the flow properties are constant. As an observer moves across a wave the flow properties change and in the second region a new value, which is again constant, is observed for each flow property. The waves divide the total flow field into regions or *cells of uniform flow*. For example, in Figure 10.10, which illustrates the basic features of characteristics versus waves, values for the various flow properties

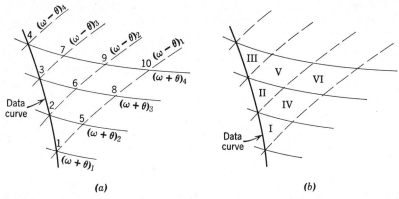

(a)   (b)

Fig. 10.10 Characteristics and weak waves as characteristics. (*a*) Characteristics *lattice*: flow properties found successively at points 5, 6, 7, 8, 9, and 10. (*b*) Wave *field*: flow properties found successively in cells IV, V, and VI.

are known along the data curve. Consider the waves in Figure 10.10(b) to be expansion waves from the upper and lower boundaries of the flow channel, and assume that these waves are drawn so that each causes a two-degree deflection in the flow direction. Those from the upper boundary give a $\Delta\theta = +2°$ and those from the lower boundary give $\Delta\theta = -2°$. Then cell II has flow with a direction $4°$ upward from the flow direction in cell I, and cell III has a flow direction upwards an additional $4°$. Each time a wave is crossed the flow is turned $2°$ in the appropriate direction.

If compression waves are also encountered, they may be superimposed in Figure 10.10(b) to give a complete wave field. In Figure 10.11, compression waves from the lower boundary of the flow channel are shown as the dashed lines and these waves are of such strength that the flow is turned upward $2°$ as it crosses each wave. This suggests numbering the cells with four numbers, $\begin{pmatrix} f & h \\ g & i \end{pmatrix}$; f indicates the number of expansion waves developed at the upper boundary which are crossed in reaching the cell, g indicates the number of expansion waves developed at the lower boundary which must be crossed, h the number of compression waves from the upper boundary, and i the number of compression waves from the lower boundary which must be crossed to reach the cell in question. Figure 10.11 shows such a numbering system, using cell I of Figure 10.10 as the reference cell.

For all waves causing equal deflection, δ,

$$\theta = \theta_1 + \delta(f - g - h + i) \tag{10.36}$$

and

$$\omega = \omega_1 + \delta(f + g - h - i) \tag{10.37}$$

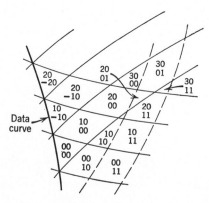

Fig. 10.11   Cell-numbering in a wave field.

Thus plotting the wave field (for weak waves) makes it possible to find both θ and ω in each cell or region and then the Mach number and the other flow properties. The real beauty of this field method lies in the fact that a weak wave may be canceled at a wall by turning the wall (inward or outward) so that the flow direction is parallel to the wall. This technique is especially valuable in "contouring" a supersonic nozzle as described in the previous section.

Problems

10.1 In a rectangular section with upper and lower walls as shown, the flow (with $k = 1.4$) along the arc AB is at constant Mach number of 1.1 and at every point normal to the arc. Use the method of characteristics to find the length L to the point where the flow has a Mach number of 1.8. (Assume continued divergence at a 10^0 half angle.) Check the result obtained for consistency with the one-dimensional theory.

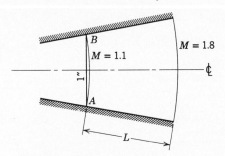

Figure for Problem 10.1.

10.2 For the configuration of Problem 10.1, what is the Mach number at a distance, $L = 2$ inches? Check with the one-dimensional theory.

10.3 Design a Prandtl-Meyer turn nozzle for air ($k = 1.4$) from $M = 1.0$ to $M = 1.8$. Find x, y, and l_2/l_1.

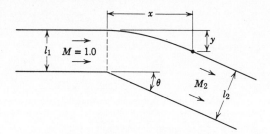

Figure for Problem 10.3.

10.4 Design a Prandtl-Meyer turn nozzle to expand air from $M = 1.2$ to $M = 2.4$. (See Problem 10.3.)

10.5 Use the method of characteristics to "contour" the diverging section of an air nozzle to give uniform and parallel flow at $M = 2.4$, by assuming a Prandtl-Meyer expansion at the throat ($M = 1.0$).

10.6 Use the method of characteristics to "contour" the diverging section of a nozzle to give uniform and parallel flow at $M = 2.0$ by assuming a flow of air at $M = 1.1$ along an arc (as along AB in Problem 10.1).

10.7 Show the wave pattern for several regions following the underexpansion at the flow exit shown. Indicate the Mach number, the pressure, and the flow direction in each region.

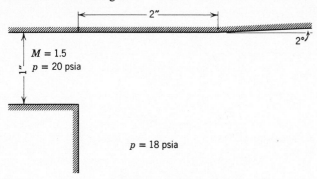

$M = 1.5$
$p = 20$ psia

$p = 18$ psia

Figure for Problem 10.7.

References

1. H. W. Liepmann and A. Roshko: *Elements of Gasdynamics*, John Wiley and Sons, New York, 1957.
2. S. Pai: *Introduction to the Theory of Compressible Flow*, D. Van Nostrand, Princeton, N.J., 1959.

11

generalized one-dimensional gas dynamics

11.1 Introduction

Throughout this text, four basic concepts, or laws, governing fluid flow have been used. In each of the specialized types of flow resulting in Fanno lines, Rayleigh lines, normal shocks, isothermal flows, etc., an analysis was made, based on the four fundamental laws as applied with a particular set of boundary conditions. Various techniques have been suggested to generalize the approach and study how some of the "simple" processes can be combined.

The method presented here is essentially that of Benedict and Steltz and it will be shown that the analysis solves the same problems as the previous special ones. It is evident that a thorough knowledge of the basic principles is most desirable, both to the understanding and the use of the generalized techniques. This approach has the advantage of pointing out the presence of common bonds between the various "simple" flows. It has the

181

added advantage of offering possible solutions to some (but certainly not all) combined or "nonsimple" type of flow problems.

11.2 The generalized flow equation

As in many of the flow analyses previously discussed, it is suitable to consider the continuity equation for steady, one-dimensional flow as one of the starting points.

$$\frac{d\rho}{\rho} + \frac{dA}{A} + \frac{dV}{V} = 0 \tag{11.1}$$

Using the steady flow energy equation for the variation from the static to stagnation state,

$$dh + \frac{V\,dV}{g_0} = dh_0 \tag{11.2}$$

which leads (for a perfect gas) to

$$\frac{dV}{V} = \frac{d(T_0 - T)}{2(T_0 - T)} = \frac{1}{2}\frac{dT_0}{T_0} + \frac{1}{2}\frac{d\left(1 - \dfrac{T}{T_0}\right)}{1 - \dfrac{T}{T_0}} \tag{11.3}$$

Again using the perfect gas relationship and the concept of stagnation state, the relative density change can be written:

$$\frac{d\rho}{\rho} = \frac{d(\rho/\rho_0)}{\rho/\rho_0} + \frac{d\rho_0}{\rho_0} = \frac{d(\rho/\rho_0)}{\rho/\rho_0} + \frac{dp_0}{p_0} - \frac{dT_0}{T_0} \tag{11.4}$$

Then, for any *arbitrary* flow process, a general dimensionless continuity equation may be written by substituting in equation (11.1) for $d\rho/\rho$ and dV/V

$$\frac{d(\rho/\rho_0)}{\rho/\rho_0} + \frac{dp_0}{p_0} - \frac{1}{2}\frac{dT_0}{T_0} + \frac{dA}{A} + \frac{1}{2}\frac{d\left(1 - \dfrac{T}{T_0}\right)}{1 - \dfrac{T}{T_0}} = 0 \tag{11.5}$$

Equation (11.5), although quite general, is simple to integrate and evaluate. In either its differential form or its integrated form, it is properly referred to as *the generalized flow equation*. Integrating

$$\frac{p_0}{\sqrt{T_0}} A \frac{\rho}{\rho_0} \sqrt{1 - \frac{T}{T_0}} = \text{Constant} \tag{11.6}$$

Note that the portion of the equation which relates the static state to the stagnation state may be expressed in terms of the pressure ratio, p/p_0

$$\frac{\rho}{\rho_0} \sqrt{1 - \frac{T}{T_0}} = \left(\frac{p}{p_0}\right)^{1/k} \sqrt{1 - \left(\frac{p}{p_0}\right)^{(k-1)/k}} \tag{11.7}$$

Similarly, $\rho/\rho_0\sqrt{1 - (T/T_0)}$ may be expressed in terms of the Mach number at any given point:

$$\rho/\rho_0\sqrt{1 - \frac{T}{T_0}} = \frac{\sqrt{\frac{k-1}{2}}\, M}{\left(1 + \frac{k-1}{2} M^2\right)^{(k+1)/(2k-1)}} \tag{11.8}$$

The generalized flow equation is then

$$\frac{p_0}{\sqrt{T_0}} A\left(\frac{p}{p_0}\right)^{1/k} \sqrt{1 - \left(\frac{p}{p_0}\right)^{(k-1)/k}}$$

$$= \frac{p_0}{\sqrt{T_0}} A \frac{\sqrt{\frac{k-1}{2}}\, M}{\left(1 + \frac{k-1}{2} M^2\right)^{(k+1)/2(k-1)}} = \text{Constant} \tag{11.9}$$

11.3 The reference state and the generalized compressible flow function

Just as in the cases of the various "simple" flows, it is of great convenience to define a reference state (real or projected imaginary) in the generalized flow in addition to the stagnation state. It has been noted that even though it is extremely valuable, the concept of stagnation state cannot be used in connection with certain flow variables. The ratio of flow area to the flow area at a reference state has no meaning if the reference state is the stagnation state. In adiabatic flows, the flow velocity ratio and impulse function ratio have no meaning when stagnation conditions are used for the reference state. This difficulty also is experienced with nearly all properties when the stagnation temperature is changing during the flow process.

In order to find a suitable reference state for generalized flow, it is advantageous and convenient to consider the second law of thermodynamics. In Chapter 2 it was pointed out that

$$ds = ds_e + ds_i \tag{11.10}$$

where $ds_e = \delta Q/T$ and may be either positive or negative. Thus ds_i must always be positive or in the limit zero as the process involved approaches a reversible one. The first law may be used to eliminate the quantity ds_e, since

$$\delta Q = T\, ds_e = c_p\, dT + \frac{V\, dV}{g_0} \tag{11.11}$$

for any flow with no external work. The total entropy change for any pure substance may be written

$$ds = \frac{c_p \, dT}{T} - \frac{dp}{\rho T} \qquad (11.12)$$

Combining equations (11.10), (11.11), and (11.12) yields,

$$ds_i = - \frac{dp}{\rho T} - \frac{V \, dV}{g_0 T} \qquad (11.13)$$

The thermodynamic reference state for generalized flow is defined as that state were the entropy production rate due to friction is zero. That is, $ds_i = 0$. Then equation (11.13) may be written

$$\frac{dp}{\rho} = - \frac{V \, dV}{g_0} \qquad (11.14)$$

Employing the continuity equation at the reference state (for the condition of constant area),

$$\frac{dV}{V} = - \frac{d\rho}{\rho}$$

equation (11.14) may be written

$$\frac{dp}{d\rho} = \frac{V^2}{g_0}$$

or

$$V^* = \sqrt{g_0(dp/d\rho)} \qquad (11.15)$$

Thus the velocity at the reference state is defined in much the same way as the velocity at the sonic point in isentropic flow. There is a distinct difference, however. In the development here it was necessary only to take $ds_i = 0$, and hence the total entropy is other than zero if there is a heat transfer.

If the flow is adiabatic, then $dp/d\rho$ may be replaced by $(\partial p/\partial \rho)_s$ since $ds_i = 0$, and then $V^* = a$. This is the condition encountered in Chapter 5 in isentropic flow and in Chapter 6 in Fanno flow. The two reference points were not the same and the generalized flow approach does not imply that they are the same. The reference state for the generalized analysis is defined as that state having a velocity given by equation (11.15) and also having the requirement that the rate of change of the flow area is zero. Thus, in varying area isentropic flow, the reference state occurs in the throat area of a converging-diverging nozzle, while in constant area adiabatic flow, the reference state occurs at the point where the "friction length" (and hence the entropy) has become a maximum. In both cases the Mach number is equal to 1.0 in agreement with the results found in Chapters 5 and 6.

It is not a requirement of the definition of the thermodynamic reference state that the Mach number be 1.0. As an example, consider the isothermal flow of a perfect gas in a constant-area duct, as described in section 8.5. The velocity at the reference state, as given by equation (11.15), is then

$$V^* = \sqrt{g_0 \frac{p}{\rho}} = \sqrt{g_0 RT} = \sqrt{\frac{a^2}{k}} \tag{11.16}$$

Thus, at the reference state in isothermal flow, the Mach number at the reference state is $\sqrt{1/k}$, which again agrees with previous theory.

Having defined and discussed the concept of the reference state, it is now appropriate to return to the generalized flow equation and include the reference state concept with it. Equation (11.9) may be written as

$$\frac{p_{01}}{\sqrt{T_{01}}} A_1 \left(\frac{p_1}{p_{01}}\right)^{1/k} \left[1 - \left(\frac{p_1}{p_{01}}\right)^{(k-1)/k}\right]^{\frac{1}{2}} = \frac{p_{02}}{\sqrt{T_{02}}} A_2 \left(\frac{p_2}{p_{02}}\right)^{1/k}$$

$$\times \left[1 - \left(\frac{p_2}{p_{02}}\right)^{(k-1)/k}\right]^{\frac{1}{2}} \tag{11.17}$$

It is convenient to define a pressure ratio function

$$P = \left(\frac{p}{p_0}\right)^{1/k} \left[1 - \left(\frac{p}{p_0}\right)^{(k-1)/k}\right]^{\frac{1}{2}} \tag{11.18}$$

It is easy to show that this function is a maximum (with p the independent variable) when

$$\frac{p}{p_0} = \left(\frac{2}{k+1}\right)^{k/(k-1)}$$

Then

$$P_{\max} = \left(\frac{2}{k+1}\right)^{1/(k-1)} \left(\frac{k-1}{k+1}\right)^{\frac{1}{2}} \tag{11.19}$$

By dividing both sides of equation (11.17) by $P_{\max}$, it is evident that

$$\left(\frac{T_{02}}{T_{01}}\right)^{\frac{1}{2}} \frac{p_{01}}{p_{02}} \frac{A_1}{A_2} \frac{\left(\dfrac{p_1}{p_{01}}\right)^{1/k} \left[1 - \left(\dfrac{p_1}{p_{01}}\right)^{(k-1)/k}\right]^{\frac{1}{2}}}{\left(\dfrac{2}{k+1}\right)^{1/(k-1)} \left(\dfrac{k-1}{k+1}\right)^{\frac{1}{2}}}$$

$$= \frac{\left(\dfrac{p_2}{p_{02}}\right)^{1/k} \left[1 - \left(\dfrac{p_2}{p_{02}}\right)^{(k-1)/k}\right]^{\frac{1}{2}}}{\left(\dfrac{2}{k+1}\right)^{1/(k-1)} \left(\dfrac{k-1}{k+1}\right)^{\frac{1}{2}}} \tag{11.20}$$

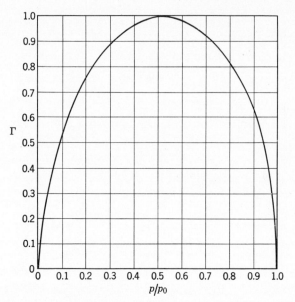

Fig. 11.1 Generalized compressible flow function, Γ ($k = 1.4$).

or more simply

$$\left(\frac{T_{02}}{T_{01}}\right)^{\!\!\frac{1}{2}} \frac{p_{01}}{p_{02}} \frac{A_1}{A_2}\Gamma_1 = \Gamma_2 \tag{11.21}$$

where Γ is the *generalized compressible flow function*. This function is based on the principle of continuity and the conservation of energy.

It is now in order to investigate the Γ function and observe its variation with pressure ratio. Differentiating the definition,

$$\Gamma = \frac{\left(\dfrac{p}{p_0}\right)^{\!1/k}\!\left[1 - \left(\dfrac{p}{p_0}\right)^{\!(k-1)/k}\right]^{\frac{1}{2}}}{\left(\dfrac{2}{k+1}\right)^{\!1/(k-1)}\!\left(\dfrac{k-1}{k+1}\right)^{\!\frac{1}{2}}} \tag{11.22}$$

it is evident that Γ is a maximum when

$$\frac{p}{p_0} = \left(\frac{2}{k+1}\right)^{\!k/(k-1)}$$

and thus $\Gamma_{\max} = 1.00$.

Figure 11.1 shows the variation of Γ with pressure ratio (for $k = 1.4$).

It is quite a simple matter to tabulate the values of Γ as the pressure ratio p/p_0 changes, and almost as easy to tabulate Γ as a function of Mach number. Such a tabulation is found in the isentropic table in the Appendix.

11.4 Application of generalized compressible flow function to specific processes

Adiabatic flow with no friction (isentropic). It has already been seen that for this condition $dT_0 = 0$ and $dp_0 = 0$. Thus the generalized flow equation may be written

$$\frac{A_1}{A_2} \Gamma_1 = \Gamma_2 \tag{11.23}$$

Knowing inlet conditions, i.e., M_1, or p_1/p_{01}, the tabulated Γ_1 may be found from the table in the Appendix, and this along with the specified area ratio determines Γ_2. Knowing Γ_2, it is easy to re-enter the isentropic tables and find values for all properties at the thus defined point 2. Figure 11.2 compares the isentropic process on the Ts and Γ versus p/p_0 diagrams.

It is evident that for a computed Γ_2 the solution may be either subsonic or supersonic. The usual care and thought are necessary, here as before, with the requirement of a minimum area section in one case being apparent.

Adiabatic flow with friction. For this type of flow process the generalized flow equation becomes

$$\left(\frac{p_{01}}{p_{02}}\right)\left(\frac{A_1}{A_2}\right)\Gamma_1 = \Gamma_2 \tag{11.24}$$

For the condition of constant area, as in Chapter 6, it is necessary in a practical problem to locate point 2 through some knowledge of the entropy increase. In Chapter 6, the factor $fL_{\max}/D$ was used to locate the second point and thus determine the ratio p_{01}/p_{02} from the Fanno tables. It is equally necessary here to make some preliminary calculations to find the entropy increase and determine p_{01}/p_{02}. (*Note:* Remember that for any adiabatic flow of a perfect gas $p_{01}/p_{02} = e^{\Delta s/R}$.)

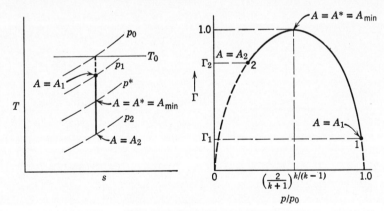

Fig. 11.2 Isentropic process.

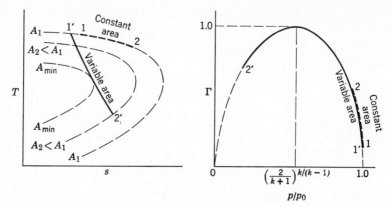

Fig. 11.3 Adiabatic flow with friction.

For a known stagnation pressure ratio with constant area, Γ_2 may be immediately found from equation (11.24) and hence the remaining properties can all be found in terms of the values at the initial state. Figure 11.3 shows such a constant area adiabatic flow with friction as well as a variable area case on both Ts and Γ versus p/p_0 diagrams.

Also with the variable area adiabatic flows, some information must be known regarding the entropy increase to make it possible to determine p_{01}/p_{02}. This factor with the given area ratio determines Γ_2, as in equation (11.24), and hence the values of the other properties can be expressed in terms of the initial state. Of course the inverse type of problem is also possible. If the Mach number or temperature is known at the end of the adiabatic process, Γ_2 can be found from the tables, and then the value of p_{01}/p_{02} (and the entropy increase) can be found from equation (11.24).

Heating or cooling processes. The generalized flow equation,

$$\left(\frac{T_{02}}{T_{01}}\right)^{\!1/2} \frac{p_{01}}{p_{02}} \frac{A_1}{A_2} \Gamma_1 = \Gamma_2 \qquad (11.21)$$

is repeated for easy reference in studying this process. The basic key here is again the ratio p_{01}/p_{02}, but since the process is not adiabatic, the simple relations between stagnation pressure ratio and entropy increase are invalid. The stagnation pressure changes with heat addition and also with friction, and evaluation of the over-all ratio p_{01}/p_{02} becomes very difficult, if not impossible. In a particular problem both p_{01} and p_{02} might be measured; then the general equation (11.21) can be solved for Γ_2 and the remaining properties at the end of the process.

The simple heating or simple cooling process, i.e., constant area and no friction, was handled in Chapter 8. The same problem is easily handled

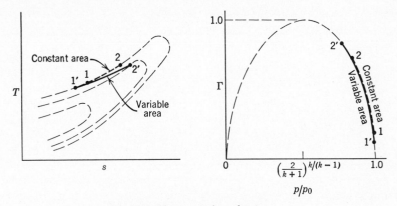

Fig. 11.4 Heating without friction.

with the Γ function. Equation (11.21) may be written, for constant area,

$$\left(\frac{T_{02}}{T_{01}}\right)^{\!1/2} \frac{p_{01}}{p_{02}} \Gamma_1 = \Gamma_2 \tag{11.25}$$

and, as usual with the generalized flow concept, the key is determining p_{01}/p_{02}. The stagnation temperature ratio may generally be found from the amount of heating or cooling; Γ_1 and the ratio of the inlet stagnation temperature to the critical state stagnation temperature are generally known or can be found from initial flow conditions. Then the relation

$$\frac{T_{02}}{T_0{}^*} = \frac{T_{02}}{T_{01}} \frac{T_{01}}{T_0{}^*} \tag{11.26}$$

may be used to find $T_{02}/T_0{}^*$, and hence M_2 and Γ_2. Equation (11.25) defines the stagnation pressure ratio after T_{02}/T_{01}, Γ_1, and Γ_2 are known, and thus all properties at point 2 are fixed. Figure 11.4 presents Ts and Γ versus p/p_0 diagrams for heating processes without friction for both constant area and changing area.

In the case of heating with an area change, equation (11.21) is still valid and most general. However, it is difficult in this case to evaluate Γ_2. The technique outlined above, for constant area, breaks down at the point of determining M_2, since M_2 depends on the area change as well as the ratio of $T_{02}/T_0{}^*$ for a constant area process. Usually the heating portion of the process takes place at nearly constant area and then the process can be analyzed by these techniques. An initial isentropic change to that area at which the heat transfer is to occur can be used to determine a new Γ_{1a}, i.e.,

$$\frac{A_1}{A_{1a}} \Gamma_1 = \Gamma_{1a}$$

Then a heating (or cooling) process at constant area, A_{1a} may be analyzed as outlined above to determine point $2a$, and finally an isentropic change to the final area A_2 completes the problem.

$$\frac{A_{1a}}{A_2} \Gamma_{2a} = \Gamma_2$$

Such a procedure is shown in Figure 11.5.

A similar technique may be used with the generalized flow equation for heating or cooling with friction, by first taking an adiabatic flow with friction and then a heating or cooling without friction, or vice versa.

Isothermal processes. Just as in the other cases which have been analyzed with the generalized compressible flow equation, the determination of the stagnation pressure ratio for the process usually holds the key to the solution. For a constant-area isothermal process,

$$\left(\frac{T_{02}}{T_{01}}\right)^{\!\frac{1}{2}} \frac{p_{01}}{p_{02}} \Gamma_1 = \Gamma_2 \tag{11.27}$$

In constant-area isothermal flow it is impossible for the Mach number to do anything other than approach $\sqrt{1/k}$. As pointed out above, the reference state for generalized flow is found where $M = \sqrt{1/k}$, if the flow is isothermal. The values of $(T_0/T_0{}^*)_{\text{isoth}}$, which are tabulated as a column in the Rayleigh table in the Appendix, are valuable in connection with this analysis. Figure 11.6 illustrates this process.

For a given process as illustrated, the ratio of the stagnation temperatures or the amount of heat addition is usually known. From known initial conditions, Γ_1 and $(T_{01}/T_0{}^*)_{\text{isoth}}$ can be determined. For the usual case $(T_{02}/T_0{}^*)_{\text{isoth}}$ then may be found from

$$\left(\frac{T_{02}}{T_0{}^*}\right)_{\text{isoth}} = \left(\frac{T_{01}}{T_0{}^*}\right)_{\text{isoth}} \frac{T_{02}}{T_{01}} \tag{11.28}$$

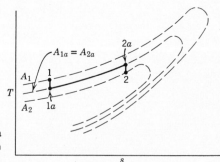

Fig. 11.5 Heating with area change (all heat transferred at an intermediate area).

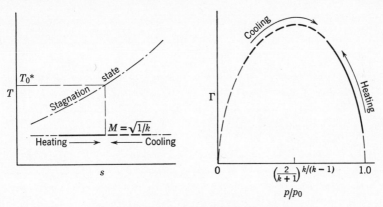

Fig. 11.6 Constant-area isothermal process.

With $(T_{02}/T_0{}^*)_{\text{isoth}}$ known, Γ_2 is obtained and the ratio

$$\frac{p_{01}}{p_{02}} = \frac{\Gamma_2}{\Gamma_1}\left(\frac{T_{01}}{T_{02}}\right)^{\!1\!/\!2}$$

can be computed. Γ_2, p_{01}/p_{02}, and T_{01}/T_{02} are sufficient to determine all properties at the end of the process in terms of the initial properties.

Normal shocks. The generalized compressible flow function may be used in determining the changes which occur across a normal shock, but here again the key to the problem is the stagnation pressure ratio. For a normal shock the equation is (as for any adiabatic constant-area process):

$$\frac{p_{01}}{p_{02}}\Gamma_1 = \Gamma_2$$

For known upstream conditions (ahead of the shock), Γ_1 can be found and also p_{01}/p_{02} from the shock tables. Γ_2 which is thus determined fixes the values of other properties for the state of the fluid following the shock. Figure 11.7 shows a normal shock process on both Ts and Γ versus p/p_0 diagrams. Notice that for normal shocks, Γ_2 must always be larger than Γ_1, a requirement of the second law of thermodynamics.

In the cases of flow with simple heating or cooling as along a Rayleigh line, cases of isothermal flow, and cases of normal shock processes, quantities which were developed in earlier chapters are needed and used. The values of $T_0/T_0{}^*$ for Rayleigh flow must be used in analyzing the flow on the generalized basis presented in this chapter. Since such values are readily available in the tables, this is no particular disadvantage. In fact, one of the advantages of this generalized approach is that one table can be used in place of the four separate ones for isentropic, Fanno, Rayleigh,

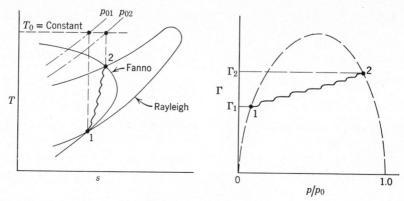

Fig. 11.7 Normal shock.

and normal shocks. Such a generalized table has been suggested by Benedict and Steltz. It should include a tabulation, probably with Mach number the independent variable, of p/p_0, T/T_0, Γ, $(T_0/T_0{}^*)_{\text{Rayleigh}}$, $(T_0/T_0{}^*)_{\text{isoth}}$ and p_{01}/p_{02} for a normal shock. Having such a table would make it possible to solve most of, but not all, the problems of the simple flow process very handily.

The real value of the generalized flow approach is in the solution of the generalized problem. Certainly an area change in a flow duct can be measured, the stagnation temperature ratio is usually obtainable from known heating or cooling effects, and only the stagnation pressure ratio presents a problem. Knowledge of either the resulting Mach number or this stagnation pressure ratio is necessary to solve the generalized problem.

Problems

11.1 In the expansion of air through a converging-diverging nozzle which has an exit area 1.75 times the throat area, the air enters with a Mach number of 0.1 and is discharged at $M = 1.95$. The duct supplying this nozzle has an area five times the throat area of the nozzle. Assume adiabatic flow and use the generalized compressible flow approach to find the entropy increase for 1 lb of air as it flows through this nozzle. What is the nozzle efficiency?

11.2 Air expands through a converging-diverging nozzle with an over-all area ratio, (A_2/A_1), of 3.0. Inlet conditions are: Mach number, 0.15; $T_0 = 1000°R$; $p_0 = 100$ psia. Assume isentropic flow and find for the nozzle exit section: (*a*) the Mach number, (*b*) the total and static pressure, (*c*) the total and static temperature.

11.3 Work problem 5.6 by using the concept of the generalized compressible flow function.

11.4 Use the Γ function to solve problem 5.7.

11.5 In the adiabatic flow of air in a constant-area duct, at a certain section the air is found to be flowing with a Mach number of 0.25, a temperature of 987°R, and a pressure of 95.7 psia. Estimate the temperature, the pressure, and the Mach number where the stagnation pressure is 55 psia.

11.6 In a certain adiabatic flow (which includes both an area change and friction), air experiences a drop in stagnation pressure such that the ratio p_{02}/p_{01} is 0.55. The initial conditions are: Mach number, 0.25; stagnation temperature, 1000°R; stagnation pressure, 100 psia. The inlet and exit areas have been measured and the ratio A_2/A_1 is found to be 1.35. Find static pressure, static temperature, and Mach number at the exit.

11.7 Air is cooled during the frictionless flow through a constant-area duct such that the final stagnation temperature. Initially the ratio of static to stagnation pressure is 0.30, and the stagnation temperature at this state is 1000°R. Assume an inlet static pressure of 2 psia, and find the resulting temperature, pressure, and Mach number.

11.8 In a certain frictionless flow duct, the exit area is 0.7 times the inlet area. Air enters this duct with a Mach number of 0.25 and experiences a heat addition such that the stagnation temperature is doubled. For an inlet stagnation temperature of 500°R and a stagnation pressure of 10 psia, find the exit temperature, pressure, and Mach number, if all the heat is transferred at the inlet area.

11.9 Solve problem 11.8 if all the heat is transferred at the exit area.

11.10 In a certain constant-area isothermal flow of air, the Mach number entering the portion of the duct under study is 0.15, the pressure is 20 psia, and the temperature is 600°R. Leaving the portion of the duct being studied, the Mach number is found to be 0.75. (a) Find the heat addition per pound of air. (b) Find the pressure at the second section, (c) Find the temperature at that point. (d) Find the entropy increase.

11.11 Consider the isothermal flow of air in a constant-area duct in which the stagnation temperature increases by 15%. For an inlet Mach number of 0.10, inlet temperature of 600°R, and inlet pressure of 25 psia, find the exit pressure and the entropy change per pound of air.

11.12 During the isothermal flow of air through a certain passage, the area is found to increase 20% while the stagnation temperature decreases 20%. Initial conditions are: Mach number, 1.10; pressure, 5 psia; temperature, 500°R. Find the resulting pressure, temperature, and Mach number.

11.13 Consider a normal shock process for air with upstream conditions such that Mach number is 2.5; temperature, 444°R; and pressure, 5.58 psia. Find the pressure following the shock and the entropy change across the shock.

11.14 Solve problem 7.8 by using the concepts of generalized flow.

11.15 Use the Γ function to solve problem 7.14.

References

1. R. P. Benedict and W. G. Steltz: A Generalized Approach to One Dimensional Gas Dynamics, ASME Paper 60-WA-300.
2. A. H. Shapiro: *The Dynamics and Thermodynamics of Compressible Fluid Flow*, Vol. I, Ronald Press, New York, 1953.

appendix

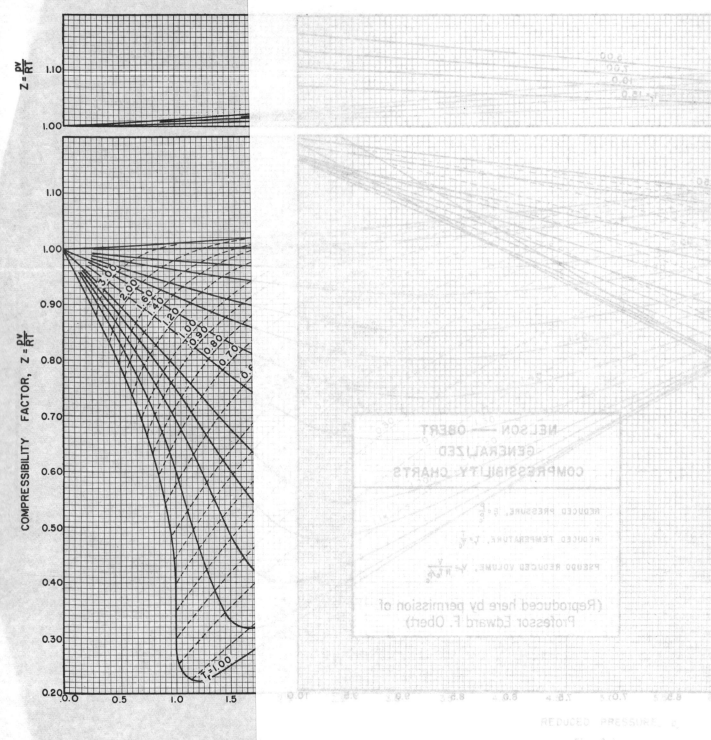

NELSON — OBERT
GENERALIZED
COMPRESSIBILITY CHARTS

REDUCED PRESSURE, $P_r = \frac{P}{P_c}$

REDUCED TEMPERATURE, $T_r = \frac{T}{T_c}$

PSEUDO REDUCED VOLUME, $V_r = \frac{V}{RT_c/P_c}$

(Reproduced here by permission of
Professor Edward F. Obert)

COMPRESSIBILITY FACTOR, $Z = \frac{pv}{RT}$

$Z = \frac{pv}{RT}$

REDUCED PRESSURE

Fig. A-1.

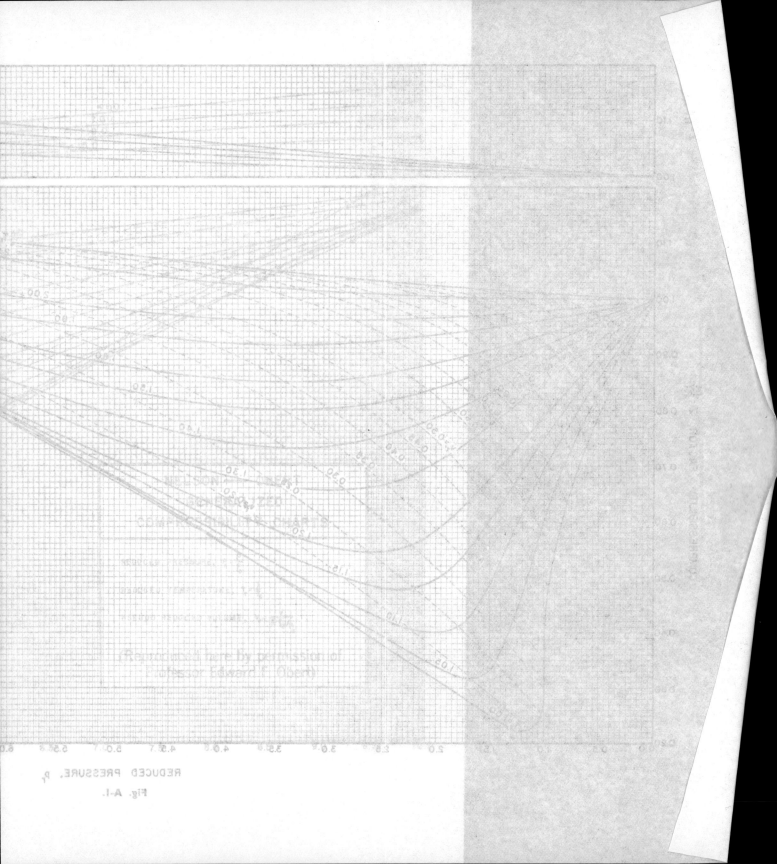

Table A.I
Thermodynamic Properties of Air at Low Pressure*

T	h	p_r	u	v_r	ϕ
200	47.67	0.04320	33.96	1714.9	0.36303
220	52.46	0.06026	37.38	1352.5	0.38584
240	57.25	0.08165	40.80	1088.8	0.40666
260	62.03	0.10797	44.21	892.0	0.42582
280	66.82	0.13986	47.63	741.6	0.44356
300	71.61	0.17795	51.04	624.5	0.46007
320	76.40	0.22290	54.46	531.8	0.47550
340	81.18	0.27545	57.87	457.2	0.49002
360	85.97	0.3363	61.29	396.6	0.50369
380	90.75	0.4061	64.70	346.6	0.51663
400	95.53	0.4858	68.11	305.0	0.52890
420	100.32	0.5760	71.52	270.1	0.54058
440	105.11	0.6776	74.93	240.6	0.55172
460	109.90	0.7913	78.36	215.33	0.56235
480	114.69	0.9182	81.77	193.65	0.57255
500	119.48	1.0590	85.20	174.90	0.58233
520	124.27	1.2147	88.62	158.58	0.59173
540	129.06	1.3860	92.04	144.32	0.60078
560	133.86	1.5742	95.47	131.78	0.60950
580	138.66	1.7800	98.90	120.70	0.61793
600	143.47	2.005	102.34	110.88	0.62607
620	148.28	2.249	105.78	102.12	0.63395
640	153.09	2.514	109.21	94.30	0.64159
660	157.92	2.801	112.67	87.27	0.64902
680	162.73	3.111	116.12	80.96	0.65621
700	167.56	3.446	119.58	75.25	0.66321
720	172.39	3.806	123.04	70.07	0.67002
740	177.23	4.193	126.51	65.38	0.67665
760	182.08	4.607	129.99	61.10	0.68312
780	186.94	5.051	133.47	57.20	0.68942
800	191.81	5.526	136.97	53.63	0.69558
820	196.69	6.033	140.47	50.35	0.70160
840	201.56	6.573	143.98	47.34	0.70747
860	206.46	7.149	147.50	44.57	0.71323

* Abridged from Table 1 in *Gas Tables*, by Joseph H. Keenan and Joseph Kaye. Copyright 1948, by Joseph H. Keenan and Joseph Kaye. Published by John Wiley and Sons, New York, who gave permission for this reproduction.

Table A.I (Continued)

T	h	p_r	u	v_r	ϕ
880	211.35	7.761	151.02	42.01	0.71886
900	216.26	8.411	154.57	39.64	0.72438
920	221.18	9.102	158.12	37.44	0.72979
940	226.11	9.834	161.68	35.41	0.73509
960	231.06	10.610	165.26	33.52	0.74030
980	236.02	11.430	168.83	31.76	0.74540
1000	240.98	12.298	172.43	30.12	0.75042
1020	245.97	13.215	176.04	28.59	0.75536
1040	250.95	14.182	179.66	27.17	0.76019
1060	255.96	15.203	183.29	25.82	0.76496
1080	260.97	16.278	186.93	24.58	0.76964
1100	265.99	17.413	190.58	23.40	0.77426
1120	271.03	18.604	194.25	22.30	0.77880
1140	276.08	19.858	197.94	21.27	0.78326
1160	281.14	21.18	201.63	20.293	0.78767
1180	286.21	22.56	205.33	19.377	0.79201
1200	291.30	24.01	209.05	18.514	0.79628
1220	296.41	25.53	212.78	17.700	0.80050
1240	301.52	27.13	216.53	16.932	0.80466
1260	306.65	28.80	220.28	16.205	0.80876
1280	311.79	30.55	224.05	15.518	0.81280
1300	316.94	32.39	227.83	14.868	0.81680
1320	322.11	34.31	231.63	14.253	0.82075
1340	327.29	36.31	235.43	13.670	0.82464
1360	332.48	38.41	239.25	13.118	0.82848
1380	337.68	40.59	243.08	12.593	0.83229
1400	342.90	42.88	246.93	12.095	0.83604
1420	348.14	45.26	250.79	11.622	0.83975
1440	353.37	47.75	254.66	11.172	0.84341
1460	358.63	50.34	258.54	10.743	0.84704
1480	363.89	53.04	262.44	10.336	0.85062
1500	369.17	55.86	266.34	9.948	0.85416
1520	374.47	58.78	270.26	9.578	0.85767
1540	379.77	61.83	274.20	9.226	0.86113
1560	385.08	65.00	278.13	8.890	0.86456
1580	390.40	68.30	282.09	8.569	0.86794
1600	395.74	71.73	286.06	8.263	0.87130
1620	401.09	75.29	290.04	7.971	0.87462

Table A.I (*Continued*)

T	h	p_r	u	v_r	ϕ
1640	406.45	78.99	294.03	7.691	0.87791
1660	411.82	82.83	298.02	7.424	0.88116
1680	417.20	86.82	302.04	7.168	0.88439
1700	422.59	90.95	306.06	6.924	0.88758
1720	428.00	95.24	310.09	6.690	0.89074
1740	433.41	99.69	314.13	6.465	0.89387
1760	438.83	104.30	318.18	6.251	0.89697
1780	444.26	109.08	322.24	6.045	0.90003
1800	449.71	114.03	326.32	5.847	0.90308
1820	455.17	119.16	330.40	5.658	0.90609
1840	460.63	124.47	334.50	5.476	0.90908
1860	466.12	129.95	338.61	5.302	0.91203
1880	471.60	135.64	342.73	5.134	0.91497
1900	477.09	141.51	346.85	4.974	0.91788
1920	482.60	147.59	350.98	4.819	0.92076
1940	488.12	153.87	355.12	4.670	0.92362
1960	493.64	160.37	359.28	4.527	0.92645
1980	499.17	167.07	363.43	4.390	0.92926
2000	504.71	174.00	367.61	4.258	0.93205
2020	510.26	181.16	371.79	4.130	0.93481
2040	515.82	188.54	375.98	4.008	0.93756
2060	521.39	196.16	380.18	3.890	0.94026
2080	526.97	204.02	384.39	3.777	0.94296
2100	532.55	212.1	388.60	3.667	0.94564
2120	538.15	220.5	392.83	3.561	0.94829
2140	543.74	229.1	397.05	3.460	0.95092
2160	549.35	238.0	401.29	3.362	0.95352
2180	554.97	247.2	405.53	3.267	0.95611
2200	560.59	256.6	409.78	3.176	0.95868
2220	566.23	266.3	414.05	3.088	0.96123
2240	571.86	276.3	418.31	3.003	0.96376
2260	577.51	286.6	422.59	2.921	0.96626
2280	583.16	297.2	426.87	2.841	0.96876
2300	588.82	308.1	431.16	2.765	0.97123
2320	594.49	319.4	435.46	2.691	0.97369
2340	600.16	330.9	439.76	2.619	0.97611
2360	605.84	342.8	444.07	2.550	0.97853
2380	611.53	355.0	448.38	2.483	0.98092
2400	617.22	367.6	452.70	2.419	0.98331

Table A.I (*Continued*)

T	h	p_r	u	v_r	ϕ
2420	622.92	380.5	457.02	2.356	0.98567
2440	628.62	393.7	461.36	2.296	0.98802
2460	634.34	407.3	465.70	2.237	0.99035
2480	640.05	421.3	470.05	2.180	0.99266
2500	645.78	435.7	474.40	2.125	0.99497
2550	660.12	473.3	485.31	1.9956	1.00064
2600	674.49	513.5	496.26	1.8756	1.00623
2650	688.90	556.3	507.25	1.7646	1.01172
2700	703.35	601.9	518.26	1.6617	1.01712
2750	717.83	650.4	529.31	1.5662	1.02244
2800	732.33	702.0	540.40	1.4775	1.02767
2850	746.88	756.7	551.52	1.3951	1.03282
2900	761.45	814.8	562.66	1.3184	1.03788
2950	776.05	876.4	573.84	1.2469	1.04288
3000	790.68	941.4	585.04	1.1803	1.04779
3100	820.03	1083.4	607.53	1.0600	1.05741
3200	849.48	1241.7	630.12	0.9546	1.06676
3300	879.02	1418.0	652.81	0.8621	1.07585
3400	908.66	1613.2	675.60	0.7807	1.08470
3500	938.40	1829.3	698.48	0.7087	1.09332
3600	968.21	2067.9	721.44	0.6449	1.10172
3700	998.11	2330.3	744.48	0.5882	1.10991
3800	1028.09	2618.4	767.60	0.5376	1.11791
3900	1058.14	2934.4	790.80	0.4923	1.12571
4000	1088.26	3280	814.06	0.4518	1.13334
4100	1118.46	3656	837.40	0.4154	1.14079
4200	1148.72	4067	860.81	0.3826	1.14809
4300	1179.04	4513	884.28	0.3529	1.15522
4400	1209.42	4997	907.81	0.3262	1.16221
4500	1239.86	5521	931.39	0.3019	1.16905
4600	1270.36	6089	955.04	0.2799	1.17575
4700	1300.92	6701	978.73	0.2598	1.18232
4800	1331.51	7362	1002.48	0.2415	1.18876
4900	1362.17	8073	1026.28	0.2248	1.19508
5000	1392.87	8837	1050.12	0.20959	1.20129
5100	1423.62	9658	1074.02	0.19561	1.20738
5200	1454.41	10539	1097.96	0.18279	1.21336

Table A.1 (Continued)

T	h	p_r	u	v_r	ϕ
5300	1485.26	11481	1121.95	0.17101	1.21923
5400	1516.14	12490	1145.98	0.16015	1.22500
5500	1547.07	13568	1170.04	0.15016	1.23068
5600	1578.03	14719	1194.16	0.14093	1.23626
5700	1609.04	15946	1218.31	0.13242	1.24174
5800	1640.09	17252	1242.50	0.12454	1.24714
5900	1671.17	18643	1266.73	0.11723	1.25246
6000	1702.29	20120	1291.00	0.11047	1.25769
6100	1733.45	21691	1315.30	0.10418	1.26284
6200	1764.65	23357	1339.64	0.09833	1.26791
6300	1795.88	25123	1364.02	0.09289	1.27291
6400	1827.14	26994	1388.43	0.08783	1.27783
6500	1858.44	28974	1412.87	0.08310	1.28268

Table A.2

One-Dimensional Isentropic Flow Functions for a Perfect Gas†
(Constant Specific Heat and Molecular Weight)

(a) $k = 1.4$

M	M^*	$\dfrac{A}{A^*}$	$\dfrac{p}{p_0}$	$\dfrac{\rho}{\rho_0}$	$\dfrac{T}{T_0}$	$\dfrac{I}{I^*}$	$\left(\dfrac{A}{A^*}\right)\left(\dfrac{p}{p_0}\right)$	f_w	f_I	Γ
0	0	∞	1.00000	1.00000	1.00000	∞	∞	0	∞	0
0.01	0.01096	57.874	.99993	.99995	.99998	45.650	57.870	.01183	84.526	.01775
.02	.02191	28.942	.99972	.99980	.99992	22.834	28.934	.02366	42.280	.03477
.03	.03286	19.300	.99937	.99955	.99982	15.232	19.288	.03548	28.205	.05176
.04	.04381	14.482	.99888	.99920	.99968	11.435	14.465	.04728	21.173	.06911
.05	.05476	11.592	.99825	.99875	.99950	9.1584	11.571	.05907	16.958	.08628
.06	.06570	9.6659	.99748	.99820	.99928	7.6428	9.6415	.07084	14.152	.10355
.07	.07664	8.2915	.99658	.99755	.99902	6.5620	8.2631	.08258	12.151	.12069
.08	.08758	7.2616	.99553	.99680	.99872	5.7529	7.2291	.09429	10.652	.13777
.09	.09851	6.4613	.99435	.99596	.99838	5.1249	6.4248	.10597	9.4894	.15479
.10	.10943	5.8218	.99303	.99502	.99800	4.6236	5.7812	.11761	8.5613	.17180
.11	.12035	5.2992	.99157	.99398	.99758	4.2146	5.2546	.12921	7.8039	.18873
.12	.13126	4.8643	.98998	.99284	.99714	3.8747	4.8157	.14077	7.1746	.20559
.13	.14216	4.4968	.98826	.99160	.99664	3.5880	4.4440	.15227	6.6438	.22242
.14	.15306	4.1824	.98640	.99027	.99610	3.3432	4.1255	.16372	6.1903	.23910
.15	.16395	3.9103	.98441	.98884	.99552	3.1317	3.8493	.17511	5.7988	.25574
.16	.17483	3.6727	.98228	.98731	.99490	2.9474	3.6076	.18644	5.4576	.27228
.17	.18569	3.4635	.98003	.98569	.99425	2.7855	3.3943	.19970	5.1578	.28873
.18	.19654	3.2779	.97765	.98398	.99356	2.6422	3.2046	.20889	4.8925	.30507
.19	.20738	3.1122	.97514	.98217	.99283	2.5146	3.0348	.22001	4.6562	.32129
.20	.21822	2.9635	.97250	.98027	.99206	2.4004	2.8820	.23105	4.4447	.33745
.21	.22904	2.8293	.96973	.97828	.99125	2.2976	2.7437	.24201	4.2543	.35346
.22	.23984	2.7076	.96685	.97621	.99041	2.2046	2.6178	.25289	4.0822	.36934
.23	.25063	2.5968	.96383	.97403	.98953	2.1203	2.5029	.26368	3.9260	.38509
.24	.26141	2.4956	.96070	.97177	.98861	2.0434	2.3975	.27438	3.7837	.40073
.25	.27216	2.4027	.95745	.96942	.98765	1.9732	2.3005	.28498	3.6537	.41619
.26	.28291	2.3173	.95408	.96699	.98666	1.9088	2.2109	.29549	3.5344	.43153
.27	.29364	2.2385	.95060	.96446	.98563	1.8496	2.1279	3.0589	3.4248	.44672
.28	.30435	2.1656	.94700	.96185	.98456	1.7950	2.0508	.31619	3.3238	.46177
.29	.31504	2.0979	.94329	.95916	.98346	1.7446	1.9789	.32638	3.2304	.47666
.30	.32572	2.0351	.93947	.95638	.98232	1.6979	1.9119	.33647	3.1440	.49139
.31	.33638	1.9765	.93554	.95352	.98114	1.6546	1.8491	.34644	3.0638	.50594
.32	.34701	1.9218	.93150	.95058	.97993	1.6144	1.7902	.35629	2.9893	.52034
.33	.35762	1.8707	.92736	.94756	.97868	1.5769	1.7348	.36602	2.9199	.53453
.34	.36821	1.8229	.92312	.94446	.97740	1.5420	1.6828	.37563	2.8552	.54859
.35	.37879	1.7780	.91877	.94128	.97608	1.5094	1.6336	.38512	2.7948	·56244
.36	.38935	1.7358	.91433	.93803	.97473	1.4789	1.5871	.39448	2.7383	.57612
.37	.39988	1.6961	.90979	.93470	.97335	1.4503	1.5431	.40371	2.6855	.58959
.38	.41039	1.6587	.90516	.93129	.97193	1.4236	1.5014	.41281	2.6359	.60289
.39	.42087	1.6234	.90044	.92782	.97048	1.3985	1.4618	.42178	2.5894	.61597

† Portions of this table were calculated originally as a part of Project Meteor and appeared as a part of MIT Meteor Report No. 14, 1947, by A. H. Shapiro, W. R. Hawthorne, and C. M. Edelman. They have been reproduced in *Gas Tables*, by J. H. Keenan and J. Kaye, published by John Wiley and Sons, 1948. These values are reproduced here by permission of A. H. Shapiro and John Wiley and Sons.

Table A.2 (*Continued*)

Isentropic Flow

(*a*) *k* = 1.4

M	M*	$\frac{A}{A^*}$	$\frac{p}{p_0}$	$\frac{\rho}{\rho_0}$	$\frac{T}{T_0}$	$\frac{I}{I^*}$	$\left(\frac{A}{A^*}\right)\left(\frac{p}{p_0}\right)$	f_w	f_I	Γ
0.40	.43133	1.5901	.89562	92428	.96899	1.3749	1.4241	.43061	2.5458	.62888
.41	.44177	1.5587	.89071	.92066	.96747	1.3527	1.3883	.43930	2.5047	.64157
.42	.45218	1.5289	.88572	.91697	.96592	1.3318	1.3542	.44786	2.4661	.65406
.43	.46256	1.5007	.88065	.91322	.96434	1.3122	1.3216	.45627	2.4297	.66634
.44	.47292	1.4740	.87550	.90940	.96272	1.2937	1.2905	.46454	2.3955	.67842
.45	.48326	1.4487	.87027	.90552	.96108	1.2763	1.2607	.47266	2.3632	.69029
.46	.49357	1.4246	.86496	.90157	.95940	1.2598	1.2322	.48064	2.3327	.70194
.47	.50385	1.4018	.85958	.89756	.95769	1.2443	1.2050	.48847	2.3040	.71337
.48	.51410	1.3801	.85413	.89349	.95595	1.2296	1.1788	.49615	2.2768	.72459
.49	.52432	1.3594	.84861	.88936	.95418	1.2158	1.1537	.50368	2.2512	.73559
.50	.53452	1.3398	.84302	.88517	.95238	1.2027	1.12951	.51105	2.2269	.74635
.51	.54469	1.3212	.83737	.88092	.95055	1.1903	1.10631	.51828	2.2040	.75690
.52	.55482	1.3034	.83166	.87662	.94869	1.1786	1.08397	.52535	2.1823	.76722
.53	.56493	1.2864	.82589	.87227	.94681	1.1675	1.06245	.53226	2.1618	.77733
.54	.57501	1.2703	.82005	.86788	.94489	1.1571	1.04173	.53902	2.1424	.78720
.55	.58506	1.2550	.81416	.86342	.94295	1.1472	1.02174	.54563	2.1241	.79685
.56	.59508	1.2403	.80822	.85892	.94098	1.1378	1.00244	.55207	2.1067	.80626
.57	.60506	1.2263	.80224	.85437	.93898	1.1289	.98381	.55836	2.0903	.81544
.58	.61500	1.2130	.79621	.84977	.93696	1.1205	.96581	.56449	2.0748	.82439
.59	.62491	1.2003	.79012	.84513	.93491	1.1126	.94839	.57046	2.0601	.83311
.60	.63480	1.1882	.78400	.84045	.93284	1.10504	.93155	.57628	2.0461	.84161
.61	.64466	1.1766	.77784	.83573	.93074	1.09793	.91525	.58193	2.0330	.84987
.62	.65448	1.1656	.77164	.83096	.92861	1.09120	.89946	.58743	2.0205	.85789
.63	.66427	1.1551	.76540	.82616	.92646	1.08485	.88416	.59276	2.0087	.86568
.64	.67402	1.1451	.75913	.82132	.92428	1.07883	.86932	.59794	1.9976	.87325
.65	.68374	1.1356	.75283	.81644	.92208	1.07314	.85493	.60296	1.9871	.88057
.66	.69342	1.1265	.74650	.81153	.91986	1.06777	.84096	.60782	1.9771	.88767
.67	.70307	1.1178	.74014	.80659	.91762	1.06271	.82740	.61252	1.9677	.89455
.68	.71268	1.1096	.73376	.80162	.91535	1.05792	.81421	.61707	1.9589	.90118
.69	·72225	1.1018 '	.72735	.79662	.91306	1.05340	.80141	.62145	1.9505	.90759
.70	.73179	1.09437	.72092	.79158	.91075	1.04915	.78896	.62568	1.9426	.91376
.71	.74129	1.08729	.71448	.78652	.90842	1.04514	.77685	.62976	1.9352	.91971
.72	.75076	1.08057	.70802	.78143	.90606	1.04137	.76507	.63368	1.9282	.92544
.73	.76019	1.07419	.70155	.77632	.90368	1.03783	.75360	.63744	1.9217	.93093
.74	.76958	1.06814	.69507	.77119	.90129	1.03450	.74243	.64105	1.9155	.93620
.75	.77893	1.06242	.68857	.76603	.89888	1.03137	.73155	.64450	1.9097	.94125
.76	.78825	1.05700	.68207	.76086	.89644	1.02844	.72095	.64781	1.9043	.94607
.77	.79753	1.05188	.67556	.75567	.89399	1.02570	.71062	.65096	1.8992	.95068
.78	.80677	1.04705	.66905	.75046	.89152	1.02314	.70054	.65396	1.8945	.95506
.79	.81597	1.04250	.66254	.74524	.88903	1.02075	.69070	.65681	1.8901	.95923

Table A.2 (*Continued*)

Isentropic Flow

(*a*) $k = 1.4$

M	M^*	$\dfrac{A}{A^*}$	$\dfrac{p}{p_0}$	$\dfrac{\rho}{\rho_0}$	$\dfrac{T}{T_0}$	$\dfrac{I}{I^*}$	$\left(\dfrac{A}{A^*}\right)\left(\dfrac{p}{p_0}\right)$	f_w	f_I	Γ
0.80	.82514	1.03823	.65602	.74000	.88652	1.01853	.68110	.65952	1.8859	.96318
.81	.83426	1.03422	.64951	.73474	.88400	1.01646	.67173	.66208	1.8821	.96691
.82	.84334	1.03046	.64300	.72947	.88146	1.01455	.66259	.66449	1.8786	.97043
.83	.85239	1.02696	.63650	.72419	.87890	1.01278	.65366	.66676	1.8753	.97375
.84	.86140	1.02370	.63000	.71890	.87633	1.01115	.64493	.66888	1.8723	.97685
.85	.87037	1.02067	.62351	.71361	.87374	1.00966	.63640	.67087	1.8695	.97975
.86	.87929	1.01787	.61703	.70831	.87114	1.00829	.62806	.67271	1.8670	.98244
.87	.88817	1.01530	.61057	.70300	.86852	1.00704	.61991	.67441	1.8647	.98493
.88	.89702	1.01294	.60412	.69769	.86589	1.00591	.61193	.67598	1.8626	.98722
.89	.90583	1.01080	.59768	.69237	.86324	1.00490	.60413	.67742	1.8607	.98932
.90	.91460	1.00886	.59126	.68704	.86058	1.00399	.59650	.67872	1.8590	.99121
.91	.92333	1.00713	.58486	.68171	.85791	1.00318	.58903	.67988	1.8575	.99292
.92	.93201	1.00560	.57848	.67639	.85523	1.00248	.58171	.68092	1.8562	.99443
.93	.94065	1.00426	.57212	.67107	.85253	1.00188	.57455	.68183	1.8551	.99576
.94	.94925	1.00311	.56578	.66575	.84982	1.00136	.56754	.68261	1.8542	.99690
.95	.95781	1.00214	.55946	.66044	.84710	1.00093	.56066	.68327	1.8534	.99786
.96	.96633	1.00136	.55317	.65513	.84437	1.00059	.55392	.68380	1.8527	.99864
.97	.97481	1.00076	.54691	.64982	.84162	1.00033	.54732	.68421	1.8522	.99924
.98	.98325	1.00033	.54067	.64452	.83887	1.00014	.54085	.68450	1.8519	.99966
.99	.99165	1.00008	.53446	.63923	.83611	1.00003	.53450	.68467	1.8517	.99991
1.00	1.00000	1.00000	.52828	.63394	.83333	1.00000	.52828	.68473	1.8516	1.00000
1.01	1.00831	1.00008	.52213	.62866	.83055	1.00003	.52218	.68467	1.8517	.99991
1.02	1.01658	1.00033	.51602	.62339	.82776	1.00013	.51619	.68451	1.8519	.99967
1.03	1.02481	1.00074	.50994	.61813	.82496	1.00030	.51031	.68423	1.8522	.99926
1.04	1.03300	1.00130	.50389	.61288	.82215	1.00053	.50454	.68384	1.8526	.99869
1.05	1.04114	1.00202	.49787	.60765	.81933	1.00082	.49888	.68334	1.8531	.99797
1.06	1.04924	1.00290	.49189	.60243	.81651	1.00116	.49332	.68275	1.8538	.99710
1.07	1.05730	1.00394	.48595	.59722	.81368	1.00155	.48787	.68205	1.8545	.99608
1.08	1.06532	1.00512	.48005	.59203	.81084	1.00200	.48251	.68124	1.8553	.99490
1.09	1.07330	1.00645	.47418	.58685	.80800	1.00250	.47724	.68034	1.8563	.99359
1.10	1.08124	1.00793	.46835	.58169	.80515	1.00305	.47206	.67935	1.8573	.99214
1.11	1.08914	1.00955	.46256	.57655	.80230	1.00365	.46698	.67826	1.8584	.99054
1.12	1.09699	1.01131	.45682	.57143	.79944	1.00429	.46199	.67707	1.8596	.98881
1.13	1.10480	1.01322	.45112	.56632	.79657	1.00497	.45708	.67580	1.8608	.98695
1.14	1.11256	1.01527	.44545	.56123	.79370	1.00569	.45225	.67443	1.8622	.98496
1.15	1.1203	1.01746	.43983	.55616	.79083	1.00646	.44751	.67298	1.8636	.98284
1.16	1.1280	1.01978	.43425	.55112	.78795	1.00726	.44284	.67145	1.8651	.98060
1.17	1.1356	1.02224	.42872	.54609	.78507	1.00810	.43825	.66983	1.8666	.97824
1.18	1.1432	1.02484	.42323	.54108	.78218	1.00897	.43374	.66814	1.8682	.97576
1.19	1.1508	1.02757	.41778	.53610	.77929	1.00988	.42930	.66636	1.8699	.97317

Table A.2 (*Continued*)

Isentropic Flow

(*a*) $k = 1.4$

M	M^*	$\dfrac{A}{A^*}$	$\dfrac{p}{p_0}$	$\dfrac{\rho}{\rho_0}$	$\dfrac{T}{T_0}$	$\dfrac{I}{I^*}$	$\left(\dfrac{A}{A^*}\right)\left(\dfrac{p}{p_0}\right)$	f_w	f_I	Γ
1.20	1.1583	1.03044	.41238	.53114	.77640	1.01082	.42493	.66450	1.8717	.97056
1.21	1.1658	1.03344	.40702	.52620	.77350	1.01178	.42063	.66258	1.8735	.96764
1.22	1.1732	1.03657	.40171	.52129	.77061	1.01278	.41640	.66057	1.8753	.96472
1.23	1.1806	1.03983	.39645	.51640	.76771	1.01381	.41224	.65850	1.8772	.96169
1.24	1.1879	1.04323	.39123	.51154	.76481	1.01486	.40814	.65636	1.8792	.95856
1.25	1.1952	1.04676	.38606	.50670	.76190	1.01594	.40411	.65415	1.8812	.95533
1.26	1.2025	1.05041	.38094	.50189	.75900	1.01705	.40014	.65187	1.8832	.95201
1.27	1.2097	1.05419	.37586	.49710	.75610	1.01818	.39622	.64953	1.8853	.94860
1.28	1.2169	1.05810	.37083	.49234	.75319	1.01933	.39237	.64713	1.8874	.94509
1.29	1.2240	1.06214	.36585	.48761	.75029	1.02050	.38858	.64467	1.8896	.94149
1.30	1.2311	1.06631	.36092	.48291	.74738	1.02170	.38484	.64215	1.8918	.93782
1.31	1.2382	1.07060	.35603	.47823	.74448	1.02292	.38116	.63958	1.8941	.93406
1.32	1.2452	1.07502	.35119	.47358	.74158	1.02415	.37754	.63695	1.8963	.93021
1.33	1.2522	1.07957	.34640	.46895	.73867	1.02540	.37397	.63427	1.8987	.92630
1.34	1.2591	1.08424	.34166	.46436	.73577	1.02666	.37044	.63153	1.9010	.92230
1.35	1.2660	1.08904	.33697	.45980	.73287	1.02794	.36697	.62875	1.9034	.91824
1.36	1.2729	1.09397	.33233	.45527	.72997	1.02924	.36355	.62592	1.9058	.91411
1.37	1.2797	1.09902	.32774	.45076	.72707	1.03056	.36018	.62304	1.9082	.90990
1.38	1.2865	1.10420	.32319	.44628	.72418	1.03189	.35686	.62012	1.9107	.90564
1.39	1.2932	1.10950	.31869	.44183	.72128	1.03323	.35359	.61716	1.9132	.90131
1.40	1.2999	1.1149	.31424	.43742	.71839	1.03458	.35036	.61415	1.9157	.89692
1.41	1.3065	1.1205	.30984	.43304	.71550	1.03595	.34717	.61110	1.9182	.89247
1.42	1.3131	1.1262	.30549	.42869	.71261	1.03733	.34403	.60802	1.9208	.88797
1.43	1.3197	1.1320	.30119	.42436	.70973	1.03872	.34093	.60490	1.9233	.88341
1.44	1.3262	1.1379	.29693	.42007	.70685	1.04012	.33787	.60175	1.9259	.87881
1.45	1.3327	1.1440	.29272	.41581	.70397	1.04153	.33486	.59856	1.9285	.87415
1.46	1.3392	1.1502	.28856	.41158	.70110	1.04295	.33189	.59534	1.9312	.86945
1.47	1.3456	1.1565	.28445	.40738	.69823	1.04438	.32896	.59209	1.9338	.86471
1.48	1.3520	1.1629	.28039	.40322	.69537	1.04581	.32607	.58881	1.9365	.85992
1.49	1.3583	1.1695	.27637	.39909	.69251	1.04725	.32321	.58551	1.9391	.85509
1.50	1.3646	1.1762	.27240	.39498	.68965	1.04870	.32039	.58217	1.9418	.85022
1.51	1.3708	1.1830	.26848	.39091	.68680	1.05016	.31761	.57881	1.9445	.84531
1.52	1.3770	1.1899	.26461	.38687	.68396	1.05162	.31487	.57543	1.9472	.84038
1.53	1.3832	1.1970	.26078	.38287	.68112	1.05309	.31216	.57203	1.9499	.83540
1.54	1.3894	1.2042	.25700	.37890	.67828	1.05456	.30948	.56860	1.9527	.83040
1.55	1.3955	1.2115	.25326	.37496	.67545	1.05604	.30685	.56516	1.9554	.82537
1.56	1.4016	1.2190	.24957	.37105	.67262	1.05752	.30424	.56170	1.9581	.82031
1.57	1.4076	1.2266	.24593	.36717	.66980	1.05900	.30167	.55822	1.9609	.81523
1.58	1.4135	1.2343	.24233	.36332	.66699	1.06049	.29913	.55472	1.9636	.81012
1.59	1.4195	1.2422	.23878	.35951	.66418	1.06198	.29662	.55121	1.9664	.80500

Table A.2 (Continued)

Isentropic Flow

(a) $k = 1.4$

M	M^*	$\dfrac{A}{A^*}$	$\dfrac{p}{p_0}$	$\dfrac{\rho}{\rho_0}$	$\dfrac{T}{T_0}$	$\dfrac{I}{I^*}$	$\left(\dfrac{A}{A^*}\right)\left(\dfrac{p}{p_0}\right)$	f_w	f_I	Γ
1.60	1.4254	1.2502	.23527	.35573	.66138	1.06348	.29414	.54768	1.9692	.79985
1.61	1.4313	1.2583	.23181	.35198	.65858	1.06498	.29169	.54414	1.9719	.79468
1.62	1.4371	1.2666	.22839	.34826	.65579	1.06648	.28928	.54060	1.9747	.78950
1.63	1.4429	1.2750	.22501	.34458	.65301	1.06798	.28690	.53704	1.9775	.78430
1.64	1.4487	1.2835	.22168	.34093	.65023	1.06948	.28454	.53347	1.9803	.77909
1.65	1.4544	1.2922	.21839	.33731	.64746	1.07098	.28221	.52989	1.9831	.77386
1.66	1.4601	1.3010	.21515	.33372	.64470	1.07249	.27991	.52630	1.9859	.76863
1.67	1.4657	1.3099	.21195	.33016	.64194	1.07399	.27764	.52271	1.9886	.76338
1.68	1.4713	1.3190	.20879	.32664	.63919	1.07550	.27540	.51911	1.9914	.75813
1.69	1.4769	1.3282	.20567	.32315	.63645	1.07701	.27318	.51551	1.9942	.75287
1.70	1.4825	1.3376	.20259	.31969	.63372	1.07851	.27099	.51191	1.9970	.74760
1.71	1.4880	1.3471	.19955	.31626	.63099	1.08002	.26882	.50830	1.9998	.74233
1.72	1.4935	1.3567	.19656	.31286	.62827	1.08152	.26668	.50469	2.0026	.73707
1.73	1.4989	1.3665	.19361	.30950	.62556	1.08302	.26457	.50108	2.0054	.73179
1.74	1.5043	1.3764	.19070	.30617	.62286	1.08453	.26248	.49747	2.0082	.72651
1.75	1.5097	1.3865	.18782	.30287	.62016	1.08603	.26042	.49386	2.0109	.72124
1.76	1.5150	1.3967	.18499	.29959	.61747	1.08753	.25838	.49025	2.0137	.71597
1.77	1.5203	1.4071	.18220	.29635	.61479	1.08903	.25636	.48664	2.0165	.71071
1.78	1.5256	1.4176	.17944	.29314	.61211	1.09053	.25436	.48304	2.0193	.70544
1.79	1.5308	1.4282	.17672	.28997	.60945	1.09202	.25239	.47944	2.0220	.70018
1.80	1.5360	1.4390	.17404	.28682	.60680	1.09352	.25044	.47584	2.0248	.69493
1.81	1.5412	1.4499	.17140	.28370	.60415	1.09500	.24851	.47225	2.0276	.68969
1.82	1.5463	1.4610	.16879	.28061	.60151	1.09649	.24660	.46867	2.0303	.68446
1.83	1.5514	1.4723	.16622	.27756	.59888	1.09798	.24472	.46509	2.0331	.67923
1.84	1.5564	1.4837	.16369	.27453	.59626	1.09946	.24286	.46152	2.0358	.67401
1.85	1.5614	1.4952	.16120	.27153	.59365	1.1009	.24102	.45795	2.0385	.66881
1.86	1.5664	1.5069	.15874	.26857	.59105	1.1024	.23919	.45440	2.0413	.66361
1.87	1.5714	1.5188	.15631	.26563	.58845	1.1039	.23739	.45085	2.0440	.65843
1.88	1.5763	1.5308	.15392	.26272	.58586	1.1054	.23561	.44731	2.0467	.65327
1.89	1.5812	1.5429	.15156	.25984	.58329	1.1068	.23385	.44379	2.0494	.64812
1.90	1.5861	1.5552	.14924	.25699	.58072	1.1083	.23211	.44027	2.0521	.64298
1.91	1.5909	1.5677	.14695	.25417	.57816	1.1097	.23039	.43676	2.0548	.63786
1.92	1.5957	1.5804	.14469	.25138	.57561	1.1112	.22868	.43327	2.0575	.63275
1.93	1.6005	1.5932	.14247	.24862	.57307	1.1126	.22699	.42978	2.0602	.62767
1.94	1.6052	1.6062	.14028	.24588	.57054	1.1141	.22532	.42631	2.0629	.62260
1.95	1.6099	1.6193	.13813	.24317	.56802	1.1155	.22367	.42285	2.0656	.61755
1.96	1.6146	1.6326	.13600	.24049	.56551	1.1170	.22204	.41941	2.0682	.61251
1.97	1.6193	1.6461	.13390	.23784	.56301	1.1184	.22042	.41598	2.0709	.60750
1.98	1.6239	1.6597	.13184	.23522	.56051	1.1198	.21882	.41256	2.0735	.60251
1.99	1.6285	1.6735	.12981	.23262	.55803	1.1213	.21724	.40916	2.0762	.59754

Table A.2 (Continued)

Isentropic Flow

(a) $k = 1.4$

M	M^*	$\dfrac{A}{A^*}$	$\dfrac{p}{p_0}$	$\dfrac{\rho}{\rho_0}$	$\dfrac{T}{T_0}$	$\dfrac{I}{I^*}$	$\left(\dfrac{A}{A^*}\right)\left(\dfrac{p}{p_0}\right)$	f_w	f_I	Γ
2.00	1.6330	1.6875	.12780	.23005	.55556	1.1227	.21567	.40577	2.0788	.59259
2.01	1.6375	1.7017	.12583	.22751	.55310	1.1241	.21412	.40239	2.0814	.58767
2.02	1.6420	1.7160	.12389	.22499	.55064	1.1255	.21259	.39903	2.0840	.58276
2.03	1.6465	1.7305	.12198	.22250	.54819	1.1269	.21107	.39569	2.0866	.57788
2.04	1.6509	1.7452	.12009	.22004	.54576	1.1283	.20957	.39236	2.0892	.57302
2.05	1.6553	1.7600	.11823	.21760	.54333	1.1297	.20808	.38905	2.0918	.56818
2.06	1.6597	1.7750	.11640	.21519	.54091	1.1311	.20661	.38576	2.0944	.56337
2.07	1.6640	1.7902	.11460	.21281	.53850	1.1325	.20515	.38248	2.0970	.55859
2.08	1.6683	1.8056	.11282	.21045	.53611	1.1339	.20371	.37922	2.0995	.55383
2.09	1.6726	1.8212	.11107	.20811	.53373	1.1352	.20228	.37598	2.1021	.54909
2.10	1.6769	1.8369	.10935	.20580	.53135	1.1366	.20087	.37276	2.1046	.54438
2.11	1.6811	1.8529	.10766	.20352	.52898	1.1380	.19947	.36955	2.1071	.53971
2.12	1.6853	1.8690	.10599	.20126	.52663	1.1393	.19809	.36636	2.1096	.53504
2.13	1.6895	1.8853	.10434	.19902	.52428	1.1407	.19672	.36319	2.1121	.53041
2.14	1.6936	1.9018	.10272	.19681	.52194	1.1420	.19537	.36004	2.1146	.52580
2.15	1.6977	1.9185	.10113	.19463	.51962	1.1434	.19403	.35690	2.1171	.52122
2.16	1.7018	1.9354	.09956	.19247	.51730	1.1447	.19270	.35379	2.1196	.51668
2.17	1.7059	1.9525	.09802	.19033	.51499	1.1460	.19138	.35069	2.1221	.51216
2.18	1.7099	1.9698	.09650	.18821	.51269	1.1474	.19008	.34761	2.1245	.50766
2.19	1.7139	1.9873	.09500	.18612	.51041	1.1487	.18879	.34455	2.1270	.50320
2.20	1.7179	2.0050	.09352	.18405	.50813	1.1500	.18751	.34152	2.1294	.49876
2.21	1.7219	2.0229	.09207	.18200	.50586	1.1513	.18624	.33850	2.1318	.49435
2.22	1.7258	2.0409	.09064	.17998	.50361	1.1526	.18499	.33550	2.1342	.48997
2.23	1.7297	2.0592	.08923	.17798	.50136	1.1539	.18375	.33252	2.1366	.48562
2.24	1.7336	2.0777	.08784	.17600	.49912	1.1552	.18252	.32956	2.1390	.48129
2.25	1.7374	2.0964	.08648	.17404	.49689	1.1565	.18130	.32662	2.1414	.47700
2.26	1.7412	2.1154	.08514	.17211	.49468	1.1578	.18009	.32370	2.1438	.47273
2.27	1.7450	2.1345	.08382	.17020	.49247	1.1590	.17890	.32080	2.1461	.46850
2.28	1.7488	2.1538	.08252	.16830	.49027	1.1603	.17772	.31792	2.1485	.46429
2.29	1.7526	2.1734	.08123	.16643	.48809	1.1616	.17655	.31506	2.1508	.46012
2.30	1.7563	2.1931	.07997	.16458	.48591	1.1629	.17539	.31222	2.1532	.45597
2.31	1.7600	2.2131	.07873	.16275	.48374	1.1641	.17424	.30940	2.1555	.45185
2.32	1.7637	2.2333	.07751	.16095	.48158	1.1653	.17310	.30660	2.1578	.44776
2.33	1.7673	2.2537	.07631	.15916	.47944	1.1666	.17197	.30382	2.1601	.44370
2.34	1.7709	2.2744	.07513	.15739	.47730	1.1678	.17085	.30106	2.1624	.43967
2.35	1.7745	2.2953	.07396	.15564	.47517	1.1690	.16975	.29832	2.1646	.43568
2.36	1.7781	2.3164	.07281	.15391	.47305	1.1703	.16866	.29560	2.1669	.43171
2.37	1.7817	2.3377	.07168	.15220	.47095	1.1715	.16757	.29291	2.1691	.42777
2.38	1.7852	2.3593	.07057	.15052	.46885	1.1727	.16649	.29023	2.1714	.42386
2.39	1.7887	2.3811	.06948	.14885	.46676	1.1739	.16543	.28757	2.1736	.41998

Table A.2 (*Continued*)

Isentropic Flow

(*a*) k = 1.4

M	M*	$\dfrac{A}{A^*}$	$\dfrac{p}{p_0}$	$\dfrac{\rho}{\rho_0}$	$\dfrac{T}{T_0}$	$\dfrac{I}{I^*}$	$\left(\dfrac{A}{A^*}\right)\left(\dfrac{p}{p_0}\right)$	f_w	f_I	Γ
2.40	1.7922	2.4031	.06840	.14720	.46468	1.1751	.16437	.28494	2.1758	.41613
2.41	1.7957	2.4254	.06734	.14557	.46262	1.1763	.16332	.28232	2.1780	.41231
2.42	1.7991	2.4479	.06630	.14395	.46056	1.1755	.16229	.27973	2.1802	.40852
2.43	1.8025	2.4706	.06527	.14235	.45851	1.1786	.16126	.27715	2.1824	.40476
2.44	1.8059	2.4936	.06426	.14078	.45647	1.1798	.16024	.27460	2.1846	.40103
2.45	1.8093	2.5168	.06327	.13922	.45444	1.1810	.15923	.27206	2.1867	.39732
2.46	1.8126	2.5403	.06229	.13768	.45242	1.1821	.15823	.26955	2.1889	.39365
2.47	1.8159	2.5640	.06133	.13616	.45041	1.1833	.15724	.26705	2.1910	.39001
2.48	1.8192	2.5880	.06038	.13465	.44841	1.1844	.15626	.26458	2.1932	.38640
2.49	1.8225	2.6122	.05945	.13316	.44642	1.1856	.15528	.26212	2.1953	.38281
2.50	1.8258	2.6367	.05853	.13169	.44444	1.1867	.15432	.25969	2.1974	.37926
2.51	1.8290	2.6615	.05763	.13023	.44247	1.1879	.15337	.25728	2.1995	.37573
2.52	1.8322	2.6865	.05674	.12879	.44051	1.1890	.15242	.25488	2.2016	.37224
2.53	1.8354	2.7117	.05586	.12737	.43856	1.1901	.15148	.25251	2.2037	.36877
2.54	1.8386	2.7372	.05500	.12597	.43662	1.1912	.15055	.25016	2.2057	.36533
2.55	1.8417	2.7630	.05415	.12458	.43469	1.1923	.14963	.24782	2.2078	.36192
2.56	1.8448	2.7891	.05332	.12321	.43277	1.1934	.14871	.24551	2.2098	.35854
2.57	1.8479	2.8154	.05250	.12185	.43085	1.1945	.14780	.24321	2.2119	.35519
2.58	1.8510	2.8420	.05169	.12051	.42894	1.1956	.14691	.24094	2.2139	.35187
2.59	1.8541	2.8689	.05090	.11418	.42705	1.1967	.14601	.23868	2.2159	.34857
2.60	1.8572	2.8960	.05012	.11787	.42517	1.1978	.14513	.23644	2.2179	.34531
2.61	1.8602	2.9234	.04935	.11658	.42330	1.1989	.14426	.23423	2.2199	.34207
2.62	1.8632	2.9511	.04859	.11530	.42143	1.2000	.14339	.23203	2.2219	.33886
2.63	1.8662	2.9791	.04784	.11403	.41957	1.2011	.14253	.22985	2.2238	.33567
2.64	1.8692	3.0074	.04711	.11278	.41772	1.2021	.14168	.22769	2.2258	.33252
2.65	1.8721	3.0359	.04639	.11154	.41589	1.2031	.14083	.22555	2.2277	.32939
2.66	1.8750	3.0647	.04568	.11032	.41406	1.2042	.13999	.22342	2.2297	.32629
2.67	1.8779	3.0938	.04498	.10911	.41224	1.2052	.13916	.22132	2.2316	.32322
2.68	1.8808	3.1233	.04429	.10792	.41043	1.2062	.13834	.21924	2.2335	.32018
2.69	1.8837	3.1530	.04361	.10674	.40863	1.2073	.13752	.21717	2.2354	.31716
2.70	1.8865	3.1830	.04295	.10557	.40684	1.2083	.13671	.21512	2.2373	.31417
2.71	1.8894	3.2133	.04230	.10442	.40505	1.2093	.13591	.21309	2.2392	.31120
2.72	1.8922	3.2440	.04166	.10328	.40327	1.2103	.13511	.21108	2.2411	.30826
2.73	1.8950	3.2749	.04102	.10215	.40151	1.2113	.13432	.20909	2.2430	.30536
2.74	1.8978	3.3061	.04039	.10104	.39976	1.2123	.13354	.20711	2.2448	.30247
2.75	1.9005	3.3376	.03977	.09994	.39801	1.2133	.13276	.20515	2.2467	.29961
2.76	1.9032	3.3695	.03917	.09885	.39627	1.2143	.13199	.20321	2.2485	.29678
2.77	1.9060	3.4017	.03858	.09777	.39454	1.2153	.13123	.20129	2.2503	.29397
2.78	1.9087	3.4342	.03800	.09671	.39282	1.2163	.13047	.19939	2.2522	.29119
2.79	1.9114	3.4670	.03742	.09566	.39111	1.2173	.12972	.19750	2.2540	.28843

Table A.2 (*Continued*)

Isentropic Flow

(a) k = 1.4

M	M*	$\frac{A}{A^*}$	$\frac{p}{p_0}$	$\frac{\rho}{\rho_0}$	$\frac{T}{T_0}$	$\frac{I}{I^*}$	$\left(\frac{A}{A^*}\right)\left(\frac{p}{p_0}\right)$	f_w	f_l	Γ
.80	1.9140	3.5001	.03685	.09462	.38941	1.2182	.12897	.19563	2.2558	.28570
.81	1.9167	3.5336	.03629	.09360	.38771	1.2192	.12823	.19378	2.2575	.28300
.82	1.9193	3.5674	.03574	.09259	.38603	1.2202	.12750	.19194	2.2593	.28032
.83	1.9220	3.6015	.03520	.09158	.38435	1.2211	.12678	.19012	2.2611	.27766
.84	1.9246	3.6359	.03467	.09059	.38268	1.2221	.12605	.18832	2.2628	.27503
.85	1.9271	3.6707	.03415	.08962	.38102	1.2230	.12534	.18654	2.2646	.27243
.86	1.9297	3.7058	.03363	.08865	.37937	1.2240	.12463	.18477	2.2663	.26984
.87	1.9322	3.7413	.03312	.08769	.37773	1.2249	.12393	.18302	2.2681	.26729
.88	1.9348	3.7771	.03262	.08674	.37610	1.2258	.12323	.18128	2.2698	.26475
.89	1.9373	3.8133	.03213	.08581	.37448	1.2268	.12254	.17957	2.2715	.26224
.90	1.9398	3.8498	.03165	.08489	.37286	1.2277	.12185	.17786	2.2732	.25976
.91	1.9423	3.8866	.03118	.08398	.37125	1.2286	.12117	.17618	2.2749	.25729
.92	1.9448	3.9238	.03071	.08308	.36965	1.2295	.12049	.17451	2.2766	.25485
.93	1.9472	3.9614	.03025	.08218	.36806	1.2304	.11982	.17285	2.2782	.25244
.94	1.9497	3.9993	.02980	.08130	.36648	1.2313	.11916	.17121	2.2799	.25004
.95	1.9521	4.0376	.02935	.08043	.36490	1.2322	.11850	.16959	2.2815	.24767
.96	1.9545	4.0763	.02891	.07957	.36333	1.2331	.11785	.16798	2.2832	.24532
.97	1.9569	4.1153	.02848	.07872	.36177	1.2340	.11720	.16639	2.2848	.24300
.98	1.9593	4.1547	.02805	.07788	.36022	1.2348	.11656	.16481	2.2865	.24069
.99	1.9616	4.1944	.02764	.07705	.35868	1.2357	.11591	.16325	2.2881	.23841
.00	1.9640	4.2346	.02722	.07623	.35714	1.2366	.11528	.16170	2.2897	.23615
.10	1.9866	4.6573	.02345	.06852	.34223	1.2450	.10921	.14702	2.3053	.21471
.20	2.0079	5.1210	.0223	.06165	.32808	1.2530	.10359	.13371	2.3200	.19528
.30	2.0279	5.6287	.01748	.05554	.31466	1.2605	.09837	.12165	2.3340	.17766
.40	2.0466	6.1837	.01512	.05009	.30193	1.2676	.09353	.11073	2.3471	.16171
.50	2.0642	6.7896	.01311	.04523	.28986	1.2743	.08902	.10085	2.3596	.14728
.60	2.0808	7.4501	.01138	.04089	.27840	1.2807	.08482	.09191	2.3714	.13423
.70	2.0964	8.1691	.00990	.03702	.26752	1.2867	.08090	.08382	2.3825	.12241
.80	2.1111	8.9506	.00863	.03355	.25720	1.2924	.07723	.07650	2.3931	.11172
.90	2.1250	9.7990	.00753	.03044	.24740	1.2978	.07380	.06988	2.4030	.10205
.00	2.1381	10.719	.00658	.02766	.23810	1.3029	.07059	.06388	2.4125	.09329
.10	2.1505	11.715	.00577	.02516	.22925	1.3077	.06758	.05845	2.4215	.08536
.20	2.1622	12.792	.00506	.02292	.22085	1.3123	.06475	.05353	2.4300	.07818
.30	2.1732	13.955	.00445	.02090	.21286	1.3167	.06209	.04907	2.4380	.07166
.40	2.1837	15.210	.00392	.01909	.20525	1.3208	.05959	.04502	2.4457	.06575
.50	2.1936	16.562	.00346	.01745	.19802	1.3247	.05723	.04134	2.4529	.06038
.60	2.2030	18.018	.00305	.01597	.19113	1.3284	.05500	.03800	2.4598	.05550
.70	2.2119	19.583	.00270	.01463	.18457	1.3320	.05289	.03497	2.4664	.05107
.80	2.2204	21.264	.00240	.01343	.17832	1.3354	.05091	.03220	2.4726	.04703
.90	2.2284	23.067	.00213	.01233	.17235	1.3386	.04904	.02968	2.4786	.04335
.00	2.2361	25.000	$189(10)^{-5}$	.01134	.16667	1.3416	.04725	.02739	2.4842	.04000
.00	2.2953	53.180	$633(10)^{-6}$	.00519	.12195	1.3655	.03368	.01288	2.5284	.01880
.00	2.3333	104.143	$242(10)^{-6}$	.00261	.09259	1.3810	.02516	.00657	2.5570	.00960
.00	2.3591	190.109	$102(10)^{-6}$	.00141	.07246	1.3915	.01947	.00360	2.5765	.00526
.00	2.3772	327.189	$474(10)^{-7}$	.000815	.05814	1.3989	.01550	.00209	2.5903	.00306
.00	2.3904	535.938	$236(10)^{-7}$	.000495	.04762	1.4044	.01263	.00128	2.6004	.00187
∞	2.4495	∞	0	0	0	1.4289	0	0	2.6458	0

Table A.2 (*Continued*)

Isentropic Flow

(*b*) *k* = 1.0

M	M^*	$\dfrac{A}{A^*}$	$\dfrac{p}{p_0} = \dfrac{\rho}{\rho_0}$	$\dfrac{T}{T_0}$	$\dfrac{I}{I^*}$	$\left(\dfrac{A}{A^*}\right)\left(\dfrac{p}{p_0}\right)$	f_I
0	0	∞	1.0000	1.000	∞	∞	∞
0.05	.05	12.146	.9989		10.025	12.136	20.050
.10	.10	6.096	.9951		5.050	6.065	10.100
.15	.15	4.089	.9888		3.408	4.044	6.8167
.20	.20	3.094	.9802		2.600	3.033	5.2000
.25	.25	2.503	.9693		2.125	2.426	4.2500
.30	.30	2.115	.9561		1.817	2.022	3.6333
.35	.35	1.842	.9406		1.604	1.733	3.2071
.40	.40	1.643	.9231		1.450	1.516	2.9000
.45	.45	1.491	.9037		1.336	1.348	2.6722
.50	.50	1.375	.8825		1.250	1.2131	2.5000
.55	.55	1.283	.8597		1.184	1.1028	2.3682
.60	.60	1.210	.8353		1.133	1.0109	2.2667
.65	.65	1.153	.8096		1.0942	.9331	2.1885
.70	.70	1.107	.7827		1.0643	.8665	2.1286
.75	.75	1.0714	.7549		1.0417	.8087	2.0833
.80	.80	1.0441	.7262		1.0250	.7582	2.0500
.85	.85	1.0240	.6968		1.0132	.7136	2.0265
.90	.90	1.0104	.6670		1.0056	.6739	2.0111
.95	.95	1.0025	.6369		1.0013	.6385	2.0026
1.00	1.00	1.0000	.6065		1.0000	.6065	2.0000
1.05	1.05	1.0025	.5762		1.0012	.5777	2.0024
1.10	1.10	1.0097	.5461		1.0045	.5514	2.0091
1.15	1.15	1.0217	.5163		1.0098	.5274	2.0196
1.20	1.20	1.0384	.4868		1.0167	.5054	2.0333
1.25	1.25	1.0598	.4578		1.0250	.4852	2.0500
1.30	1.30	1.0861	.4295		1.0346	.4666	2.0692
1.35	1.35	1.117	.4020		1.0453	.4493	2.0907
1.40	1.40	1.154	.3753		1.0571	.4332	2.1143
1.45	1.45	1.197	.3495		1.0698	.4183	2.1397
1.50	1.50	1.245	.3247		1.0833	.4044	2.1667
1.55	1.55	1.300	.3008		1.0976	.3913	2.1952
1.60	1.60	1.363	.2780		1.113	.3791	2.2250
1.65	1.65	1.434	.2563		1.218	.3676	2.2561
1.70	1.70	1.514	.2357		1.144	.3568	2.2882

Table A.2 (Continued)
Isentropic Flow
(b) $k = 1.0$

M	M^*	$\dfrac{A}{A^*}$	$\dfrac{p}{p_0} = \dfrac{\rho}{\rho_0}$	$\dfrac{T}{T_0}$	$\dfrac{I}{I^*}$	$\left(\dfrac{A}{A^*}\right)\left(\dfrac{p}{p_0}\right)$	f_I
1.75	1.75	1.603	.2163	1.000	1.161	.3466	2.3214
1.80	1.80	1.703	.1979		1.178	.3370	2.3556
1.85	1.85	1.815	.1806		1.195	.3279	2.3905
1.90	1.90	1.941	.1645		1.213	.3192	2.4263
1.95	1.95	2.082	.1494		1.231	.3110	2.4628
2.00	2.00	2.241	.1353		1.250	.3033	2.5000
2.05	2.05	2.419	.1223		1.269	.2959	2.5378
2.10	2.10	2.620	.1102		1.288	.2888	2.5762
2.15	2.15	2.846	.09914		1.307	.2821	2.6151
2.20	2.20	3.100	.08892		1.327	.2757	2.6545
2.25	2.25	3.388	.07956		1.347	.2696	2.6944
2.30	2.30	3.714	.07100		1.367	.2637	2.7348
2.35	2.35	4.083	.06321		1.387	.2581	2.7755
2.40	2.40	4.502	.05614		1.408	.2527	2.8167
2.45	2.45	4.979	.04973		1.429	.2475	2.8582
2.50	2.50	5.522	.04394		1.450	.2426	2.9000
2.55	2.55	6.142	.03873		1.471	.2379	2.9422
2.60	2.60	6.852	.03405		1.492	.2333	2.9846
2.65	2.65	7.665	.02986		1.513	.2289	3.0274
2.70	2.70	8.600	.02612		1.535	.2247	3.0704
2.75	2.75	9.676	.02279		1.557	.2206	3.1136
2.80	2.80	10.92	.01984		1.579	.2166	3.1571
2.85	2.85	12.35	.01723		1.600	.2128	3.2009
2.90	2.90	14.02	.01492		1.622	.2092	3.2448
2.95	2.95	15.95	.01289		1.644	.2056	3.2890
3.00	3.00	18.20	$1111(10)^{-5}$		1.667	.2022	3.3333
3.50	3.50	79.22	$219(10)^{-5}$		1.893	.1733	3.7857
4.00	4.00	452.0	$335(10)^{-6}$		2.125	.1516	4.2500
4.50	4.50	3364	$401(10)^{-7}$		2.361	.1348	4.7222
5.00	5.00	32550	$373(10)^{-8}$		2.600	.1213	5.2000
6.00	6.00	$664(10)^4$	$152(10)^{-10}$		3.083	.1010	6.1667
7.00	7.00	$378(10)^7$	$229(10)^{-13}$		3.571	.08665	7.1429
8.00	8.00	$599(10)^{10}$	$127(10)^{-16}$		4.062	.07578	8.1250
9.00	9.00	$262(10)^{14}$	$258(10)^{-20}$		4.556	.06741	9.1111
10.00	10.00	$314(10)^{18}$	$193(10)^{-24}$		5.050	.06065	10.100
∞	∞	∞	0	1.000	∞	0	∞

Table A.2 (Continued)

Isentropic Flow

(c) $k = 1.1$

M	M^*	$\dfrac{A}{A^*}$	$\dfrac{p}{p_0}$	$\dfrac{\rho}{\rho_0}$	$\dfrac{T}{T_0}$	$\dfrac{I}{I^*}$	$\left(\dfrac{A}{A^*}\right)\left(\dfrac{p}{p_0}\right)$	f_w	f_I	Γ
0	0	∞	1.0000	1.0000	1.0000	∞	∞	0	∞	0
0.05	0.05123	11.999	.9986	.9988	.9999	9.785	11.982	.05237	19.120	.08312
.10	.1024	6.023	.9945	.9950	.9995	4.931	5.990	.10433	9.6371	.16601
.15	.1536	4.042	.9877	.9888	.9989	3.332	3.992	.15547	6.5101	.24735
.20	.2047	3.059	.9783	.9802	.9980	2.545	2.993	.20541	4.9721	.32695
.25	.2558	2.476	.9663	.9693	.9969	2.083	2.393	.25375	4.0697	.40382
.30	.3067	2.094	.9518	.9561	.9955	1.784	1.993	.30015	3.4850	.47768
.35	.3575	1.825	.9350	.9408	.9939	1.577	1.707	.34429	3.0818	.54792
.40	.4082	1.628	.9161	.9234	.9921	1.429	1.492	.38585	2.7920	.61409
.45	.4588	1.480	.8951	.9042	.9900	1.319	1.325	.42459	2.5778	.67570
.50	.5092	1.365	.8723	.8832	.9877	1.237	1.1908	.46028	2.4163	.73250
.55	.5594	1.275	.8478	.8606	.9851	1.174	1.0812	.49272	2.2931	.78416
.60	.6094	1.204	.8218	.8366	.9823	1.125	.9897	.52179	2.1987	.83040
.65	.6592	1.148	.7945	.8113	.9793	1.0882	.9121	.54737	2.1263	.87111
.70	.7087	1.104	.7662	.7850	.9761	1.0599	.8456	.56940	2.0710	.90617
.75	.7579	1.0689	.7370	.7578	.9727	1.0387	.7878	.58786	2.0295	.93554
.80	.8069	1.0425	.7071	.7298	.9690	1.0231	.7372	.60277	1.9991	.95927
.85	.8557	1.0231	.6768	.7013	.9651	1.0122	.6924	.61417	1.9778	.97741
.90	.9041	1.0100	.6462	.6724	.9610	1.0051	.6526	.62215	1.9640	.99011
.95	.9522	1.0024	.6154	.6431	.9568	1.0012	.6169	.62684	1.9564	.99756
1.00	1.0000	1.0000	.5847	.6139	.9524	1.0000	.5847	.62836	1.9540	1.0000
1.05	1.0474	1.0023	.5542	.5847	.9478	1.0011	.5555	.62689	1.9561	.99766
1.10	1.0945	1.0092	.5240	.5557	.9430	1.0041	.5289	.62263	1.9620	.99087
1.15	1.141	1.0204	.4944	.5271	.9380	1.0087	.5046	.61576	1.9711	.97994
1.20	1.188	1.0360	.4654	.4989	.9328	1.0148	.4822	.60650	1.9830	.96520
1.25	1.234	1.0559	.4371	.4713	.9275	1.0221	.4616	.59509	1.9972	.94704
1.30	1.279	1.0801	.4097	.4443	.9221	1.0305	.4425	.58174	2.0135	.92580
1.35	1.324	1.1088	.3832	.4180	.9165	1.0397	.4249	.56669	2.0316	.90185
1.40	1.369	1.4121	.3576	.3926	.9107	1.0497	.4084	.55017	2.0512	.87557
1.45	1.413	1.1802	.3330	.3680	.9048	1.0604	.3930	.53241	2.0721	.84730
1.50	1.457	1.223	.3095	.3443	.8989	1.0717	.3787	.51361	2.0942	.81738
1.55	1.501	1.272	.2871	.3216	.8928	1.0836	.3652	.49400	2.1172	.78617
1.60	1.544	1.326	.2658	.2999	.8865	1.0958	.3526	.47377	2.1411	.75398
1.65	1.586	1.387	.2456	.2791	.8801	1.108	.3407	.45311	2.1657	.72110
1.70	1.628	1.454	.2266	.2593	.8737	1.121	.3294	.43219	2.1909	.68781

Table A.2 (Continued)

Isentropic Flow

(c) $k = 1.1$

M	M^*	$\dfrac{A}{A^*}$	$\dfrac{p}{p_0}$	$\dfrac{\rho}{\rho_0}$	$\dfrac{T}{T_0}$	$\dfrac{I}{I^*}$	$\left(\dfrac{A}{A^*}\right)\left(\dfrac{p}{p_0}\right)$	f_w	f_l	Γ
1.75 1.670		1.528	.2086	.2406	.8672	1.134	.3188	.41118	2.2166	.65436
1.80 1.711		1.610	.1917	.2228	.8606	1.147	.3088	.39022	2.2426	.62100
1.85 1.752		1.701	.1759	.2060	.8539	1.161	.2993	.36943	2.2692	.58793
1.90 1.792		1.801	.1612	.1902	.8471	1.175	.2902	.34895	2.2959	.55532
1.95 1.832		1.911	.1474	.1754	.8402	1.189	.2816	.32886	2.3229	.52335
2.00 1.871		2.032	.1346	.1615	.8333	1.203	.2735	.30926	2.3500	.49217
2.05 1.910		2.165	.1227	.1485	.8264	1.217	.2657	.29022	2.3773	.46187
2.10 1.948		2.312	.1117	.1363	.8194	1.231	.2582	.27181	2.4046	.43257
2.15 1.986		2.473	.1015	.1250	.8123	1.245	.2511	.25408	2.4320	.40434
2.20 2.023		2.651	.09218	.1145	.8052	1.259	.2444	.23705	2.4593	.37725
2.25 2.060		2.846	.08357	.10473	.7980	1.273	.2379	.22077	2.4866	.35133
2.30 2.096		3.061	.07566	.09568	.7908	1.286	.2317	.20525	2.5138	.32664
2.35 2.132		3.299	.06842	.08731	.7836	1.300	.2257	.19050	2.5410	.30316
2.40 2.167		3.560	.06179	.07959	.7764	1.314	.2200	.17652	2.5680	.28092
2.45 2.202		3.848	.05574	.07247	.7692	1.328	.2145	.16331	2.5949	.25990
2.50 2.236		4.165	.05022	.06592	.7619	1.342	.2092	.15087	2.6216	.24010
2.55 2.270		4.515	.04520	.05990	.7546	1.356	.2041	.13917	2.6481	.22148
2.60 2.303		4.902	.04064	.05438	.7473	1.369	.1992	.12820	2.6745	.20402
2.65 2.336		5.328	.03650	.04932	.7401	1.382	.1945	.11793	2.7006	.18768
2.70 2.368		5.799	.03276	.04470	.7329	1.395	.1900	.10835	2.7265	.17243
2.75 2.400		6.320	.02936	.04047	.7256	1.408	.1856	.09943	2.7522	.15823
2.80 2.432		6.895	.02630	.03661	.7184	1.422	.1814	.09113	2.7777	.14502
2.85 2.463		7.532	.02354	.03310	.7112	1.435	.1773	.08342	2.8029	.13276
2.90 2.493		8.237	.02104	.02989	.7040	1.448	.1733	.07629	2.8278	.12141
2.95 2.523		9.016	.01880	.02698	.6968	1.460	.1695	.06969	2.8525	.11091
3.0 2.553		9.880	$1679(10)^{-5}$	.02434	.6897	1.472	.1658	.06360	2.8769	.10121
3.5 2.824		25.83	$522(10)^{-5}$	.008414	.6202	1.589	.1348	.02432	3.1053	.03871
4.0 3.055		71.74	$156(10)^{-5}$	.002801	.5556	1.691	.1116	.00876	3.3046	.01394
4.5 3.250		205.7	$456(10)^{-6}$	.000918	.4969	1.779	.09382	.00305	3.4763	.00486
5.0 3.416		597.3	$134(10)^{-6}$	.000301	.4444	1.854	.08004	.00105	3.6232	.00167
6.0 3.674		4911	$121(10)^{-7}$	$338(10)^{-7}$	.3571	1.973	.05942	$127(10)^{-6}$	3.8557	$202(10)^{-6}$
7.0 3.862		37920	$121(10)^{-8}$	$419(10)^{-8}$	.2899	2.060	.04588	$165(10)^{-8}$	4.0259	$263(10)^{-7}$
8.0 4.000		$263(10)^{3}$	$139(10)^{-9}$	$585(10)^{-9}$	.2381	2.125	.03653	$240(10)^{-8}$	4.1523	$381(10)^{-8}$
9.0 4.104		$161(10)^{4}$	$184(10)^{-10}$	$927(10)^{-10}$	.1980	2.174	.02971	$389(10)^{-9}$	4.2476	$620(10)^{-9}$
0.0 4.183		$889(10)^{4}$	$275(10)^{-11}$	$165(10)^{-10}$	.1667	2.211	.02444	$708(10)^{-10}$	4.3207	$113(10)^{-9}$
∞ 4.583		∞	0	0	0	2.400	0	0	4.6904	0

Table A.2 (Continued)

Isentropic Flow

(d) $k = 1.2$

M	M^*	$\dfrac{A}{A^*}$	$\dfrac{p}{p_0}$	$\dfrac{\rho}{\rho_0}$	$\dfrac{T}{T_0}$	$\dfrac{I}{I^*}$	$\left(\dfrac{A}{A^*}\right)\left(\dfrac{p}{p_0}\right)$	f_w	f_I	Γ
0	0	∞	1.0000	1.0000	1.0000	∞	∞	0	∞	0
0.05	0.05243	11.857	.9985	.9988	.9998	9.562	11.839	.05470	18.310	.08452
.10	.1048	5.953	.9949	.9950	.9991	4.822	5.917	.10894	9.2336	.16797
.15	.1571	3.996	.9866	.9888	.9978	3.260	3.942	.16230	6.2431	.25025
.20	.2093	3.026	.9763	.9802	.9960	2.493	2.954	.21433	4.7739	.33051
.25	.2614	2.451	.9633	.9693	.9938	2.044	2.361	.26464	3.9131	.40806
.30	.3133	2.073	.9477	.9562	.9911	1.753	1.965	.31283	3.3565	.48236
.35	.3649	1.809	.9296	.9409	.9879	1.553	1.681	.35857	2.9735	.55291
.40	.4162	1.615	.9092	.9236	.9843	1.409	1.468	.40155	2.6989	.61918
.45	.4672	1.469	.8867	.9046	.9802	1.304	1.302	.44149	2.4964	.68076
.50	.5179	1.356	.8623	.8839	.9756	1.224	1.170	.47817	2.3443	.73731
.55	.5683	1.268	.8363	.8616	.9706	1.164	1.0606	.51141	2.2288	.78858
.60	.6183	1.199	.8088	.8379	.9653	1.118	.9694	.54108	2.1405	.83433
.65	.6678	1.144	.7801	.8131	.9595	1.0826	.8922	.56710	2.0731	.87444
.70	.7618	1.100	.7505	.7873	.9533	1.0559	.8258	.58942	2.0220	.90885
.75	.7654	1.0666	.7201	.7606	.9467	1.0360	.7681	.60804	1.9837	.93758
.80	.8134	1.0410	.6892	.7333	.9398	1.0214	.7174	.62302	1.9558	.96067
.85	.8609	1.0222	.6580	.7055	.9326	1.0112	.6726	.63443	1.9364	.97825
.90	.9078	1.0096	.6267	.6774	.9251	1.0047	.6327	.64238	1.9238	.99052
.95	.9542	1.0023	.5954	.6492	.9172	1.0011	.5968	.64702	1.9170	.99768
1.00	1.0000	1.0000	.5644	.6209	.9091	1.0000	.5644	.64853	1.9149	.10000
1.05	1.0451	1.0022	.5339	.5928	.9007	1.0010	.5351	.64709	1.9167	.99778
1.10	1.0896	1.0087	.5039	.5449	.8921	1.0037	.5083	.64291	1.9219	.99134
1.15	1.134	1.0194	.4746	.5374	.8832	1.0079	.4838	.63622	1.9299	.98102
1.20	1.177	1.0340	.4461	.5104	.8741	1.0133	.4613	.62723	1.9403	.96716
1.25	1.219	1.0525	.4185	.4839	.8648	1.0197	.4405	.61619	1.9526	.95014
1.30	1.261	1.0749	.3918	.4581	.8554	1.0270	.4212	.60333	1.9666	.93030
1.35	1.302	1.101	.3662	.4330	.8458	1.0350	.4033	.58888	1.9820	.90801
1.40	1.342	1.131	.3417	.4087	.8361	1.0437	.3767	.57306	1.9986	.88363
1.45	1.382	1.166	.3182	.3852	.8263	1.0529	.3712	.55609	2.0161	.85747
1.50	1.421	1.205	.2959	.3625	.8163	1.0625	.3566	.53819	2.0345	.82986
1.55	1.459	1.248	.2747	.3407	.8063	1.0724	.3430	.51954	2.0535	.80111
1.60	1.497	1.296	.2547	.3199	.7962	1.0826	.3302	.50034	2.0730	.77150
1.65	1.534	1.349	.2358	.3000	.7860	1.0930	.3181	.48076	2.0930	.74130
1.70	1.570	1.407	.2180	.2810	.7758	1.1036	.3067	.46094	2.1132	.71075

Table A.2 (Continued)

Isentropic Flow

(d) $k = 1.2$

M	M^*	$\dfrac{A}{A^*}$	$\dfrac{p}{p_0}$	$\dfrac{\rho}{\rho_0}$	$\dfrac{T}{T_0}$	$\dfrac{I}{I^*}$	$\left(\dfrac{A}{A^*}\right)\left(\dfrac{p}{p_0}\right)$	f_w	f_I	Γ
1.75	1.606	1.470	.2013	.2629	.7656	1.114	.2960	.44105	2.1337	.68007
1.80	1.641	1.539	.1856	.2458	.7553	1.125	.2858	.42119	2.1544	.64946
1.85	1.675	1.615	.1710	.2295	.7450	1.136	.2762	.40149	2.1751	.61908
1.90	1.708	1.698	.1573	.2141	.7347	1.147	.2671	.38205	2.1959	.58911
1.95	1.741	1.787	.1446	.1996	.7245	1.158	.2584	.36296	2.2167	.55966
2.00	1.773	1.884	.1328	.1859	.7143	1.168	.2502	.34428	2.2374	.53087
2.05	1.804	1.989	.1218	.1730	.7041	1.179	.2423	.32609	2.2580	.50281
2.10	1.835	2.103	.1117	.1609	.6940	1.190	.2348	.30843	2.2785	.47559
2.15	1.865	2.226	.1023	.1496	.6839	1.201	.2277	.29135	2.2988	.44924
2.20	1.894	2.359	.09362	.1390	.6739	1.212	.2209	.27487	2.3189	.42384
2.25	1.923	2.504	.08563	.1290	.6639	1.222	.2144	.25902	2.3389	.39940
2.30	1.951	2.660	.07826	.1197	.6540	1.232	.2082	.24382	2.3586	.37596
2.35	1.978	2.829	.07148	.1110	.6442	1.242	.2022	.22928	2.3780	.35354
2.40	2.005	3.011	.06526	.1029	.6345	1.252	.1965	.21540	2.3972	.33213
2.45	2.031	3.208	.05955	.09529	.6249	1.262	.1910	.20217	2.4161	.31174
2.50	2.057	3.421	.05431	.08825	.6154	1.272	.1858	.18960	2.4348	.29235
2.55	2.082	3.650	.04951	.08170	.6060	1.282	.1808	.17767	2.4532	.27395
2.60	2.106	3.898	.04512	.07562	.5967	1.291	.1759	.16636	2.4712	.25652
2.65	2.130	4.166	.04110	.06997	.5875	1.300	.1712	.15567	2.4890	.24004
2.70	2.154	4.455	.03743	.06472	.5784	1.309	.1667	.14557	2.5065	.22447
2.75	2.177	4.767	.03408	.05985	.5694	1.318	.1624	.13605	2.5236	.20978
2.80	2.199	5.103	.03102	.05534	.5605	1.327	.1583	.12708	2.5405	.19595
2.85	2.220	5.466	.02823	.05116	.5518	1.335	.1543	.11864	2.5571	.18294
2.90	2.241	5.858	.02569	.04729	.5432	1.343	.1505	.11071	2.5733	.17071
2.95	2.262	6.280	.02337	.04370	.5347	1.352	.1467	.10327	2.5893	.15923
3.00	2.283	6.735	.02126	.04039	.5263	1.360	.1432	.09629	2.6049	.14847
3.5	2.461	13.76	.008242	.01834	.4494	1.434	.1134	.04713	2.7452	.07268
4.0	2.602	28.35	.003237	.008417	.3846	1.493	.09178	.02287	2.8590	.03527
4.5	2.714	57.96	.001305	.003948	.3306	1.541	.07563	.01119	2.9509	.01725
5.0	2.803	116.3	.000544	.001904	.2857	1.580	.06327	.00557	3.0253	.00860
6.0	2.934	434.7	$106(10)^{-6}$	$486(10)^{-6}$	.2174	1.637	.04608	$149(10)^{-5}$	3.1355	$229(10)^{-5}$
7.0	3.023	1458	$237(10)^{-7}$	$140(10)^{-6}$	.1695	1.677	.03456	$442(10)^{-6}$	3.2106	$681(10)^{-6}$
8.0	3.084	4451	$609(10)^{-8}$	$451(10)^{-7}$	.1351	1.704	.02711	$145(10)^{-6}$	3.2635	$224(10)^{-6}$
9.0	3.129	12411	$176(10)^{-8}$	$160(10)^{-7}$	.1099	1.724	.02184	$524(10)^{-7}$	3.3019	$808(10)^{-7}$
10.0	3.162	31659	$564(10)^{-9}$	$621(10)^{-8}$	.09091	1.739	.01789	$205(10)^{-7}$	3.3304	$136(10)^{-7}$
∞	3.317	∞	0	0	0	1.809	0	0	3.4641	0

Table A.2 (Continued)

Isentropic Flow

(e) $k = 1.3$

M	M^*	$\dfrac{A}{A^*}$	$\dfrac{p}{p_0}$	$\dfrac{\rho}{\rho_0}$	$\dfrac{T}{T_0}$	$\dfrac{I}{I^*}$	$\left(\dfrac{A}{A^*}\right)\left(\dfrac{p}{p_0}\right)$	f_w	f_I	Γ
0	0	∞	1.0000	1.0000	1.0000	∞	∞	0	∞	0
0.05	0.0536	11.721	.9984	.9988	.9996	9.354	11.702	.05693	17.595	.08540
.10	.1072	5.885	.9936	.9951	.9985	4.720	5.848	.11336	8.8779	.16990
.15	.1606	3.952	.9855	.9889	.9966	3.194	3.895	.16883	6.0080	.25300
.20	.2138	2.994	.9744	.9803	.9940	2.445	2.917	.22287	4.5995	.33400
.25	.2668	2.426	.9603	.9694	.9907	2.007	2.330	.27503	3.7756	.41220
.30	.3195	2.054	.9435	.9563	.9867	1.724	1.938	.32491	3.2438	.48694
.35	.3719	1.793	.9241	.9411	.9820	1.530	1.657	.37216	2.8786	.55775
.40	.4239	1.602	.9023	.9240	.9766	1.391	1.446	.41644	2.6175	.62410
.45	.4754	1.459	.8784	.9051	.9705	1.289	1.281	.45748	2.4255	.68560
.50	.5264	1.348	.8526	.8845	.9638	1.213	1.1491	.49506	2.2818	.74192
.55	.5769	1.261	.8251	.8625	.9566	1.155	1.0407	.52900	2.1730	.79280
.60	.6267	1.193	.7962	.8392	.9488	1.111	.9501	.55920	2.0902	.83805
.65	.6759	1.139	.7662	.8148	.9404	1.0777	.8731	.58558	2.0272	.87758
.70	.7245	1.0972	.7354	.7895	.9315	1.0524	.8069	.60813	1.9796	.91138
.75	.7724	1.0644	.7040	.7634	.9222	1.0336	.7493	.62687	1.9442	.93946
.80	.8195	1.0395	.6723	.7367	.9124	1.0199	.6988	.64188	1.9185	.96196
.85	.8658	1.0214	.6403	.7096	.9022	1.0104	.6540	.65327	1.9006	.97903
.90	.9113	1.0092	.6084	.6823	.8917	1.0043	.6140	.66118	1.8892	.99088
.95	.9561	1.0022	.5768	.6549	.8808	1.0010	.5781	.66578	1.8830	.99777
1.00	1.0000	1.0000	.5457	.6276	.8696	1.0000	.5457	.66726	1.8811	1.00000
1.05	1.0430	1.0021	.5152	.6004	.8581	1.0009	.5163	.66558	1.8828	.99788
1.10	1.0852	1.0083	.4854	.5735	.8464	1.0034	.4895	.66176	1.8874	.99176
1.15	1.127	1.0183	.4565	.5470	.8345	1.0072	.4649	.65524	1.8945	.98198
1.20	1.167	1.0321	.4285	.5210	.8224	1.0120	.4423	.64651	1.9036	.96890
1.25	1.206	1.0495	.4015	.4956	.8102	1.0177	.4214	.63582	1.9143	.95288
1.30	1.245	1.0704	.3756	.4709	.7978	1.0241	.4021	.62341	1.9265	.93428
1.35	1.283	1.0948	.3509	.4468	.7853	1.0312	.3842	.60950	1.9398	.91343
1.40	1.320	1.123	.3273	.4235	.7728	1.0388	.3675	.59432	1.9540	.89068
1.45	1.356	1.154	.3049	.4010	.7603	1.0467	.3519	.57807	1.9689	.86634
1.50	1.391	1.189	.2836	.3793	.7477	1.0549	.3374	.56097	1.9844	.84070
1.55	1.425	1.228	.2635	.3585	.7351	1.0634	.3237	.54318	2.0004	.81405
1.60	1.458	1.271	.2446	.3385	.7225	1.0720	.3109	.52489	2.0166	.78664
1.65	1.491	1.318	.2268	.3194	.7100	1.0808	.2989	.50625	2.0331	.75871
1.70	1.523	1.369	.2101	.3011	.6976	1.0897	.2875	.48741	2.0498	.73046

Table A.2 (Continued)

Isentropic Flow

(e) k = 1.3

M	M^*	$\dfrac{A}{A^*}$	$\dfrac{p}{p_0}$	$\dfrac{\rho}{\rho_0}$	$\dfrac{T}{T_0}$	$\dfrac{I}{I^*}$	$\left(\dfrac{A}{A^*}\right)\left(\dfrac{p}{p_0}\right)$	f_w	f_I	Γ
1.75	1.554	1.424	.1944	.2836	.6852	1.0986	.2768	.46849	2.0665	.70211
1.80	1.584	1.484	.1797	.2670	.6729	1.108	.2667	.44961	2.0833	.67382
1.85	1.613	1.549	.1660	.2513	.6607	1.116	.2571	.43087	2.1000	.64573
1.90	1.641	1.618	.1533	.2364	.6487	1.125	.2481	.41236	2.1166	.61799
1.95	1.669	1.693	.1415	.2222	.6368	1.134	.2395	.39415	2.1331	.59069
2.00	1.696	1.773	.1305	.2087	.6250	1.143	.2313	.37631	2.1495	.56396
2.05	1.722	1.859	.1203	.1960	.6134	1.152	.2236	.35889	2.1656	.53785
2.10	1.747	1.951	.1108	.1841	.6019	1.160	.2162	.34193	2.1816	.51244
2.15	1.772	2.050	.1020	.1728	.5905	1.168	.2092	.32548	2.1973	.48778
2.20	1.796	2.156	.0939	.1621	.5793	1.176	.2025	.30956	2.2127	.46392
2.25	1.819	2.268	.08645	.1521	.5684	1.184	.1961	.29418	2.2280	.44088
2.30	1.842	2.388	.07955	.1427	.5576	1.192	.1900	.27937	2.2429	.41868
2.35	1.864	2.517	.07318	.1338	.5470	1.200	.1842	.26513	2.2576	.39734
2.40	1.885	2.654	.06731	.1254	.5365	1.208	.1786	.25146	2.2720	.37686
2.45	1.906	2.799	.06190	.1176	.5262	1.216	.1733	.23837	2.2860	.35724
2.50	1.926	2.954	.05692	.1103	.5161	1 223	.1682	.22585	2.2999	.33847
2.55	1.946	3.119	.05234	.1034	.5062	1.230	.1633	.21389	2.3134	.32055
2.60	1.965	3.295	.04813	.09693	.4965	1.237	.1586	.20248	2.3266	.30345
2.65	1.983	3.482	.04426	.09087	.4870	1.244	.1541	.19161	2.3395	.28716
2.70	2.001	3.681	.04070	.08520	.4777	1.250	.1498	.18127	2.3522	.27166
2.75	2.019	3.892	.03743	.07988	.4686	1.257	.1457	.17144	2.3645	.25692
2.80	2.036	4.116	.03442	.07490	.4596	1.264	.1417	.16210	2.3766	.24293
2.85	2.052	4.354	.03166	.07024	.4508	1.270	.1379	.15323	2.3883	.22964
2.90	2.068	4.607	.02913	.06587	.4422	1.276	.1342	.14483	2.3998	.21705
2.95	2.084	4.875	.02680	.06178	.4338	1.282	.1307	.13686	2.4111	.20511
3.0	2.099	5.160	.02466	.05796	.4255	1.288	.12726	.12932	2.4220	.19381
3.5	2.228	9.110	.01090	.03092	.3524	1.338	.09926	.07325	2.5178	.10977
4.0	2.326	15.94	.00498	.01692	.2941	1.378	.07934	.04185	2.5923	.06272
4.5	2.402	27.39	.00236	.00954	.2477	1.409	.06471	.02436	2.6505	.03651
5.0	2.460	45.95	.00117	.00555	.2105	1.433	.05372	.01452	2.6962	.02176
6.0	2.543	120.1	$321(10)^{-6}$	.00206	.15625	1.468	.03856	$556(10)^{-5}$	2.7619	$833(10)^{-5}$
7.0	2.598	285.3	$101(10)^{-6}$	$847(10)^{-6}$	.11976	1.491	.02882	$234(10)^{-5}$	2.8054	$350(10)^{-5}$
8.0	2.635	625.2	$360(10)^{-7}$	$382(10)^{-6}$	.09434	1.507	.02251	$107(10)^{-5}$	2.8353	$160(10)^{-5}$
9.0	2.662	1275	$141(10)^{-7}$	$186(10)^{-6}$	.07605	1.519	.01798	$527(10)^{-6}$	2.8566	$790(10)^{-6}$
10.0	2.681	2438	$605(10)^{-8}$	$968(10)^{-7}$	.06250	1.527	.01475	$276(10)^{-6}$	2.8724	$414(10)^{-6}$
∞	2.769	∞	0	0	0	1.565	0	0	2.9439	0

Table A.2 (Continued)

Isentropic Flow

(f) k = 1.67

M	M*	$\frac{A}{A^*}$	$\frac{p}{p_0}$	$\frac{\rho}{\rho_0}$	$\frac{T}{T_0}$	$\frac{I}{I^*}$	$\left(\frac{A}{A^*}\right)\left(\frac{p}{p_0}\right)$	f_w	f_I	Γ
0	0	∞	1.0000	1.0000	1.0000	0	∞	0	∞	0
0.05	0.05775	11.265	.9979	.9988	.9992	8.687	11.242	.06451	15.535	.08881
.10	.1154	5.661	.9917	.9950	.9967	4.392	5.614	.12837	7.8543	.17670
.15	.1727	3.805	.9815	.9888	.9925	2.982	3.735	.19096	5.3326	.26279
.20	.2296	2.887	.9674	.9803	.9868	2.293	2.793	.25169	4.1002	.34637
.25	.2859	2.344	.9497	.9695	.9795	1.892	2.226	.31000	3.3831	.42661
.30	.3415	1.989	.9286	.9566	.9708	1.635	1.847	.36541	2.9234	.50825
.35	.3963	1.741	.9046	.9417	.9606	1.460	1.575	.41747	2.6102	.57450
.40	.4502	1.560	.8780	.9250	.9491	1.336	1.370	.46584	2.3883	.64107
.45	.5031	1.424	.8491	.9067	.9364	1.245	1.209	.51024	2.2268	.70217
.50	.5549	1.320	.8184	.8869	.9227	1.178	1.0803	.55047	2.1073	.75753
.55	.6055	1.239	.7862	.8658	.9080	1.128	.9742	.58640	2.0179	.80697
.60	.6548	1.176	.7529	.8437	.8924	1.0909	.8853	.61798	1.9508	.85045
.65	.7029	1.126	7190	.8207	.8760	1.0628	.8097	.64524	1.9004	.88799
.70	.7496	1.0874	.6847	.7970	.8590	1.0422	.7445	.66824	1.8630	.91960
.75	.7949	1.0576	.6503	.7728	.8414	1.0265	.6877	.68711	1.8355	.94557
.80	.8388	1.0351	.6162	.7483	.8234	1.0155	.6378	.70203	1.8159	.96610
.85	.8812	1.0189	.5826	.7236	.8051	1.0080	.5936	.71320	1.8025	.98147
.90	.9222	1.0080	.5497	.6988	.7866	1.0033	.5541	.72086	1.7940	.99201
.95	.9618	1.0019	.5177	.6742	.7679	1.0008	.5187	.72526	1.7895	.99806
1.00	1.0000	1.0000	.4867	.6497	.7491	1.0000	.4867	.72666	1.7882	1.00000
1.05	1.0368	1.0018	.4568	.6255	.7303	1.0007	.4576	.72535	1.7893	.99819
1.10	1.0721	1.0071	.4282	.6017	.7116	1.0024	.4312	.72158	1.7925	.99301
1.15	1.106	1.0154	.4009	.5784	.6930	1.0051	.4070	.71563	1.7973	.98482
1.20	1.139	1.0266	.3749	.5557	.6746	1.0085	.3849	.70776	1.8033	.97398
1.25	1.170	1.0406	.3502	.5335	.6564	1.0124	.3646	.69820	1.8103	.96084
1.30	1.200	1.0573	.3269	.5119	.6385	1.0167	.3457	.68721	1.8181	.94571
1.35	1.229	1.0765	.3049	.4910	.6209	1.0213	.3282	.67499	1.8264	.92889
1.40	1.257	1.0981	.2842	.4707	.6036	1.0262	.3121	.66174	1.8351	.81066
1.45	1.283	1.122	.2647	.4511	.5867	1.0313	.2972	.64765	1.8441	.89127
1.50	1.309	1.148	.2465	.4323	.5702	1.0364	.2830	.63290	1.8533	.87097
1.55	1.333	1.176	.2295	.4142	.5541	1.0416	.2700	.61763	1.8626	.84995
1.60	1.356	1.207	.2136	.3968	.5383	1.0468	.2579	.60198	1.8719	.82842
1.65	1.379	1.240	.1988	.3801	.5230	1.0520	.2465	.58607	1.8812	.80652
1.70	1.400	1.275	.1850	.3640	.5081	1.0572	.2358	.57001	1.8904	.78443

Table A.2 (Continued)

Isentropic Flow

(f) k = 1.67

M	M*	$\frac{A}{A^*}$	$\frac{p}{p_0}$	$\frac{\rho}{\rho_0}$	$\frac{T}{T_0}$	$\frac{I}{I^*}$	$\left(\frac{A}{A^*}\right)\left(\frac{p}{p_0}\right)$	f_w	f_I	Γ
1.75	1.420	1.312	.1721	.3486	.4936	1.0623	.2257	.55390	1.8995	.76225
1.80	1.440	1.351	.1601	.3339	.4795	1.0673	.2163	.53782	1.9085	.74012
1.85	1.459	1.392	.1490	.3198	.4658	1.0722	.2075	.52183	1.9173	.71812
1.90	1.477	1.436	.1386	.3063	.4526	1.0770	.1991	.50600	1.9259	.69634
1.95	1.494	1.482	.1290	.2934	.4398	1.0817	.1912	.49038	1.9343	.67484
2.00	1.511	1.530	.1201	.2811	.4274	1.0863	.1838	.47502	1.9425	.65370
2.05	1.527	1.580	.1119	2694	.4153	1.0908	.1768	.45994	1.9505	.63296
2.10	1.542	1.632	.1042	.2582	.4036	1.0952	.1701	.44519	1.9583	.61265
2.15	1.556	1.687	.09712	.2475	.3923	1.0994	.1638	.43077	1.9659	.59281
2.20	1.570	1.744	.09053	.2373	.3814	1.1035	.1579	.41671	1.9732	.57346
2.25	1.583	1.803	.08442	.2276	.3709	1.107	.1522	.40303	1.9803	.55463
2.30	1.596	1.865	.07875	.2183	.3607	1.111	.1468	.38972	1.9872	.53632
2.35	1.608	1.929	.07349	.2094	.3508	1.115	.1417	.37681	1.9939	.51855
2.40	1.620	1.995	.06862	.2010	.3413	1.119	.1369	.36428	2.0004	.50131
2.45	1.631	2.064	.06410	.1930	.3321	1.123	.1323	.35215	2.0067	.48461
2.50	1.642	2.135	.05990	.1853	.3232	1.126	.1279	.34040	2.0128	.46844
2.55	1.653	2.209	.05601	.1780	.3146	1.129	.1237	.32904	2.0186	.45281
2.60	1.663	2.285	.05239	.1710	.3063	1.132	.1197	.31806	2.0243	.43770
2.65	1.673	2.364	.04903	.1644	.2983	1.135	.1159	.30745	2.0298	.42310
2.70	1.682	2.445	.04591	.1581	.2905	1.138	.1123	.29721	2.0351	.40901
2.75	1.691	2.529	.04301	.1520	.2830	1.141	.1088	.28733	2.0403	.39542
2.80	1.699	2.616	.04032	.1462	.2757	1.144	.1055	.27781	2.0452	.38230
2.85	1.707	2.705	.03781	.1407	.2687	1.146	.1023	.26862	2.0500	.36966
2.90	1.715	2.797	.03547	.1354	.2620	1.149	.09924	.25976	2.0547	.35747
2.95	1.723	2.892	.03330	.1304	.2554	1.152	.09633	.25123	2 0592	.34573
3.0	1.730	2.990	.03128	.12560	.2491	1.154	.09354	.24300	2.0635	.33441
3.5	1.790	4.134	.01720	.08779	.1959	1.174	.07111	.17576	2.0999	.24188
4.0	1.833	5.608	.009939	.06321	.1572	1.189	.05574	.12957	2.1264	.17831
4.5	1.864	7.456	.006007	.04676	.1285	1.200	.04479	.09746	2.1460	.13413
5.0	1.887	9.721	.003778	.03542	.1067	1.208	.03672	.07475	2.1608	.10287
6.0	1.918	15.68	165(10)$^{-5}$	.02160	.07657	1.220	.02594	.04634	2.1812	.06377
7.0	1.938	23.85	807(10)$^{-6}$	.01406	.05742	1.227	.01925	.03047	2.1942	.04193
8.0	1.951	34.58	429(10)$^{-8}$	.00963	.04456	1.232	.01484	.02101	2.2028	.02892
9.0	1.960	48.24	244(10)$^{-6}$	.00687	.03554	1.235	.01177	.01506	2.2089	.02073
10.0	1.967	65.18	147(10)$^{-6}$	.00507	.02898	1.238	.00958	.01115	2.2133	.01534
∞	1.996	∞	0	0	0	1.249	0	0	2.2327	0

Table A.3

Fanno Line—One-Dimensional, Adiabatic, Constant-Area Flow of a Perfect Gas†
(Constant Specific Heat and MolecularWeight)

(a) $k = 1.4$

M	$\dfrac{T}{T^*}$	$\dfrac{p}{p^*}$	$\dfrac{p_0}{p_0^*}$	$\dfrac{V}{V^*}$	$\dfrac{I}{I^*}$	$\dfrac{fL_{max}}{D}$
0	1.2000	∞	∞	0	∞	∞
0.01	1.2000	109.544	57.874	.01095	45.650	7134.40
.02	1.1999	54.770	28.942	.02191	22.834	1778.45
.03	1.1998	36.511	19.300	.03286	15.232	787.08
.04	1.1996	27.382	14.482	.04381	11.435	440.35
.05	1.1994	21.903	11.5914	.05476	9.1584	280.02
.06	1.1991	18.251	9.6659	.06570	7.6428	193.03
.07	1.1988	15.642	8.2915	.07664	6.5620	140.66
.08	1.1985	13.684	7.2616	.08758	5.7529	106.72
.09	1.1981	12.162	6.4614	.09851	5.1249	83.496
.10	1.1976	10.9435	5.8218	.10943	4.6236	66.922
.11	1.1971	9.9465	5.2992	.12035	4.2146	54.688
.12	1.1966	9.1156	4.8643	.13126	3.8747	45.408
.13	1.1960	8.4123	4.4968	.14216	3.5880	38.207
.14	1.1953	7.8093	4.1824	.15306	3.3432	32.511
.15	1.1946	7.2866	3.9103	.16395	3.1317	27.932
.16	1.1939	6.8291	3.6727	.17482	2.9474	24.198
.17	1.1931	6.4252	3.4635	.18568	2.7855	21.115
.18	1.1923	6.0662	3.2779	.19654	2.6422	18.543
.19	1.1914	5.7448	3.1123	.20739	2.5146	16.375
.20	1.1905	5.4555	2.9635	.21822	2.4004	14.533
.21	1.1895	5.1936	2.8293	.22904	2.2976	12.956
.22	1.1885	4.9554	2.7076	.23984	2.2046	11.596
.23	1.1874	4.7378	2.5968	.25063	2.1203	10.416
.24	1.1863	4.5383	2.4956	.26141	2.0434	9.3865
.25	1.1852	4.3546	2.4027	.27217	1.9732	8.4834
.26	1.1840	4.1850	2.3173	.28291	1.9088	7.6876
.27	1.1828	4.0280	2.2385	.29364	1.8496	6.9832
.28	1.1815	3.8820	2.1656	.30435	1.7950	6.3572
.29	1.1802	3.7460	2.0979	.31504	1.7446	5.7989
.30	1.1788	3.6190	2.0351	.32572	1.6979	5.2992
.31	1.1774	3.5002	1.9765	.33637	1.6546	4.8507
.32	1.1759	3.3888	1.9219	.34700	1.6144	4.4468
.33	1.1744	3.2840	1.8708	.35762	1.5769	4.0821
.34	1.1729	3.1853	1.8229	.36822	1.5420	3.7520
.35	1.1713	3.0922	1.7780	.37880	1.5094	3.4525
.36	1.1697	3.0042	1.7358	.38935	1.4789	3.1801
.37	1.1680	2.9209	1.6961	.39988	1.4503	2.9320
.38	1.1663	2.8420	1.6587	.41039	1.4236	2.7055
.39	1.1646	2.7671	1.6234	.42087	1.3985	2.4983

† These data were calculated originally as a portion of Project Meteor, and appeared as a part of MIT Meteor Report No. 14, 1947, by A. H. Shapiro, W. R. Hawthorne, and C. M. Edelman. They have been reproduced in *Gas Tables*, by J. H. Keenan and J. Kaye, published by John Wiley and Sons, 1948. These values are reproduced here by permission of A. H. Shapiro and John Wiley and Sons.

Table A.3 (*Continued*)
Fanno Line
(*a*) *k* = 1.4

M	$\dfrac{T}{T^*}$	$\dfrac{p}{p^*}$	$\dfrac{p_0}{p_0{}^*}$	$\dfrac{V}{V^*}$	$\dfrac{I}{I^*}$	$\dfrac{fL_{max}}{D}$
0.40	1.1628	2.6958	1.5901	.43133	1.3749	2.3085
.41	1.1610	2.6280	1.5587	.44177	1.3527	2.1344
.42	1.1591	2.5634	1.5289	.45218	1.3318	1.9744
.43	1.1572	2.5017	1.5007	.46257	1.3122	1.8272
.44	1.1553	2.4428	1.4739	.47293	1.2937	1.6915
.45	1.1533	2.3865	1.4486	.48326	1.2763	1.5664
.46	1.1513	2.3326	1.4246	.49357	1.2598	1.4509
.47	1.1492	2.2809	1.4018	.50385	1.2443	1.3442
.48	1.1471	2.2314	1.3801	.51410	1.2296	1.2453
.49	1.1450	2.1838	1.3595	.52433	1.2158	1.1539
.50	1.1429	2.1381	1.3399	.53453	1.2027	1.06908
.51	1.1407	2.0942	1.3212	.54469	1.1903	.99042
.52	1.1384	2.0519	1.3034	.55482	1.1786	.91741
.53	1.1362	2.0112	1.2864	.56493	1.1675	.84963
.54	1.1339	1.9719	1.2702	.57501	1.1571	.78662
.55	1.1315	1.9341	1.2549	.58506	1.1472	.72805
.56	1.1292	1.8976	1.2403	.59507	1.1378	.67357
.57	1.1268	1.8623	1.2263	.60505	1.1289	.62286
.58	1.1244	1.8282	1.2130	.61500	1.1205	.57568
.59	1.1219	1.7952	1.2003	.62492	1.1126	.53174
.60	1.1194	1.7634	1.1882	.63481	1.10504	.49081
.61	1.1169	1.7325	1.1766	.64467	1.09793	.45270
.62	1.1144	1.7026	1.1656	.65449	1.09120	.41720
.63	1.1118	1.6737	1.1551	.66427	1.08485	.38411
.64	1.1091	1.6456	1.1451	.67402	1.07883	.35330
.65	1.10650	1.6183	1.1356	.68374	1.07314	.32460
.66	1.10383	1.5919	1.1265	.69342	1.06777	.29785
.67	1.10114	1.5662	1.1179	.70306	1.06271	.27295
.68	1.09842	1.5413	1.1097	.71267	1.05792	.24978
.69	1.09567	1.5170	1.1018	.72225	1.05340	.22821
.70	1.09290	1.4934	1.09436	.73179	1.04915	.20814
.71	1.09010	1.4705	1.08729	.74129	1.04514	.18949
.72	1.08727	1.4482	1.08057	.75076	1.04137	.17215
.73	1.08442	1.4265	1.07419	.76019	1.03783	.15606
.74	1.08155	1.4054	1.06815	.76958	1.03450	.14113
.75	1.07865	1.3848	1.06242	.77893	1.03137	.12728
.76	1.07573	1.3647	1.05700	.78825	1.02844	.11446
.77	1.07279	1.3451	1.05188	.79753	1.02570	.10262
.78	1.06982	1.3260	1.04705	.80677	1.02314	.09167
.79	1.06684	1.3074	1.04250	.81598	1.02075	.08159

Table A.3 (*Continued*)

Fanno Line

(*a*) $k = 1.4$

M	$\dfrac{T}{T^*}$	$\dfrac{p}{p^*}$	$\dfrac{p_0}{p_0{}^*}$	$\dfrac{V}{V^*}$	$\dfrac{I}{I^*}$	$\dfrac{fL_{max}}{D}$
0.80	1.06383	1.2892	1.03823	.82514	1.01853	.07229
.81	1.06080	1.2715	1.03422	.83426	1.01646	.06375
.82	1.05775	1.2542	1.03047	.84334	1.01455	.05593
.83	1.05468	1.2373	1.02696	.85239	1.01278	.04878
.84	1.05160	1.2208	1.02370	.86140	1.01115	.04226
.85	1.04849	1.2047	1.02067	.87037	1.00966	.03632
.86	1.04537	1.1889	1.01787	.87929	1.00829	.03097
.87	1.04223	1.1735	1.01529	.88818	1.00704	.02613
.88	1.03907	1.1584	1.01294	.89703	1.00591	.02180
.89	1.03589	1.1436	1.01080	.90583	1.00490	.01793
.90	1.03270	1.12913	1.00887	.91459	1.00399	.014513
.91	1.02950	1.11500	1.00714	.92332	1.00318	.011519
.92	1.02627	1.10114	1.00560	.93201	1.00248	.008916
.93	1.02304	1.08758	1.00426	.94065	1.00188	.006694
.94	1.01978	1.07430	1.00311	.94925	1.00136	.004815
.95	1.01652	1.06129	1.00215	.95782	1.00093	.003280
.96	1.01324	1.04854	1.00137	.96634	1.00059	.002056
.97	1.00995	1.03605	1.00076	.97481	1.00033	.001135
.98	1.00664	1.02379	1.00033	.98324	1.00014	.000493
.99	1.00333	1.01178	1.00008	.99164	1.00003	.000120
1.00	1.00000	1.00000	1.00000	1.00000	1.00000	0
1.01	.99666	.98844	1.00008	1.00831	1.00003	.000114
1.02	.99331	.97711	1.00033	1.01658	1.00013	.000458
1.03	.98995	.96598	1.00073	1.02481	1.00030	.001013
1.04	.98658	.95506	1.00130	1.03300	1.00053	.001771
1.05	.98320	.94435	1.00203	1.04115	1.00082	.002712
1.06	.97982	.93383	1.00291	1.04925	1.00116	.003837
1.07	.97642	.92350	1.00394	1.05731	1.00155	.005129
1.08	.97302	.91335	1.00512	1.06533	1.00200	.006582
1.09	.96960	.90338	1.00645	1.07331	1.00250	.008185
1.10	.96618	.89359	1.00793	1.08124	1.00305	.009933
1.11	.96276	.88397	1.00955	1.08913	1.00365	.011813
1.12	.95933	.87451	1.01131	1.09698	1.00429	.013824
1.13	.95589	.86522	1.01322	1.10479	1.00497	.015949
1.14	.95244	.85608	1.01527	1.11256	1.00569	.018187
1.15	.94899	.84710	1.01746	1.1203	1.00646	.02053
1.16	.94554	.83827	1.01978	1.1280	1.00726	.02298
1.17	.94208	.82958	1.02224	1.1356	1.00810	.02552
1.18	.93862	.82104	1.02484	1.1432	1.00897	.02814
1.19	.93515	.81263	1.02757	1.1508	1.00988	.03085

Table A.3 (*Continued*)

Fanno Line

(*a*) $k = 1.4$

M	$\dfrac{T}{T^*}$	$\dfrac{p}{p^*}$	$\dfrac{p_0}{p_0{}^*}$	$\dfrac{V}{V^*}$	$\dfrac{I}{I^*}$	$\dfrac{fL_{max}}{D}$
1.20	.93168	.80436	1.03044	1.1583	1.01082	.03364
1.21	.92820	.79623	1.03344	1.1658	1.01178	.03650
1.22	.92473	.78822	1.03657	1.1732	1.01278	.03942
1.23	.92125	.78034	1.03983	1.1806	1.01381	.04241
1.24	.91777	.77258	1.04323	1.1879	1.01486	.04547
1.25	.91429	.76495	1.04676	1.1952	1.01594	.04858
1.26	.91080	.75743	1.05041	1.2025	1.01705	.05174
1.27	.90732	.75003	1.05419	1.2097	1.01818	.05494
1.28	.90383	.74274	1.05809	1.2169	1.01933	.05820
1.29	.90035	.73556	1.06213	1.2240	1.02050	.06150
1.30	.89686	.72848	1.06630	1.2311	1.02169	.06483
1.31	.89338	.72152	1.07060	1.2382	1.02291	.06820
1.32	.88989	.71465	1.07502	1.2452	1.02415	.07161
1.33	.88641	.70789	1.07957	1.2522	1.02540	.07504
1.34	.88292	.70123	1.08424	1.2591	1.02666	.07850
1.35	.87944	.69466	1.08904	1.2660	1.02794	.08199
1.36	.87596	.68818	1.09397	1.2729	1.02924	.08550
1.37	.87249	.68180	1.09902	1.2797	1.03056	.08904
1.38	.86901	.67551	1.10419	1.2864	1.03189	.09259
1.39	.86554	.66931	1.10948	1.2932	1.03323	.09616
1.40	.86207	.66320	1.1149	1.2999	1.03458	.09974
1.41	.85860	.65717	1.1205	1.3065	1.03595	.10333
1.42	.85514	.65122	1.1262	1.3131	1.03733	.10694
1.43	.85168	.64536	1.1320	1.3197	1.03872	.11056
1.44	.84822	.63958	1.1379	1.3262	1.04012	.11419
1.45	.84477	.63387	1.1440	1.3327	1.04153	.11782
1.46	.84133	.62824	1.1502	1.3392	1.04295	.12146
1.47	.83788	.62269	1.1565	1.3456	1.04438	.12510
1.48	.83445	.61722	1.1629	1.3520	1.04581	.12875
1.49	.83101	.61181	1.1695	1.3583	1.04725	.13240
1.50	.82759	.60648	1.1762	1.3646	1.04870	.13605
1.51	.82416	.60122	1.1830	1.3708	1.05016	.13970
1.52	.82075	.59602	1.1899	1.3770	1.05162	.14335
1.53	.81734	.59089	1.1970	1.3832	1.05309	.14699
1.54	.81394	.58583	1.2043	1.3894	1.05456	.15063
1.55	.81054	.58084	1.2116	1.3955	1.05604	.15427
1.56	.80715	.57591	1.2190	1.4015	1.05752	.15790
1.57	.80376	.57104	1.2266	1.4075	1.05900	.16152
1.58	.80038	.56623	1.2343	1.4135	1.06049	.16514
1.59	.79701	.56148	1.2422	1.4195	1.06198	.16876

Table A.3 (Continued)

Fanno Line

(a) k = 1.4

M	$\dfrac{T}{T^*}$	$\dfrac{p}{p^*}$	$\dfrac{p_0}{p_0{}^*}$	$\dfrac{V}{V^*}$	$\dfrac{I}{I^*}$	$\dfrac{fL_{max}}{D}$
1.60	.79365	.55679	1.2502	1.4254	1.06348	.17236
1.61	.79030	.55216	1.2583	1.4313	1.06498	.17595
1.62	.78695	.54759	1.2666	1.4371	1.06648	.17953
1.63	.78361	.54308	1.2750	1.4429	1.06798	.18311
1.64	.78028	.53862	1.2835	1.4487	1.06948	.18667
1.65	.77695	.53421	1.2922	1.4544	1.07098	.19022
1.66	.77363	.52986	1.3010	1.4601	1.07249	.19376
1.67	.77033	.52556	1.3099	1.4657	1.07399	.19729
1.68	.76703	.52131	1.3190	1.4713	1.07550	.20081
1.69	.76374	.51711	1.3282	1.4769	1.07701	.20431
1.70	.76046	.51297	1.3376	1.4825	1.07851	.20780
1.71	.75718	.50887	1.3471	1.4880	1.08002	.21128
1.72	.75392	.50482	1.3567	1.4935	1.08152	.21474
1.73	.75067	.50082	1.3665	1.4989	1.08302	.21819
1.74	.74742	.49686	1.3764	1.5043	1.08453	.22162
1.75	.74419	.49295	1.3865	1.5097	1.08603	.22504
1.76	.74096	.48909	1.3967	1.5150	1.08753	.22844
1.77	.73774	.48527	1.4070	1.5203	1.08903	.23183
1.78	.73453	.48149	1.4175	1.5256	1.09053	.23520
1.79	.73134	.47776	1.4282	1.5308	1.09202	.23855
1.80	.72816	.47407	1.4390	1.5360	1.09352	.24189
1.81	.72498	.47042	1.4499	1.5412	1.09500	.24521
1.82	.72181	.46681	1.4610	1.5463	1.09649	.24851
1.83	.71865	.46324	1.4723	1.5514	1.09798	.25180
1.84	.71551	.45972	1.4837	1.5564	1.09946	.25507
1.85	.71238	.45623	1.4952	1.5614	1.1009	.25832
1.86	.70925	.45278	1.5069	1.5664	1.1024	.26156
1.87	.70614	.44937	1.5188	1.5714	1.1039	.26478
1.88	.70304	.44600	1.5308	1.5763	1.1054	.26798
1.89	.69995	.44266	1.5429	1.5812	1.1068	.27116
1.90	.69686	.43936	1.5552	1.5861	1.1083	.27433
1.91	.69379	.43610	1.5677	1.5909	1.1097	.27748
1.92	.69074	.43287	1.5804	1.5957	1.1112	.28061
1.93	.68769	.42967	1.5932	1.6005	1.1126	.28372
1.94	.68465	.42651	1.6062	1.6052	1.1141	.28681
1.95	.68162	.42339	1.6193	1.6099	1.1155	.28989
1.96	.67861	.42030	1.6326	1.6146	1.1170	.29295
1.97	.67561	.41724	1.6461	1.6193	1.1184	.29599
1.98	.67262	.41421	1.6597	1.6239	1.1198	.29901
1.99	.66964	.41121	1.6735	1.6284	1.1213	.30201

Table A.3 (*Continued*)

Fanno Line

(*a*) $k = 1.4$

M	$\dfrac{T}{T^*}$	$\dfrac{p}{p^*}$	$\dfrac{p_0}{p_0{}^*}$	$\dfrac{V}{V^*}$	$\dfrac{I}{I^*}$	$\dfrac{fL_{max}}{D}$
2.00	.66667	.40825	1.6875	1.6330	1.1227	.30499
2.01	.66371	.40532	1.7017	1.6375	1.1241	.30796
2.02	.66076	.40241	1.7160	1.6420	1.1255	.31091
2.03	.65783	.39954	1.7305	1.6465	1.1269	.31384
2.04	.65491	.39670	1.7452	1.6509	1.1283	.31675
2.05	.65200	.39389	1.7600	1.6553	1.1297	.31965
2.06	.64910	.39110	1.7750	1.6597	1.1311	.32253
2.07	.64621	.38834	1.7902	1.6640	1.1325	.32538
2.08	.64333	.38562	1.8056	1.6683	1.1339	.32822
2.09	.64047	.38292	1.8212	1.6726	1.1352	.33104
2.10	.63762	.38024	1.8369	1.6769	1.1366	.33385
2.11	.63478	.37760	1.8528	1.6811	1.1380	.33664
2.12	.63195	.37498	1.8690	1.6853	1.1393	.33940
2.13	.62914	.37239	1.8853	1.6895	1.1407	.34215
2.14	.62633	.36982	1.9018	1.6936	1.1420	.34488
2.15	.62354	.36728	1.9185	1.6977	1.1434	.34760
2.16	.62076	.36476	1.9354	1.7018	1.1447	.35030
2.17	.61799	.36227	1.9525	1.7059	1.1460	.35298
2.18	.61523	.35980	1.9698	1.7099	1.1474	.35564
2.19	.61249	.35736	1.9873	1.7139	1.1487	.35828
2.20	.60976	.35494	2.0050	1.7179	1.1500	.36091
2.21	.60704	.35254	2.0228	1.7219	1.1513	.36352
2.22	.60433	.35017	2.0409	1.7258	1.1526	.36611
2.23	.60163	.34782	2.0592	1.7297	1.1539	.36868
2.24	.59895	.34550	2.0777	1.7336	1.1552	.37124
2.25	.59627	.34319	2.0964	1.7374	1.1565	.37378
2.26	.59361	.34091	2.1154	1.7412	1.1578	.37630
2.27	.59096	.33865	2.1345	1.7450	1.1590	.37881
2.28	.58833	.33641	2.1538	1.7488	1.1603	.38130
2.29	.58570	.33420	2.1733	1.7526	1.1616	.38377
2.30	.58309	.33200	2.1931	1.7563	1.1629	.38623
2.31	.58049	.32983	2.2131	1.7600	1.1641	.38867
2.32	.57790	.32767	2.2333	1.7637	1.1653	.39109
2.33	.57532	.32554	2.2537	1.7673	1.1666	.39350
2.34	.57276	.32342	2.2744	1.7709	1.1678	.39589
2.35	.57021	.32133	2.2953	1.7745	1.1690	.39826
2.36	.56767	.31925	2.3164	1.7781	1.1703	.40062
2.37	.56514	.31720	2.3377	1.7817	1.1715	.40296
2.38	.56262	.31516	2.3593	1.7852	1.1727	.40528
2.39	.56011	.31314	2.3811	1.7887	1.1739	.40760

Table A.3 (*Continued*)

Fanno Line

(*a*) $k = 1.4$

M	$\dfrac{T}{T^*}$	$\dfrac{p}{p^*}$	$\dfrac{p_0}{p_0{}^*}$	$\dfrac{V}{V^*}$	$\dfrac{I}{I^*}$	$\dfrac{fL_{max}}{D}$
2.40	.55762	.31114	2.4031	1.7922	1.1751	.40989
2.41	.55514	.30916	2.4254	1.7956	1.1763	.41216
2.42	.55267	.30720	2.4479	1.7991	1.1775	.41442
2.43	.55021	.30525	2.4706	1.8025	1.1786	.41667
2.44	.54776	.30332	2.4936	1.8059	1.1798	.41891
2.45	.54533	.30141	2.5168	1.8092	1.1810	.42113
2.46	.54291	.29952	2.5403	1.8126	1.1821	.42333
2.47	.54050	.29765	2.5640	1.8159	1.1833	.42551
2.48	.53810	.29579	2.5880	1.8192	1.1844	.42768
2.49	.53571	.29395	2.6122	1.8225	1.1856	.42983
2.50	.53333	.29212	2.6367	1.8257	1.1867	.43197
2.51	.53097	.29031	2.6615	1.8290	1.1879	.43410
2.52	.52862	.28852	2.6865	1.8322	1.1890	.43621
2.53	.52627	.28674	2.7117	1.8354	1.1901	.43831
2.54	.52394	.28498	2.7372	1.8386	1.1912	.44040
2.55	.52163	.28323	2.7630	1.8417	1.1923	.44247
2.56	.51932	.28150	2.7891	1.8448	1.1934	.44452
2.57	.51702	,27978	2.8154	1.8479	1.1945	.44655
2.58	.51474	.27808	2.8420	1.8510	1.1956	.44857
2.59	.51247	.27640	2.8689	1.8541	1.1967	.45059
2.60	.51020	.27473	2.8960	1.8571	1.1978	.45259
2.61	.50795	.27307	2.9234	1.8602	1.1989	.45457
2.62	.50571	.27143	2.9511	1.8632	1.2000	.45654
2.63	.50349	.26980	2.9791	1.8662	1.2011	.45850
2.64	.50127	.26818	3.0074	1.8691	1.2021	.46044
2.65	.49906	.26658	3.0359	1.8721	1.2031	.46237
2.66	.49687	.26499	3.0647	1.8750	1.2042	.46429
2.67	.49469	.26342	3.0938	1.8779	1.2052	.46619
2.68	.49251	.26186	3.1234	1.8808	1.2062	.46807
2.69	.49035	.26032	3.1530	1.8837	1.2073	.46996
2.70	.48820	.25878	3.1830	1.8865	1.2083	.47182
2.71	.48606	.25726	3.2133	1.8894	1.2093	.47367
2.72	.48393	.25575	3.2440	1.8922	1.2103	.47551
2.73	.48182	.25426	3.2749	1.8950	1.2113	.47734
2.74	.47971	.25278	3.3061	1.8978	1.2123	.47915
2.75	.47761	.25131	3.3376	1.9005	1.2133	.48095
2.76	.47553	.24985	3.3695	1.9032	1.2143	.48274
2.77	.47346	.24840	3.4017	1.9060	1.2153	.48452
2.78	.47139	.24697	3.4342	1.9087	1.2163	.48628
2.79	.46933	.24555	3.4670	1.9114	1.2173	.48803

Table A.3 (Continued)

Fanno Line

(a) $k = 1.4$

M	$\dfrac{T}{T^*}$	$\dfrac{p}{p^*}$	$\dfrac{p_0}{p_0{}^*}$	$\dfrac{V}{V^*}$	$\dfrac{I}{I^*}$	$\dfrac{fL_{max}}{D}$
2.80	.46729	.24414	3.5001	1.9140	1.2182	.48976
2.81	.46526	.24274	3.5336	1.9167	1.2192	.49148
2.82	.46324	.24135	3.5674	1.9193	1.2202	.49321
2.83	.46122	.23997	3.6015	1.9220	1.2211	.49491
2.84	.45922	.23861	3.6359	1.9246	1.2221	.49660
2.85	.45723	.23726	3.6707	1.9271	1.2230	.49828
2.86	.45525	.23592	3.7058	1.9297	1.2240	.49995
2.87	.45328	.23458	3.7413	1.9322	1.2249	.50161
2.88	.45132	.23326	3.7771	1.9348	1.2258	.50326
2.89	.44937	.23196	3.8133	1.9373	1.2268	.50489
2.90	.44743	.23066	3.8498	1.9398	1.2277	.50651
2.91	.44550	.22937	3.8866	1.9423	1.2286	.50812
2.92	.44358	.22809	3.9238	1.9448	1.2295	.50973
2.93	.44167	.22682	3.9614	1.9472	1.2304	.51133
2.94	.43977	.22556	3.9993	1.9497	1.2313	.51291
2.95	.43788	.22431	4.0376	1.9521	1.2322	.51447
2.96	.43600	.22307	4.0763	1.9545	1.2331	.51603
2.97	.43413	.22185	4.1153	1.9569	1.2340	.51758
2.98	.43226	.22063	4.1547	1.9592	1.2348	.51912
2.99	.43041	.21942	4.1944	1.9616	1.2357	.52064
3.0	.42857	.21822	4.2346	1.9640	1.2366	.52216
3.5	.34783	.16850	6.7896	2.0642	1.2743	.58643
4.0	.28571	.13363	10.719	2.1381	1.3029	.63306
4.5	.23762	.10833	16.562	2.1936	1.3247	.66764
5.0	.20000	.08944	25.000	2.2361	1.3416	.69381
6.0	.14634	.06376	53.180	2.2953	1.3655	.72987
7.0	.11111	.04762	104.14	2.3333	1.3810	.75281
8.0	.08696	.03686	190.11	2.3591	1.3915	.76820
9.0	.06977	.02935	327.19	2.3772	1.3989	.77898
10.0	.05714	.02390	535.94	2.3905	1.4044	.78683
∞	0	0	∞	2.4495	1.4289	.82153

Table A.3 (Continued)

Fanno Line

(b) $k = 1.0$

M	$\dfrac{T}{T^*}$	$\dfrac{p}{p^*}$	$\dfrac{p_0}{p_0{}^*}$	$\dfrac{V}{V^*}$	$\dfrac{I}{I^*}$	$\dfrac{fL_{max}}{D}$
0	1.000	∞	∞	0	∞	∞
0.05		20.000	12.146	.0500	10.025	393.01
.10		10.000	6.096	.1000	5.050	94.39
.15		6.667	4.089	.1500	3.408	39.65
.20		5.000	3.094	.2000	2.600	20.78
.25		4.000	2.503	.2500	2.125	12.227
.30		3.333	2.115	.3000	1.817	7.703
.35		2.857	1.842	.3500	1.604	5.064
.40		2.500	1.643	.4000	1.450	3.417
.45		2.222	1.492	.4500	1.336	2.341
.50		2.000	1.375	.5000	1.250	1.614
.55		1.818	1.283	.5500	1.184	1.110
.60		1.667	1.210	.6000	1.133	.7561
.65		1.539	1.153	.6500	1.0942	.5053
.70		1.429	1.107	.7000	1.0643	.3275
.75		1.333	1.0714	.7500	1.0417	.2024
.80		1.250	1.0441	.8000	1.0250	.1162
.85		1.176	1.0240	.8500	1.0132	.05904
.90		1.111	1.0104	.9000	1.0056	.02385
.95		1.0526	1.0026	.9500	1.0013	.00545
1.00		1.0000	1.0000	1.0000	1.0000	0
1.05		.9524	1.0025	1.0500	1.0012	.00461
1.10		.9091	1.0097	1.100	1.0045	.01707
1.15		.8695	1.0217	1.150	1.0098	.03567
1.20		.8333	1.0384	1.200	1.0167	.05909
1.25		.8000	1.0598	1.250	1.0250	.08629
1.30		.7692	1.0862	1.300	1.0346	.1164
1.35		.7407	1.118	1.350	1.0453	.1489
1.40		.7143	1.154	1.400	1.0571	.1831
1.45		.6897	1.196	1.450	1.0698	.2188
1.50		.6667	1.245	1.500	1.0833	.2554
1.55		.6452	1.300	1.550	1.0976	.2927
1.60		.6250	1.363	1.600	1.112	.3306
1.65		.6061	1.434	1.650	1.128	.3689
1.70		.5882	1.514	1.700	1.144	.4073

Table A.3 (Continued)

Fanno Line

(b) $k = 1.0$

M	$\dfrac{T}{T^*}$	$\dfrac{p}{p^*}$	$\dfrac{p_0}{p_0{}^*}$	$\dfrac{V}{V^*}$	$\dfrac{I}{I^*}$	$\dfrac{fL_{max}}{D}$
1.75	1.000	.5714	1.603	1.750	1.161	.4458
1.80		.5556	1.703	1.800	1.178	.4842
1.85		.5406	1.815	1.850	1.195	.5225
1.90		.5263	1.941	1.900	1.213	.5607
1.95		.5128	2.082	1.950	1.231	.5986
2.00		.5000	2.241	2.000	1.250	.6363
2.05		.4878	2.419	2.050	1.269	.6736
2.10		.4762	2.620	2.100	1.288	.7106
2.15		.4651	2.846	2.150	1.308	.7472
2.20		.4545	3.100	2.200	1.327	7835
2.25		.4444	3.388	2.250	1.347	.8194
2.30		.4348	3.714	2.300	1.367	.8549
2.35		.4256	4.083	2.350	1.388	.8900
2.40		.4167	4.502	2.400	1.408	.9246
2.45		.4082	4.979	2.450	1.429	.9588
2.50		.4000	5.522	2.500	1.450	.9926
2.55		.3922	6.142	2.550	1.471	1.0260
2.60		.3847	6.852	2.600	1.492	1.0590
2.65		.3774	7.665	2.650	1.514	1.0916
2.70		.3704	8.600	2.700	1.535	1.1237
2.75		.3636	9.676	2.750	1.557	1.155
2.80		.3571	10.92	2.800	1.579	1.187
2.85		.3509	12.35	2.850	1.600	1.218
2.90		.3449	14.02	2.900	1.622	1.248
2.95		.3390	15.95	2.950	1.644	1.279
3.00		.3333	18.20	3.000	1.667	1.308
3.50		.2857	79.22	3.500	1.893	1.587
4.00		.2500	452.01	4.000	2.125	1.835
4.50		.2222	3364	4.500	2.361	2.058
5.00		.2000	32550	5.000	2.600	2.259
6.00		.1667	$664(10)^4$	6.000	3.083	2.611
7.00		.1429	$378(10)^7$	7.000	3.571	2.912
8.00		.1250	$599(10)^{10}$	8.000	4.062	3.174
9.00		.1111	$262(10)^{14}$	9.000	4.556	3.407
10.00		.1000	$314(10)^{18}$	10.000	5.050	3.615
∞	1.000	0	∞	∞	∞	∞

Table A.3 (*Continued*)

Fanno Line

(c) $k = 1.1$

M	$\dfrac{T}{T^*}$	$\dfrac{p}{p^*}$	$\dfrac{p_0}{p_0{}^*}$	$\dfrac{V}{V^*}$	$\dfrac{I}{I^*}$	$\dfrac{fL_{max}}{D}$
0	1.0500	∞	∞	0	∞	∞
0.05	1.0499	20.493	11.999	.05123	9.785	357.05
.10	1.0495	10.244	6.023	.1024	4.932	85.65
.15	1.0488	6.828	4.042	.1536	3.332	35.92
.20	1.0479	5.118	3.059	.2047	2.545	18.79
.25	1.0467	4.092	2.476	.2558	2.083	11.03
.30	1.0453	3.408	2.094	.3067	1.784	6.936
.35	1.0436	2.919	1.825	.3575	1.577	4.549
.40	1.0417	2.552	1.628	.4082	1.429	3.062
.45	1.0395	2.266	1.480	.4588	1.319	2.093
.50	1.0370	2.037	1.365	.5092	1.237	1.439
.55	1.0343	1.849	1.275	.5594	1.174	.9871
.60	1.0314	1.693	1.204	.6094	1.125	.6705
.65	1.0283	1.560	1.148	.6591	1.0882	.4468
.70	1.0249	1.446	1.104	.7086	1.0599	.2887
.75	1.0213	1.347	1.0689	.7579	1.0386	.1780
.80	1.0174	1.261	1.0425	.8069	1.0231	.1019
.85	1.0133	1.184	1.0231	.8557	1.0122	.05160
.90	1.0091	1.116	1.0100	.9041	1.0051	.02078
.95	1.0047	1.0551	1.0024	.9522	1.0012	.00472
1.00	1.0000	1.0000	1.0000	1.0000	1.0000	0
1.05	.9951	.9501	1.0023	1.0474	1.0011	.00398
1.10	.9901	.9046	1.0092	1.0945	1.0041	.01468
1.15	.9849	.8630	1.0204	1.1412	1.0087	.03058
1.20	.9795	.8247	1.0360	1.1876	1.0148	.05050
1.25	.9739	.7895	1.0559	1.234	1.0221	.07350
1.30	.9682	.7569	1.0801	1.279	1.0304	.09885
1.35	.9623	.7266	1.109	1.324	1.0397	.1260
1.40	.9563	.6985	1.142	1.369	1.0498	.1544
1.45	.9501	.6722	1.180	1.413	1.0605	.1838
1.50	.9438	.6476	1.223	1.457	1.0717	.2138
1.55	.9374	.6246	1.272	1.501	1.0835	.2443
1.60	.9309	.6030	1.326	1.544	1.0958	.2749
1.65	.9242	.5826	1.387	1.586	1.108	.3056
1.70	.9174	.5634	1.454	1.628	1.121	.3362

Table A.3 (*Continued*)

Fanno Line

(c) $k = 1.1$

M	$\dfrac{T}{T^*}$	$\dfrac{p}{p^*}$	$\dfrac{p_0}{p_0{}^*}$	$\dfrac{V}{V^*}$	$\dfrac{I}{I^*}$	$\dfrac{fL_{max}}{D}$
1.75	.9105	.5453	1.528	1.670	1.134	.3667
1.80	.9036	.5281	1.610	1.711	1.148	.3969
1.85	.8966	.5118	1.701	1.752	1.161	.4268
1.90	.8895	.4964	1.801	1.792	1.175	.4563
1.95	.8823	.4817	1.911	1.832	1.189	.4854
2.00	.8750	.4677	2.032	1.871	1.203	.5140
2.05	.8677	.4544	2.165	1.910	1.217	.5422
2.10	.8603	.4417	2.312	1.948	1.231	.5698
2.15	.8529	.4295	2.473	1.986	1.245	.5970
2.20	.8454	.4179	2.651	2.023	1.259	.6237
2.25	.8379	.4068	2.846	2.060	1.273	.6498
2.30	.8304	.3962	3.061	2.096	1.286	.6754
2.35	.8228	.3860	3.299	2.132	1.300	.7005
2.40	.8152	.3762	3.560	2.167	1.314	.7251
2.45	.8076	.3668	3.848	2.202	1.328	.7491
2.50	.8000	.3578	4.165	2.236	1.342	.7726
2.55	.7924	.3491	4.515	2.270	1.355	.7957
2.60	.7848	.3407	4.902	2.303	1.369	.8182
2.65	.7771	.3327	5.328	2.336	1.382	.8402
2.70	.7695	.3249	5.799	2.368	1.395	.8617
2.75	.7619	.3174	6.320	2.400	1.409	.8828
2.80	.7543	.3102	6.895	2.432	1.422	.9034
2.85	.7467	.3032	7.532	2.463	1.434	.9235
2.90	.7392	.2965	8.237	2.493	1.447	.9432
2.95	.7316	.2900	9.016	2.523	1.460	.9624
3.00	.7241	.2837	9.880	2.553	1.472	.9812
3.50	.6512	.2305	25.83	2.824	1.589	1.147
4.00	.5833	.1909	71.74	3.055	1.691	1.280
4.50	.5217	.1605	205.7	3.250	1.779	1.386
5.00	.4667	.1366	597.3	3.416	1.854	1.472
6.00	.3750	.1021	4911	3.674	1.973	1.601
7.00	.3043	.07881	37919	3.862	2.060	1.689
8.00	.2500	.06250	$263(10)^3$	4.000	2.125	1.752
9.00	.2079	.05067	$161(10)^4$	4.104	2.174	1.798
10.00	.1750	.04183	$889(10)^4$	4.183	2.211	1.832
∞	0	0	∞	4.583	2.400	1.997

Table A.3 (*Continued*)

Fanno Line

(*d*) $k = 1.2$

M	$\dfrac{T}{T^*}$	$\dfrac{p}{p^*}$	$\dfrac{p_0}{p_0{}^*}$	$\dfrac{V}{V^*}$	$\dfrac{I}{I^*}$	$\dfrac{fL_{max}}{D}$
0	1.1000	∞	∞	0	∞	∞
0.05	1.0997	20.974	11.857	.05243	9.562	327.09
.10	1.0989	10.483	5.953	.1048	4.822	78.36
.15	1.0975	6.984	3.996	.1571	3.260	32.81
.20	1.0956	5.234	3.026	.2093	2.493	17.13
.25	1.0932	4.182	2.451	.2614	2.044	10.04
.30	1.0902	3.480	2.073	.3133	1.753	6.298
.35	1.0867	2.978	1.809	.3649	1.553	4.121
.40	1.0827	2.601	1.615	.4162	1.409	2.768
.45	1.0782	2.307	1.469	.4672	1.304	1.887
.50	1.0732	2.072	1.356	.5179	1.224	1.294
.55	1.0677	1.879	1.268	.5683	1.164	.8855
.60	1.0618	1.717	1.199	.6183	1.118	.5999
.65	1.0554	1.581	1.144	.6678	1.0826	.3987
.70	1.0486	1.463	1.100	.7168	1.0561	.2570
.75	1.0414	1.361	1.0666	.7654	1.0360	.1579
.80	1.0338	1.271	1.0410	.8134	1.0214	.09016
.85	1.0259	1.192	1.0222	.8609	1.0112	.04554
.90	1.0176	1.121	1.0096	.9078	1.0047	.01829
.95	1.0089	1.0573	1.0023	.9542	1.0011	.00414
1.00	1.0000	1.0000	1.0000	1.0000	1.0000	0
1.05	.9908	.9480	1.0022	1.0451	1.0010	.00347
1.10	.9813	.9005	1.0087	1.0896	1.0037	.01277
1.15	.9715	.8571	1.0194	1.134	1.0079	.02657
1.20	.9615	.8172	1.0340	1.177	1.0134	.04368
1.25	.9514	.7803	1.0525	1.219	1.0197	.06338
1.30	.9410	.7462	1.0749	1.261	1.0270	.08500
1.35	.9304	.7145	1.101	1.302	1.0351	.1080
1.40	.9197	.6850	1.132	1.342	1.0437	.1320
1.45	.9089	.6575	1.166	1.382	1.0529	.1567
1.50	.8980	.6317	1.205	1.421	1.0625	.1817
1.55	.8869	.6076	1.248	1.459	1.0724	.2069
1.60	.8758	.5849	1.296	1.497	1.0826	.2323
1.65	.8646	.5635	1.349	1.534	1.0930	.2575
1.70	.8534	.5434	1.407	1.570	1.1036	.2825

Table A.3 (Continued)

Fanno Line

(d) $k = 1.2$

M	$\dfrac{T}{T^*}$	$\dfrac{p}{p^*}$	$\dfrac{p_0}{p_0^*}$	$\dfrac{V}{V^*}$	$\dfrac{I}{I^*}$	$\dfrac{fL_{max}}{D}$
1.75	.8421	.5244	1.471	1.606	1.114	.3072
1.80	.8308	.5064	1.540	1.641	1.125	.3316
1.85	.8195	.4894	1.615	1.675	1.136	.3556
1.90	.8082	.4732	1.697	1.708	1.147	.3791
1.95	.7970	.4578	1.787	1.741	1.158	.4021
2.00	.7857	.4432	1.884	1.773	1.168	.4247
2.05	.7745	.4293	1.989	1.804	1.179	.4468
2.10	.7634	.4160	2.103	1.835	1.190	.4684
2.15	.7523	.4034	2.226	1.865	1.201	.4894
2.20	.7413	.3913	2.359	1.894	1.211	.5099
2.25	.7303	.3798	2.504	1.923	1.221	.5299
2.30	.7194	.3688	2.660	1.951	1.232	.5493
2.35	.7086	.3582	2.829	1.978	1.242	.5683
2.40	.6980	.3481	3.011	2.005	1.252	.5868
2.45	.6874	.3384	3.208	2.031	1.262	.6047
2.50	.6769	.3291	3.420	2.057	1.272	.6222
2.55	.6665	.3202	3.650	2.082	1.281	.6392
2.60	.6563	.3116	3.898	2.106	1.291	.6557
2.65	.6462	.3033	4.166	2.130	1.300	.6718
2.70	.6362	.2954	4.455	2.154	1.309	.6874
2.75	.6263	.2878	4.767	2.176	1.318	.7026
2.80	.6166	.2804	5.103	2.199	1.327	.7173
2.85	.6070	.2733	5.466	2.220	1.335	.7316
2.90	.5975	.2665	5.858	2.242	1.344	.7456
2.95	.5882	.2600	6.280	2.263	1.352	.7592
3.00	.5789	.2536	6.735	2.283	1.360	.7724
3.50	.4944	.2009	13.76	2.461	1.434	.8857
4.00	.4231	.1626	28.35	2.602	1.493	.9718
4.50	.3636	.1340	57.96	2.714	1.541	1.0380
5.00	.3143	.1121	116.31	2.803	1.580	1.0896
6.00	.2391	.08150	434.7	2.934	1.637	1.163
7.00	.1864	.06168	1458	3.023	1.677	1.212
8.00	.1486	.04819	4353	3.084	1.704	1.245
9.00	.1209	.03863	13156	3.129	1.724	1.268
10.00	.1000	.03162	29601	3.162	1.739	1.286
∞	0	0	∞	3.317	1.809	1.365

Table A.3 (*Continued*)

Fanno Line

(e) $k = 1.3$

M	$\dfrac{T}{T^*}$	$\dfrac{p}{p^*}$	$\dfrac{p_0}{p_0{}^*}$	$\dfrac{V}{V^*}$	$\dfrac{I}{I^*}$	$\dfrac{fL_{max}}{D}$
0	1.150	∞	∞	0	∞	∞
0.05	1.149	21.444	11.721	.05361	9.354	301.74
.10	1.148	10.716	5.885	.1072	4.720	72.20
.15	1.146	7.137	3.952	.1606	3.194	30.18
.20	1.143	5.346	2.994	.2138	2.445	15.73
.25	1.139	4.270	2.426	.2668	2.007	9.201
.30	1.134	3.551	2.054	.3195	1.724	5.759
.35	1.129	3.036	1.793	.3719	1.530	3.760
.40	1.123	2.649	1.602	.4239	1.391	2.520
.45	1.116	2.348	1.459	.4754	1.289	1.714
.50	1.1084	2.106	1.348	.5264	1.213	1.172
.55	1.1001	1.907	1.261	.5769	1.155	.8004
.60	1.0911	1.741	1.193	.6267	1.111	.5409
.65	1.0815	1.600	1.140	.6759	1.0777	.3586
.70	1.0713	1.479	1.0972	.7245	1.0524	.2305
.75	1.0605	1.373	1.0644	.7724	1.0336	.14131
.80	1.0493	1.280	1.0395	.8195	1.0199	.08044
.85	1.0376	1.198	1.0214	.8658	1.0104	.04053
.90	1.0254	1.125	1.0092	.9113	1.0043	.01623
.95	1.0129	1.0594	1.0022	.9561	1.0010	.00367
1.00	1.0000	1.0000	1.0000	1.0000	1.0000	0
1.05	.9868	.9461	1.0021	1.0430	1.0009	.00305
1.10	.9733	.8969	1.0083	1.0852	1.0033	.01122
1.15	.9596	.8518	1.0183	1.1266	1.0071	.02324
1.20	.9457	.8104	1.0321	1.1670	1.0120	.03820
1.25	.9316	.7722	1.0495	1.206	1.0177	.05524
1.30	.9174	.7368	1.0704	1.245	1.0241	.07388
1.35	.9031	.7039	1.0948	1.283	1.0312	.09365
1.40	.8887	.6734	1.1227	1.320	1.0388	.11417
1.45	.8743	.6448	1.1543	1.356	1.0467	.13513
1.50	.8598	.6182	1.189	1.391	1.0549	.1564
1.55	.8454	.5932	1.228	1.425	1.0634	.1777
1.60	.8309	.5697	1.271	1.458	1.0721	.1989
1.65	.8165	.5477	1.318	1.491	1.0808	.2200
1.70	.8022	.5269	1.369	1.523	1.0897	.2408

Table A.3 (*Continued*)

Fanno Line

(e) $k = 1.3$

M	$\dfrac{T}{T^*}$	$\dfrac{P}{P^*}$	$\dfrac{P_0}{P_0{}^*}$	$\dfrac{V}{V^*}$	$\dfrac{I}{I^*}$	$\dfrac{fL_{\max}}{D}$
1.75	.7880	.5073	1.424	1.554	1.0986	.2613
1.80	.7739	.4887	1.484	1.584	1.108	.2814
1.85	.7599	.4712	1.549	1.613	1.116	.3010
1.90	.7460	.4546	1.618	1.641	1.125	.3202
1.95	.7323	.4388	1.693	1.669	1.134	.3390
2.00	.7188	.4239	1.773	1.696	1.143	.3573
2.05	.7054	.4097	1.859	1.722	1.151	.3751
2.10	.6922	.3962	1.951	1.747	1.160	.3924
2.15	.6791	.3833	2.050	1.772	1.168	.4092
2.20	.6662	.3710	2.156	1.796	1.176	.4255
2.25	.6536	.3593	2.268	1.819	1.184	.4413
2.30	.6412	.3482	2.388	1.842	1.192	.4566
2.35	.6290	.3375	2.517	1.864	1.200	.4715
2.40	.6170	.3273	2.654	1.885	1.208	.4860
2.45	.6051	.3175	2.800	1.906	1.215	.5000
2.50	.5935	.3082	2.954	1.926	1.223	.5136
2.55	.5822	.2992	3.119	1.946	1.230	.5267
2.60	.5711	.2906	3.295	1.965	1.237	.5394
2.65	.5601	.2824	3.482	1.983	1.244	.5517
2.70	.5493	.2745	3.681	2.001	1.250	.5636
2.75	.5388	.2669	3.892	2.019	1.257	.5752
2.80	.5285	.2596	4.116	2.036	1.263	.5864
2.85	.5184	.2526	4.354	2.052	1.270	.5972
2.90	.5085	.2459	4.607	2.068	1.276	.6077
2.95	.4988	.2394	4.875	2.084	1.282	.6179
3.00	.4894	.2332	5.160	2.099	1.288	.6277
3.50	..4053	.1819	9.110	2.228	1.338	.7110
4.00	.3382	.1454	15.94	2.326	1.378	.7726
4.50	.2848	.1186	27.39	2.402	1.409	.8189
5.00	.2421	.09841	45.95	2.460	1.433	.8543
6.00	.1797	.07065	120.1	2.543	1.468	.9037
7.00	.1377	.05302	285.3	2.598	1.491	.9355
8.00	.1085	.04117	625.2	2.635	1.507	.9570
9.00	.08745	.03286	1275	2.662	1.519	.9722
10.00	.07188	.02769	2438	2.681	1.527	.9832
∞	0	0	∞	2.769	1.565	1.0326

Table A.3 (Continued)

Fanno Line

$(f) k = 1.67$

M	$\dfrac{T}{T^*}$	$\dfrac{p}{p^*}$	$\dfrac{p_0}{p_0{}^*}$	$\dfrac{V}{V^*}$	$\dfrac{I}{I^*}$	$\dfrac{fL_{max}}{D}$
0	1.335	∞	∞	0	∞	∞
0.05	1.334	23.099	11.265	.05775	8.687	234.36
.10	1.331	11.535	5.661	.1154	4.392	55.83
.15	1.325	7.674	3.805	.1727	2.982	23.21
.20	1.317	5.739	2.887	.2296	2.293	12.11
.25	1.308	4.574	2.344	.2859	1.892	6.980
.30	1.296	3.795	1.989	.3415	1.635	4.337
.35	1.282	3.235	1.741	.3963	1.460	2.810
.40	1.267	2.814	1.560	.4502	1.336	1.868
.45	1.250	2.485	1.424	.5031	1.245	1.260
.50	1.232	2.220	1.320	.5549	1.178	.8549
.55	1.212	2.002	1.239	.6056	1.128	.5787
.60	1.191	1.819	1.176	.6548	1.0909	.3877
.65	1.169	1.664	1.126	.7029	1.0628	.2548
.70	1.146	1.530	1.0874	.7496	1.0418	.1625
.75	1.1233	1.413	1.0576	.7949	1.0265	.09870
.80	1.0993	1.311	1.0351	.8388	1.0155	.05576
.85	1.0748	1.220	1.0189	.8812	1.0080	.02780
.90	1.0501	1.139	1.0081	.9222	1.0033	.01106
.95	1.0251	1.0657	1.0019	.9618	1.0008	.00248
1.00	1.0000	1.0000	1.0000	1.0000	1.0000	0
1.05	.9749	.9404	1.0018	1.0368	1.0006	.00203
1.10	.9499	.8860	1.0070	1.0721	1.0024	.00740
1.15	.9251	.8364	1.0154	1.1061	1.0051	.01522
1.20	.9006	.7908	1.0266	1.1388	1.0084	.02481
1.25	.8763	.7489	1.0406	1.170	1.0124	.03564
1.30	.8524	.7102	1.0573	1.200	1.0167	.04733
1.35	.8289	.6744	1.0765	1.229	1.0213	.05957
1.40	.8059	.6412	1.0981	1.257	1.0262	.07212
1.45	.7833	.6104	1.1220	1.284	1.0313	.08481
1.50	.7612	.5817	1.148	1.309	1.0364	.09749
1.55	.7397	.5549	1.176	1.333	1.0416	.1101
1.60	.7187	.5298	1.207	1.356	1.0468	.1225
1.65	.6982	.5064	1.240	1.378	1.0520	.1346
1.70	.6783	.4845	1.275	1.400	1.0572	.1465

Table A.3 (Continued)

Fanno Line

(f) $k = 1.67$

M	$\dfrac{T}{T^*}$	$\dfrac{p}{p^*}$	$\dfrac{p_0}{p_0{}^*}$	$\dfrac{V}{V^*}$	$\dfrac{I}{I^*}$	$\dfrac{fL_{\max}}{D}$
1.75	.6590	.4639	1.312	1.421	1.0623	.1580
1.80	.6402	.4445	1.351	1.440	1.0673	.1692
1.85	.6219	.4263	1.392	1.459	1.0722	.1800
1.90	.6042	.4091	1.436	1.477	1.0770	.1905
1.95	.5871	.3929	1.482	1.494	1.0817	.2007
2.00	.5705	.3776	1.530	1.510	1.0863	.2105
2.05	.5544	.3632	1.580	1.526	1.0908	.2199
2.10	.5388	.3496	1.632	1.541	1.0952	.2290
2.15	.5238	.3367	1.687	1.556	1.0994	.2377
2.20	.5093	.3244	1.744	1.570	1.1035	.2461
2.25	.4952	.3128	1.803	1.583	1.107	.2542
2.30	.4816	.3017	1.865	1.596	1.111	.2620
2.35	.4684	.2912	1.929	1.608	1.115	.2694
2.40	.4557	.2813	1.995	1.620	1.119	.2766
2.45	.4434	.2718	2.064	1.631	1.122	.2835
2.50	.4315	.2628	2.135	1.642	1.126	.2901
2.55	.4200	.2542	2.209	1.653	1.129	.2965
2.60	.4089	.2460	2.285	1.663	1.132	.3026
2.65	.3982	.2381	2.364	1.672	1.135	.3085
2.70	.3878	.2306	2.445	1.682	1.138	.3141
2.75	.3778	.2235	2.529	1.691	1.141	.3196
2.80	.3681	.2167	2.616	1.699	1.144	.3248
2.85	.3587	.2102	2.705	1.707	1.146	.3299
2.90	.3497	.2039	2.797	1.715	1.149	.3348
2.95	.3410	.1979	2.892	1.723	1.152	.3395
3.00	.3325	.1922	2.990	1.730	1.154	.3440
3.50	.2616	.1461	4.134	1.790	1.174	.3810
4.00	.2099	.1145	5.608	1.833	1.189	.4071
4.50	.1715	.09203	7.456	1.864	1.200	.4261
5.00	.1424	.07547	9.721	1.887	1.208	.4402
6.00	.10222	.05329	15.68	1.918	1.220	.4594
7.00	.07666	.03955	23.85	1.938	1.227	.4714
8.00	.05949	.03049	34.58	1.951	1.232	.4793
9.00	.04745	.02420	48.24	1.960	1.235	.4849
10.00	.03870	.01996	65.18	1.967	1.238	.4889
∞	0	0	∞	1.996	1.249	.5064

Table A.4

One-Dimensional Normal Shock of a Perfect Gas*
(Constant Specific Heat and Molecular Weight)
(a) $k = 1.4$

M_x	M_y	$\dfrac{p_y}{p_x}$	$\dfrac{\rho_y}{\rho_x}$	$\dfrac{T_y}{T_x}$	$\dfrac{p_{0y}}{p_{0x}}$	$\dfrac{p_{0y}}{p_x}$
1.00	1.00000	1.00000	1.00000	1.00000	1.00000	1.8929
1.01	.99013	1.02345	1.01669	1.00665	.99999	1.9152
1.02	.98052	1.04713	1.03344	1.01325	.99998	1.9379
1.03	.97115	1.07105	1.05024	1.01981	.99997	1.9610
1.04	.96202	1.09520	1.06709	1.02634	.99994	1.9845
1.05	.95312	1.1196	1.08398	1.03284	.99987	2.0083
1.06	.94444	1.1442	1.10092	1.03931	.99976	2.0325
1.07	.93598	1.1690	1.11790	1.04575	.99962	2.0570
1.08	.92772	1.1941	1.13492	1.05217	.99944	2.0819
1.09	.91965	1.2194	1.15199	1.05856	.99921	2.1072
1.10	.91177	1.2450	1.1691	1.06494	.99892	2.1328
1.11	.90408	1.2708	1.1862	1.07130	.99858	2.1588
1.12	.89656	1.2968	1.2034	1.07764	.99820	2.1851
1.13	.88922	1.3230	1.2206	1.08396	.99776	2.2118
1.14	.88204	1.3495	1.2378	1.09027	.99726	2.2388
1.15	.87502	1.3762	1.2550	1.09657	.99669	2.2661
1.16	.86816	1.4032	1.2723	1.10287	.99605	2.2937
1.17	.86145	1.4304	1.2896	1.10916	.99534	2.3217
1.18	.85488	1.4578	1.3069	1.11544	.99455	2.3499
1.19	.84846	1.4854	1.3243	1.12172	.99371	2.3786
1.20	.84217	1.5133	1.3416	1.1280	.99280	2.4075
1.21	.83601	1.5414	1.3590	1.1343	.99180	2.4367
1.22	.82998	1.5698	1.3764	1.1405	.99073	2.4662
1.23	.82408	1.5984	1.3938	1.1468	.98957	2.4961
1.24	.81830	1.6272	1.4112	1.1531	.98835	2.5263
1.25	.81264	1.6562	1.4286	1.1594	.98706	2.5568
1.26	.80709	1.6855	1.4460	1.1657	.98568	2.5876
1.27	.80165	1.7150	1.4634	1.1720	.98422	2.6187
1.28	.79631	1.7448	1.4808	1.1782	.98268	2.6500
1.29	.79108	1.7748	1.4983	1.1846	.98106	2.6816
1.30	.78596	1.8050	1.5157	1.1909	.97935	2.7135
1.31	.78093	1.8354	1.5331	1.1972	.97758	2.7457
1.32	.77600	1.8661	1.5505	1.2035	.97574	2.7783
1.33	.77116	1.8970	1.5680	1.2099	.97382	2.8112
1.34	.76641	1.9282	1.5854	1.2162	.97181	2.8444
1.35	.76175	1.9596	1.6028	1.2226	.96972	2.8778
1.36	.75718	1.9912	1.6202	1.2290	.96756	2.9115
1.37	.75269	2.0230	1.6376	1.2354	.96534	2.9455
1.38	.74828	2.0551	1.6550	1.2418	.96304	2.9798
1.39	.74396	2.0874	1.6723	1.2482	.96065	3.0144

   * These data were calculated originally as a portion of Project Meteor and appeared as a part of MIT Meteor Report No. 14, 1947, by A. H. Shapiro, W. R. Hawthorne, and C. M. Edelman. They have been reproduced in *Gas Tables*, by J. H. Keenan and J. Kaye, published by John Wiley and Sons, 1948. These values are reproduced here by permission of A. H. Shapiro and John Wiley and Sons.

Table A.4 (*Continued*)

Normal Shock

(*a*) k = 1.4

M_x	M_y	$\dfrac{p_y}{p_x}$	$\dfrac{\rho_y}{\rho_x}$	$\dfrac{T_y}{T_x}$	$\dfrac{p_{0y}}{p_{0x}}$	$\dfrac{p_{0y}}{p_x}$
1.40	.73971	2.1200	1.6896	1.2547	.95819	3.0493
1.41	.73554	2.1528	1.7070	1.2612	.95566	3.0844
1.42	.73144	2.1858	1.7243	1.2676	.95306	3.1198
1.43	.72741	2.2190	1.7416	1.2742	.95039	3.1555
1.44	.72345	2.2525	1.7589	1.2807	.94765	3.1915
1.45	.71956	2.2862	1.7761	1.2872	.94483	3.2278
1.46	.71574	2.3202	1.7934	1.2938	.94196	3.2643
1.47	.71198	2.3544	1.8106	1.3004	.93901	3.3011
1.48	.70829	2.3888	1.8278	1.3070	.93600	3.3382
1.49	.70466	2.4234	1.8449	1.3136	.93292	3.3756
1.50	.70109	2.4583	1.8621	1.3202	.92978	3.4133
1.51	.69758	2.4934	1.8792	1.3269	.92658	3.4512
1.52	.69413	2.5288	1.8962	1.3336	.92331	3.4894
1.53	.69073	2.5644	1.9133	1.3403	.91999	3.5279
1.54	.68739	2.6003	1.9303	1.3470	.91662	3.5667
1.55	.68410	2.6363	1.9473	1.3538	.91319	3.6058
1.56	.68086	2.6725	1.9643	1.3606	.90970	3.6451
1.57	.67768	2.7090	1.9812	1.3674	.90615	3.6847
1.58	.67455	2.7458	1.9981	1.3742	.90255	3.7245
1.59	.67147	2.7828	2.0149	1.3811	.89889	3.7645
1.60	.66844	2.8201	2.0317	1.3880	.89520	3.8049
1.61	.66545	2.8575	2.0485	1.3949	.89144	3.8456
1.62	.66251	2.8951	2.0652	1.4018	.88764	3.8866
1.63	.65962	2.9330	2.0820	1.4088	.88380	3.9278
1.64	.65677	2.9712	2.0986	1.4158	.87992	3.9693
1.65	.65396	3.0096	2.1152	1.4228	.87598	4.0111
1.66	.65119	3.0482	2.1318	1.4298	.87201	4.0531
1.67	.64847	3.0870	2.1484	1.4369	.86800	4.0954
1.68	.64579	3.1261	2.1649	1.4440	.86396	4.1379
1.69	.64315	3.1654	2.1813	1.4512	.85987	4.1807
1.70	.64055	3.2050	2.1977	1.4583	.85573	4.2238
1.71	.63798	3.2448	2.2141	1.4655	.85155	4.2672
1.72	.63545	3.2848	2.2304	1.4727	.84735	4.3108
1.73	.63296	3.3250	2.2467	1.4800	.84312	4.3547
1.74	.63051	3.3655	2.2629	1.4873	.83886	4.3989
1.75	.62809	3.4062	2.2791	1.4946	.83456	4.4433
1.76	.62570	3.4472	2.2952	1.5019	.83024	4.4880
1.77	.62335	3.4884	2.3113	1.5093	.82589	4.5330
1.78	.62104	3.5298	2.3273	1.5167	.82152	4.5783
1.79	.61875	3.5714	2.3433	1.5241	.81711	4.6238

Table A.4 (Continued)

Normal Shock

(a) $k = 1.4$

M_x	M_y	$\dfrac{p_y}{p_x}$	$\dfrac{\rho_y}{\rho_x}$	$\dfrac{T_y}{T_x}$	$\dfrac{p_{0y}}{p_{0x}}$	$\dfrac{p_{0y}}{p_x}$
1.80	.61650	3.6133	2.3592	1.5316	.81268	4.6695
1.81	.61428	3.6554	2.3751	1.5391	.80823	4.7155
1.82	.61209	3.6978	2.3909	1.5466	.80376	4.7618
1.83	.60993	3.7404	2.4067	1.5542	.79926	4.8083
1.84	.60780	3.7832	2.4224	1.5617	.79474	4.8551
1.85	.60570	3.8262	2.4381	1.5694	.79021	4.9022
1.86	.60363	3.8695	2.4537	1.5770	.78567	4.9498
1.87	.60159	3.9130	2.4693	1.5847	.78112	4.9974
1.88	.59957	3.9568	2.4848	1.5924	.77656	5.0453
1.89	.59758	4.0008	2.5003	1.6001	.77197	5.0934
1.90	.59562	4.0450	2.5157	1.6079	.76735	5.1417
1.91	.59368	4.0894	2.5310	1.6157	.76273	5.1904
1.92	.59177	4.1341	2.5463	1.6236	.75812	5.2394
1.93	.58988	4.1790	2.5615	1.6314	.75347	5.2886
1.94	.58802	4.2242	2.5767	1.6394	.74883	5.3381
1.95	.58618	4.2696	2.5919	1.6473	.74418	5.3878
1.96	.58437	4.3152	2.6070	1.6553	.73954	5.4378
1.97	.58258	4.3610	2.6220	1.6633	.73487	5.4880
1.98	.58081	4.4071	2.6369	1.6713	.73021	5.5385
1.99	.57907	4.4534	2.6518	1.6794	.72554	5.5894
2.00	.57735	4.5000	2.6666	1.6875	.72088	5.6405
2.01	.57565	4.5468	2.6814	1.6956	.71619	5.6918
2.02	.57397	4.5938	2.6962	1.7038	.71152	5.7434
2.03	.57231	4.6411	2.7109	1.7120	.70686	5.7952
2.04	.57068	4.6886	2.7255	1.7203	.70218	5.8473
2.05	.56907	4.7363	2.7400	1.7286	.69752	5.8997
2.06	.56747	4.7842	2.7545	1.7369	.69284	5.9523
2.07	.56589	4.8324	2.7690	1.7452	.68817	6.0052
2.08	.56433	4.8808	2.7834	1.7536	.68351	6.0584
2.09	.56280	4.9295	2.7977	1.7620	.67886	6.1118
2.10	.56128	4.9784	2.8119	1.7704	.67422	6.1655
2.11	.55978	5.0275	2.8216	1.7789	.66957	6.2194
2.12	.55830	5.0768	2.8402	1.7874	.66492	6.2736
2.13	.55683	5.1264	2.8543	1.7960	.66029	6.3280
2.14	.55538	5.1762	2.8683	1.8046	.65567	6.3827
2.15	.55395	5.2262	2.8823	1.8132	.65105	6.4377
2.16	.55254	5.2765	2.8962	1.8219	.64644	6.4929
2.17	.55114	5.3270	2.9100	1.8306	.64185	6.5484
2.18	.54976	5.3778	2.9238	1.8393	.63728	6.6042
2.19	.54841	5.4288	2.9376	1.8481	.63270	6.6602

Table A.4 (Continued)

Normal Shock

(a) $k = 1.4$

M_x	M_y	$\dfrac{p_y}{p_x}$	$\dfrac{\rho_y}{\rho_x}$	$\dfrac{T_y}{T_x}$	$\dfrac{p_{0y}}{p_{0x}}$	$\dfrac{p_{0y}}{p_x}$
2.20	.54706	5.4800	2.9512	1.8569	.62812	6.7163
2.21	.54572	5.5314	2.9648	1.8657	.62358	6.7730
2.22	.54440	5.5831	2.9783	1.8746	.61905	6.8299
2.23	.54310	5.6350	2.9918	1.8835	.61453	6.8869
2.24	.54182	5.6872	3.0052	1.8924	.61002	6.9442
2.25	.54055	5.7396	3.0186	1.9014	.60554	7.0018
2.26	.53929	5.7922	3.0319	1.9104	.60106	7.0597
2.27	.53805	5.8451	3.0452	1.9194	.59659	7.1178
2.28	.53683	5.8982	3.0584	1.9285	.59214	7.1762
2.29	.53561	5.9515	3.0715	1.9376	.58772	7.2348
2.30	.53441	6.0050	3.0846	1.9468	.58331	7.2937
2.31	.53322	6.0588	3.0976	1.9560	.57891	7.3529
2.32	.53205	6.1128	3.1105	1.9652	.57452	7.4123
2.33	.53089	6.1670	3.1234	1.9745	.57015	7.4720
2.34	.52974	6.2215	3.1362	1.9838	.56580	7.5319
2.35	.52861	6.2762	3.1490	1.9931	.56148	7.5920
2.36	.52749	6.3312	3.1617	2.0025	.55717	7.6524
2.37	.52638	6.3864	3.1743	2.0119	.55288	7.7131
2.38	.52528	6.4418	3.1869	2.0213	.54862	7.7741
2.39	.52419	6.4974	3.1994	2.0308	.54438	7.8354
2.40	.52312	6.5533	3.2119	2.0403	.54015	7.8969
2.41	.52206	6.6094	3.2243	2.0499	.53594	7.9587
2.42	.52100	6.6658	3.2366	2.0595	.53175	8.0207
2.43	.51996	6.7224	3.2489	2.0691	.52758	8.0830
2.44	.51894	6.7792	3.2611	2.0788	.52344	8.1455
2.45	.51792	6.8362	3.2733	2.0885	.51932	8.2083
2.46	.51691	6.8935	3.2854	2.0982	.51521	8.2714
2.47	.51592	6.9510	3.2975	2.1080	.51112	8.3347
2.48	.51493	7.0088	3.3095	2.1178	.50706	8.3983
2.49	.51395	7.0668	3.3214	2.1276	.50303	8.4622
2.50	.51299	7.1250	3.3333	2.1375	.49902	8.5262
2.51	.51204	7.1834	3.3451	2.1474	.49502	8.5904
2.52	.51109	7.2421	3.3569	2.1574	.49104	8.6549
2.53	.51015	7.3010	3.3686	2.1674	.48709	8.7198
2.54	.50923	7.3602	3.3802	2.1774	.48317	8.7850
2.55	.50831	7.4196	3.3918	2.1875	.47927	8.8505
2.56	.50740	7.4792	3.4034	2.1976	.47540	8.9162
2.57	.50651	7.5391	3.4149	2.2077	.47155	8.9821
2.58	.50562	7.5992	3.4263	2.2179	.46772	9.0482
2.59	.50474	7.6595	3.4376	2.2281	.46391	9.1146

Table A.4 (Continued)
Normal Shock
(a) k = 1.4

M_x	M_y	$\dfrac{p_y}{p_x}$	$\dfrac{\rho_y}{\rho_x}$	$\dfrac{T_y}{T_x}$	$\dfrac{p_{0y}}{p_{0x}}$	$\dfrac{p_{0y}}{p_x}$
2.60	.50387	7.7200	3.4489	2.2383	.46012	9.1813
2.61	.50301	7.7808	3.4602	2.2486	.45636	9.2481
2.62	.50216	7.8418	3.4714	2.2589	.45262	9.3154
2.63	.50132	7.9030	3.4825	2.2693	.44891	9.3829
2.64	.50048	7.9645	3.4936	2.2797	.44522	9.4507
2.65	.49965	8.0262	3.5047	2.2901	.44155	9.5187
2.66	.49883	8.0882	3.5157	2.3006	.43791	9.5869
2.67	.49802	8.1504	3.5266	2.3111	.43429	9.6553
2.68	.49722	8.2128	3.5374	2.3217	.43070	9.7241
2.69	.49642	8.2754	3.5482	2.3323	.42713	9.7932
2.70	.49563	8.3383	3.5590	2.3429	.42359	9.8625
2.71	.49485	8.4014	3.5697	2.3536	.42007	9.9320
2.72	.49408	8.4648	3.5803	2.3643	.41657	10.002
2.73	.49332	8.5284	3.5909	2.3750	.41310	10.072
2.74	.49256	8.5922	3.6014	2.3858	.40965	10.142
2.75	.49181	8.6562	3.6119	2.3966	.40622	10.212
2.76	.49107	8.7205	3.6224	2.4074	.40282	10.283
2.77	.49033	8.7850	3.6328	2.4183	.39945	10.354
2.78	.48960	8.8497	3.6431	2.4292	.39610	10.426
2.79	.48888	8.9147	3.6533	2.4402	.39276	10.498
2.80	.48817	8.9800	3.6635	2.4512	.38946	10.569
2.81	.48746	9.0454	3.6737	2.4622	.38618	10.641
2.82	.48676	9.1111	3.6838	2.4733	.38293	10.714
2.83	.48607	9.1770	3.6939	2.4844	.37970	10.787
2.84	.48538	9.2432	3.7039	2.4955	.37649	10.860
2.85	.48470	9.3096	3.7139	2.5067	.37330	10.933
2.86	.48402	9.3762	3.7238	2.5179	.37013	11.006
2.87	.48334	9.4431	3.7336	2.5292	.36700	11.080
2.88	.48268	9.5102	3.7434	2.5405	.36389	11.154
2.89	.48203	9.5775	3.7532	2.5518	.36080	11.228
2.90	.48138	9.6450	3.7629	2.5632	.35773	11.302
2.91	.48074	9.7127	3.7725	2.5746	.35469	11.377
2.92	.48010	9.7808	3.7821	2.5860	.35167	11.452
2.93	.47946	9.8491	3.7917	2.5975	.34867	11.527
2.94	.47883	9.9176	3.8012	2.6090	.34570	11.603
2.95	.47821	9.986	3.8106	2.6206	.34275	11.679
2.96	.47760	10.055	3.8200	2.6322	.33982	11.755
2.97	.47699	10.124	3.8294	2.6438	.33692	11.831
2.98	.47638	10.194	3.8387	2.6555	.33404	11.907
2.99	.47578	10.263	3.8479	2.6672	.33118	11.984
3.00	.47519	10.333	3.8571	2.6790	.32834	12.061
3.50	.45115	14.125	4.2608	3.3150	.21295	16.242
4.00	.43496	18.500	4.5714	4.0469	.13876	21.068
4.50	.42355	23.458	4.8119	4.8751	.09170	26.539
5.00	.41523	29.000	5.0000	5.8000	.06172	32.654
6.00	.40416	41.833	5.2683	7.941	.02965	46.815
7.00	.39736	57.000	5.4444	10.469	.01535	63.552
8.00	.39289	74.500	5.5652	13.387	.00849	82.865
9.00	.38980	94.333	5.6512	16.693	.00496	104.753
10.00	.38757	116.50	5.7143	20.388	.00304	129.217
∞	.37796	∞	6.000	∞	0	∞

Table A.4 (*Continued*)
Normal Shock
(*b*) *k* = 1.0

M_x	M_y	$\dfrac{p_y}{p_x} = \dfrac{\rho_y}{\rho_x}$	$\dfrac{T_y}{T_x}$	$\dfrac{p_{0y}}{p_{0x}}$	$\dfrac{p_{0y}}{p_x}$
1.00	1.0000	1.000	1.000	1.0000	1.649
1.05	.9524	1.103		.9998	1.735
1.10	.9091	1.210		.9988	1.829
1.15	.8696	1.322		.9964	1.930
1.20	.8333	1.440		.9919	2.038
1.25	.8000	1.563		.9851	2.152
1.30	.7692	1.690		.9759	2.272
1.35	7407	1.822		.9640	2.398
1.40	.7143	1.960		.9494	2.530
1.45	.6897	2.103		.9321	2.667
1.50	.6667	2.250		.9122	2.810
1.55	.6452	2.402		.8899	2.958
1.60	.6250	2.560		.8653	3.112
1.65	.6061	2.723		.8386	3.271
1.70	.5882	2.890		.8100	3.436
1.75	.5714	3.062		.7798	3.606
1.80	.5556	3.240		.7482	3.781
1.85	.5406	3.423		.7155	3.961
1.90	.5263	3.610		.6819	4.146
1.95	.5128	3.802		.6478	4.337
2.00	.5000	4.000		.6134	4.532
2.05	.4878	4.203		.5789	4.733
2.10	.4762	4.410		.5446	4.940
2.15	.4651	4.622		.5106	5.151
2.20	.4545	4.840		.4772	5.367
2.25	.4444	5.063		.4446	5.588
2.30	.4347	5.290		.4129	5.814
2.35	.4255	5.522		.3822	6.045
2.40	.4167	5.760		.3527	6.282
2.45	.4082	6.003		.3244	6.524
2.50	.4000	6.250		.2975	6.771
2.55	.3921	6.502		.2720	7.022
2.60	.3846	6.760		.2479	7.279
2.65	.3774	7.023		.2252	7.541
2.70	.3704	7.290		.2040	7.807
2.75	.3636	7.562		.1842	8.079
2.80	.3571	7.840		.1658	8.356
2.85	.3508	8.123		.1488	8.638
2.90	.3448	8.410		.1332	8.925
2.95	.3390	8.702		.1188	9.217
3.00	.3333	9.000		$1055(10)^{-4}$	9.514
3.50	.2857	12.25		$2791(10)^{-5}$	12.76
4.00	.2500	16.00		$554(10)^{-5}$	16.51
4.50	.2222	20.25		$832(10)^{-6}$	20.76
5.00	.2000	25.00		$951(10)^{-7}$	25.51
6.00	.1667	36.00		$556(10)^{-9}$	36.50
7.00	.1429	49.00		$113(10)^{-11}$	49.50
8.00	.1250	64.00		$817(10)^{-15}$	64.50
9.00	.1111	81.00		$210(10)^{-18}$	81.50
10.00	.1000	100.00		$194(10)^{-22}$	100.50
∞	0	∞	1.000	0	∞

Introduction to Gas Dynamics

Table A.4 (*Continued*)

Normal Shock

(c) $k = 1.1$

M_x	M_y	$\dfrac{p_y}{p_x}$	$\dfrac{\rho_y}{\rho_x}$	$\dfrac{T_y}{T_x}$	$\dfrac{p_{0y}}{p_{0x}}$	$\dfrac{p_{0y}}{p_x}$
1.00	1.0000	1.0000	1.000	1.0000	1.0000	1.710
1.05	.9526	1.107	1.097	1.0093	.9998	1.804
1.10	.9099	1.220	1.198	1.0183	.9988	1.906
1.15	.8712	1.338	1.303	1.0271	.9965	2.015
1.20	.8360	1.461	1.410	1.0358	.9921	2.132
1.25	.8038	1.589	1.521	1.0444	.9856	2.255
1.30	.7743	1.723	1.636	1.0529	.9769	2.384
1.35	.7471	1.862	1.754	1.0615	.9657	2.520
1.40	.7221	2.006	1.875	1.0701	.9519	2.662
1.45	.6989	2.155	1.998	1.0788	.9358	2.810
1.50	.6773	2.309	2.124	1.0876	.9174	2.964
1.55	.6573	2.469	2.252	1.0965	.8969	3.124
1.60	.6386	2.634	2.383	1.1055	.8744	3.289
1.65	.6211	2.804	2.516	1.1146	.8501	3.460
1.70	.6048	2.980	2.651	1.1239	.8242	3.637
1.75	.5895	3.161	2.789	1.133	.7970	3.820
1.80	.5751	3.347	2.928	1.143	.7686	4.008
1.85	.5615	3.538	3.069	1.153	.7393	4.202
1.90	.5487	3.734	3.211	1.163	.7093	4.401
1.95	.5366	3.936	3.355	1.173	.6789	4.606
2.00	.5252	4.143	3.500	1.184	.6483	4.817
2.05	.5144	4.355	3.646	1.194	.6175	5.033
2.10	.5042	4.572	3.793	1.205	.5869	5.254
2.15	.4945	4.795	3.942	1.216	.5566	5.481
2.20	.4853	5.023	4.092	1.228	.5267	5.713
2.25	.4765	5.256	4.242	1.239	.4974	5.951
2.30	.4682	5.494	4.393	1.251	.4687	6.194
2.35	.4603	5.738	4.544	1.263	.4408	6.443
2.40	.4527	5.987	4.696	1.275	.4138	6.697
2.45	.4454	6.241	4.848	1.287	.3878	6.957
2.50	.4385	6.500	5.000	1.300	.3627	7.222
2.55	.4319	6.764	5.152	1.313	.3387	7.492
2.60	.4256	7.034	5.304	1.326	.3157	7.768
2.65	.4196	7.309	5.457	1.339	.2938	8.049
2.70	.4138	7.589	5.610	1.353	.2730	8.335
2.75	.4082	7.875	5.762	1.367	.2533	8.627
2.80	.4029	8.166	5.914	1.381	.2347	8.925
2.85	.3978	8.462	6.065	1.395	.2172	9.228
2.90	.3929	8.763	6.216	1.410	.2007	9.536
2.95	.3882	9.069	6.367	1.424	.1852	9.850
3.00	.3837	9.381	6.517	1.439	.17070	10.17
3.50	.3466	12.786	7.977	1.603	.07126	13.66
4.00	.3203	16.714	9.333	1.791	.02750	17.68
4.50	.3009	21.167	10.565	2.003	.01014	22.24
5.00	.2859	26.143	11.667	2.241	.00366	27.28
6.00	.2661	37.67	13.50	2.790	$472(10)^{-6}$	39.16
7.00	.2531	51.29	14.91	3.439	$645(10)^{-7}$	53.12
8.00	.2443	67.00	16.00	4.188	$965(10)^{-8}$	69.23
9.00	.2381	84.81	16.84	5.036	$161(10)^{-8}$	87.49
10.00	.2336	104.71	17.50	5.984	$297(10)^{-9}$	107.90
∞	.2132	∞	21.00	∞	0	∞

Table A.4 (Continued)
Normal Shock
(d) $k = 1.2$

M_x	M_y	$\dfrac{p_y}{p_x}$	$\dfrac{\rho_y}{\rho_x}$	$\dfrac{T_y}{T_x}$	$\dfrac{p_{0y}}{p_{0x}}$	$\dfrac{p_{0y}}{p_x}$
1.00	1.0000	1.000	1.000	1.0000	1.0000	1.772
1.05	.9528	1.112	1.092	1.0178	.9998	1.873
1.10	.9106	1.229	1.187	1.0351	.9989	1.982
1.15	.8726	1.352	1.285	1.0521	.9965	2.099
1.20	.8383	1.480	1.385	1.0689	.9923	2.224
1.25	.8071	1.614	1.486	1.0855	.9861	2.356
1.30	.7787	1.753	1.590	1.1022	.9777	2.495
1.35	.7527	1.897	1.696	1.1189	.9671	2.641
1.40	.7288	2.047	1.803	1.1357	.9542	2.793
1.45	.7067	2.203	1.911	1.1527	.9391	2.951
1.50	.6864	2.364	2.020	1.170	.9220	3.115
1.55	.6676	2.530	2.131	1.187	.9030	3.286
1.60	.6501	2.702	2.242	1.205	.8822	3.463
1.65	.6338	2.879	2.354	1.223	.8599	3.646
1.70	.6186	3.062	2.466	1.241	.8362	3.836
1.75	.6044	3.250	2.579	1.260	.8114	4.031
1.80	.5912	3.444	2.692	1.279	.7856	4.232
1.85	.5788	3.643	2.805	1.299	.7591	4.439
1.90	.5671	3.847	2.918	1.319	.7320	4.652
1.95	.5561	4.057	3.031	1.339	.7045	4.871
2.00	.5458	4.273	3.143	1.360	.6768	5.096
2.05	.5360	4.494	3.255	1.381	.6490	5.326
2.10	.5268	4.720	3.366	1.402	.6213	5.562
2.15	.5181	4.952	3.477	1.424	.5938	5.805
2.20	.5099	5.189	3.587	1.446	.5667	6.053
2.25	.5021	5.432	3.697	1.469	.5400	6.307
2.30	.4947	5.680	3.806	1.492	.5139	6.567
2.35	.4877	5.934	3.914	1.516	.4884	6.832
2.40	.4810	6.193	4.020	1.540	.4636	7.104
2.45	.4746	6.457	4.126	1.565	.4397	7.383
2.50	.4686	6.727	4.231	1.590	.4162	7.664
2.55	.4629	7.003	4.335	1.616	.3937	7.952
2.60	.4574	7.284	4.437	1.642	.3721	8.247
2.65	.4521	7.570	4.538	1.668	.3513	8.547
2.70	.4471	7.862	4.638	1.695	.3314	8.853
2.75	.4424	8.159	4.737	1.723	.3124	9.165
2.80	.4378	8.462	4.834	1.751	.2942	9.483
2.85	.4334	8.770	4.930	1.779	.2768	9.806
2.90	.4292	9.084	5.025	1.808	.2603	10.135
2.95	.4252	9.403	5.118	1.837	.2446	10.470
3.00	.4214	9.727	5.211	1.867	.22980	10.81
3.50	.3904	13.273	6.056	2.192	.11978	14.53
4.00	.3690	17.364	6.769	2.565	.06096	18.83
4.50	.3536	22.000	7.364	2.988	.03093	23.70
5.00	.3421	27.182	7.857	3.459	.01586	29.15
6.00	.3267	39.18	8.609	4.551	$441(10)^{-5}$	41.76
7.00	.3170	53.36	9.136	5.841	$134(10)^{-5}$	56.66
8.00	.3106	69.73	9.513	7.329	$450(10)^{-6}$	73.86
9.00	.3061	88.27	9.791	9.016	$164(10)^{-6}$	93.35
10.00	.3029	109.00	10.000	10.900	$650(10)^{-7}$	115.14
∞	.2887	∞	11.00	∞	0	∞

Table A.4 (Continued)

Normal Shock

(e) $k = 1.3$

M_x	M_y	$\dfrac{p_y}{p_x}$	$\dfrac{\rho_y}{\rho_x}$	$\dfrac{T_y}{T_x}$	$\dfrac{p_{0y}}{p_{0x}}$	$\dfrac{p_{0y}}{p_x}$
1.00	1.0000	1.000	1.000	1.0000	1.0000	1.832
1.05	.9530	1.116	1.088	1.0257	.9998	1.941
1.10	.9112	1.237	1.178	1.0507	.9989	2.058
1.15	.8739	1.364	1.269	1.0752	.9966	2.183
1.20	.8403	1.497	1.362	1.0995	.9925	2.316
1.25	.8100	1.636	1.456	1.124	.9866	2.457
1.30	.7825	1.780	1.551	1.148	.9786	2.605
1.35	.7575	1.930	1.646	1.172	.9684	2.760
1.40	.7346	2.085	1.742	1.197	.9562	2.922
1.45	.7136	2.246	1.838	1.222	.9421	3.090
1.50	.6942	2.413	1.935	1.247	.9261	3.265
1.55	.6764	2.585	2.031	1.273	.9084	3.447
1.60	.6599	2.763	2.127	1.299	.8891	3.635
1.65	.6446	2.947	2.223	1.326	.8684	3.830
1.70	.6304	3.137	2.318	1.353	.8466	4.031
1.75	.6172	3.332	2.413	1.380	.8238	4.238
1.80	.6048	3.532	2.507	1.408	.8001	4.452
1.85	.5933	3.738	2.601	1.437	.7758	4.672
1.90	.5825	3.950	2.694	1.467	.7510	4.898
1.95	.5724	4.168	2.785	1.497	.7259	5.131
2.00	.5629	4.391	2.875	1.527	.7006	5.370
2.05	.5539	4.620	2.964	1.558	.6752	5.615
2.10	.5455	4.855	3.052	1.590	.6499	5.866
2.15	.5376	5.095	3.139	1.623	.6248	6.123
2.20	.5301	5.341	3.225	1.656	.6000	6.387
2.25	.5230	5.592	3.309	1.690	.5755	6.657
2.30	.5163	5.849	3.392	1.725	.5515	6.933
2.35	.5100	6.112	3.474	1.760	.5280	7.215
2.40	.5040	6.381	3.554	1.796	.5050	7.503
2.45	.4983	6.655	3.633	1.832	.4827	7.798
2.50	.4929	6.935	3.710	1.869	.4610	8.098
2.55	.4878	7.220	3.786	1.907	.4400	8.405
2.60	.4829	7.511	3.860	1.946	.4196	8.718
2.65	.4782	7.808	3.933	1.985	.3999	9.037
2.70	.4738	8.110	4.005	2.025	.3810	9.362
2.75	.4696	8.418	4.075	2.066	.3628	9.693
2.80	.4655	8.732	4.144	2.108	.3452	10.030
2.85	.4616	9.052	4.211	2.150	.3284	10.373
2.90	.4579	9.377	4.277	2.193	.3123	10.723
2.95	.4544	9.708	4.341	2.236	.2969	11.079
3.00	.4511	10.04	4.404	2.280	.28217	11.44
3.50	.4241	13.72	4.964	2.763	.16770	15.39
4.00	.4058	17.96	5.412	3.318	.09932	19.96
4.50	.3927	22.76	5.768	3.946	.05941	25.18
5.00	.3832	28.13	6.053	4.648	.03612	30.90
6.00	.3704	40.57	6.469	6.271	$1422(10)^{-5}$	44.31
7.00	.3625	55.26	6.749	8.189	$610(10)^{-5}$	60.14
8.00	.3573	72.22	6.943	10.401	$283(10)^{-5}$	78.40
9.00	.3536	91.43	7.084	12.908	$140(10)^{-5}$	99.10
10.00	.3510	112.91	7.188	15.710	$740(10)^{-6}$	122.24
∞	.3397	∞	7.667	∞	0	∞

Table A.4 (*Continued*)
Normal Shock
(f) $k = 1.67$

M_x	M_y	$\dfrac{p_y}{p_x}$	$\dfrac{\rho_y}{\rho_x}$	$\dfrac{T_y}{T_x}$	$\dfrac{p_{0y}}{p_{0x}}$	$\dfrac{p_{0y}}{p_x}$
1.00	1.0000	1.000	1.000	1.0000	1.0000	2.055
1.05	.9535	1.128	1.075	1.0496	.9998	2.189
1.10	.9131	1.262	1.149	1.0985	.9990	2.333
1.15	.8776	1.403	1.223	1.1471	.9969	2.486
1.20	.8463	1.550	1.297	1.195	.9934	2.649
1.25	.8184	1.703	1.370	1.244	.9883	2.821
1.30	.7935	1.863	1.441	1.293	.9813	3.002
1.35	.7711	2.029	1.511	1.343	.9728	3.191
1.40	.7509	2.201	1.580	1.394	.9627	3.388
1.45	.7325	2.379	1.647	1.445	.9511	3.592
1.50	.7158	2.563	1.713	1.497	.9381	3.804
1.55	.7006	2.754	1.777	1.550	.9239	4.025
1.60	.6866	2.951	1.840	1.604	.9086	4.254
1.65	.6738	3.154	1.901	1.659	.8924	4.490
1.70	.6620	3.364	1.960	1.716	.8754	4.733
1.75	.6511	3.580	2.018	1.774	.8577	4.984
1.80	.6410	3.802	2.074	1.833	.8395	5.243
1.85	.6316	4.030	2.128	1.893	.8209	5.510
1.90	.6229	4.265	2.181	1.955	.8019	5.784
1.95	.6148	4.506	2.232	2.018	.7827	6.065
2.00	.6073	4.753	2.282	2.083	.7634	6.354
2.05	.6002	5.006	2.330	2.149	.7441	6.650
2.10	.5936	5.266	2.376	2.216	.7248	6.954
2.15	.5875	5.532	2.421	2.284	.7056	7.266
2.20	.5817	5.804	2.465	2.354	.6866	7.585
2.25	.5762	6.082	2.507	2.426	.6678	7.911
2.30	.5711	6.366	2.548	2.499	.6493	8.244
2.35	.5663	6.657	2.587	2.574	.6310	8.585
2.40	.5617	6.954	2.625	2.650	.6130	8.934
2.45	.5574	7.257	2.662	2.727	.5954	9.290
2.50	.5534	7.567	2.697	2.806	.5783	9.65
2.55	.5495	7.883	2.731	2.886	.5615	10.02
2.60	.5459	8.205	2.764	2.968	.5450	10.40
2.65	.5425	8.533	2.796	3.052	.5289	10.79
2.70	.5392	8.868	2.827	3.137	.5133	11.18
2.75	.5361	9.209	2.857	3.223	.4981	11.58
2.80	.5331	9.556	2.886	3.311	.4833	11.99
2.85	.5303	9.909	2.914	3.401	.4689	12.41
2.90	.5276	10.269	2.941	3.492	.4550	12.83
2.95	.5251	10.635	2.967	3.584	.4415	13.26
3.00	.5227	11.01	2.992	3.678	.4283	13.69
3.50	.5036	15.07	3.204	4.704	.3177	18.47
4.00	.4910	19.76	3.358	5.885	.2384	23.99
4.50	.4822	25.08	3.473	7.221	.1816	30.24
5.00	.4758	31.02	3.560	8.714	.1406	37.23
6.00	.4674	44.78	3.680	12.17	.08831	53.40
7.00	.4623	61.04	3.756	16.25	.05842	72.53
8.00	.4589	79.81	3.808	20.96	.04059	94.59
9.00	.4566	101.08	3.843	26.30	.02920	119.6
10.00	.4550	124.84	3.870	32.26	.02167	147.6
∞	.4479	∞	3.985	∞	0	∞

Table A.5

Rayleigh Line—One-Dimensional, Frictionless, Constant-Area Flow
with Stagnation Temperature Change for a Perfect Gas†

(a) $k = 1.4$

M	$\dfrac{T_0}{T_0{}^*}$	$\dfrac{T}{T^*}$	$\dfrac{p}{p^*}$	$\dfrac{p_0}{p_0{}^*}$	$\dfrac{V}{V^*}$	$\left(\dfrac{T_0}{T_0{}^*}\right)_{\text{isoth}}$
0	0	0	2.4000	1.2679	0	.87500
0.01	.000480	.000576	2.3997	1.2678	.000240	.87502
0.02	.00192	.00230	2.3987	1.2675	.000959	.87507
0.03	.00431	.00516	2.3970	1.2671	.00216	.87516
0.04	.00765	.00917	2.3946	1.2665	.00383	.87528
0.05	.01192	.01430	2.3916	1.2657	.00598	.87544
0.06	.01712	.02053	2.3880	1.2647	.00860	.87563
0.07	.02322	.02784	2.3837	1.2636	.01168	.87586
0.08	.03021	.03621	2.3787	1.2623	.01522	.87612
0.09	.03807	.04562	2.3731	1.2608	.01922	.87642
0.10	.04678	.05602	2.3669	1.2591	.02367	.87675
0.11	.05630	.06739	2.3600	1.2573	.02856	.87712
0.12	.06661	.07970	2.3526	1.2554	.03388	.87752
0.13	.07768	.09290	2.3445	1.2533	.03962	.87796
0.14	.08947	.10695	2.3359	1.2510	.04578	.87843
0.15	.10196	.12181	2.3267	1.2486	.05235	.87894
0.16	.11511	.13743	2.3170	1.2461	.05931	.87948
0.17	.12888	.15377	2.3067	1.2434	.06666	.88006
0.18	.14324	.17078	2.2959	1.2406	.07438	.88067
0.19	.15814	.18841	2.2845	1.2377	.08247	.88132
0.20	.17355	.20661	2.2727	1.2346	.09091	.88200
0.21	.18943	.22533	2.2604	1.2314	.09969	.88272
0.22	.20574	.24452	2.2477	1.2281	.10879	.88347
0.23	.22244	.26413	2.2345	1.2248	.11820	.88426
0.24	.23948	.28411	2.2209	1.2213	.12792	.88508
0.25	.25684	.30440	2.2069	1.2177	.13793	.88594
0.26	.27446	.32496	2.1925	1.2140	.14821	.88683
0.27	.29231	.34573	2.1777	1.2102	.15876	.88776
0.28	.31035	.36667	2.1626	1.2064	.16955	.88872
0.29	.32855	.38773	2.1472	1.2025	.18058	.88972

† Portions of this table were calculated originally as a portion of Project Meteor and appeared as a part of MIT Meteor Report No. 14, 1947, by A. H. Shapiro, W. R. Hawthorne, and C. M. Edelman. They have been reproduced in *Gas Tables*, by J. H. Keenan and J. Kaye, published by John Wiley and Sons, 1948. These values are reproduced here by permission of A. H. Shapiro and John Wiley and Sons.

Table A.5 (Continued)

Rayleigh Line

(a) k = 1.4

M	$\dfrac{T_0}{T_0{}^*}$	$\dfrac{T}{T^*}$	$\dfrac{p}{p^*}$	$\dfrac{p_0}{p_0{}^*}$	$\dfrac{V}{V^*}$	$\left(\dfrac{T_0}{T_0{}^*}\right)_{\text{isoth}}$
0.30	.34686	.40887	2.1314	1.1985	0.19183	.89075
0.31	.36525	.43004	2.1154	1.1945	0.20329	.89182
0.32	.38369	.45119	2.0991	1.1904	0.21494	.89292
0.33	.40214	.47228	2.0825	1.1863	0.22678	.89406
0.34	.42057	.49327	2.0657	1.1821	0.23879	.89523
0.35	.43894	.51413	2.0487	1.1779	0.25096	.89644
0.36	.45723	.53482	2.0314	1.1737	0.26327	.89768
0.37	.47541	.55530	2.0140	1.1695	0.27572	.89896
0.38	.49346	.57553	1.9964	1.1652	0.28828	.90027
0.39	.51134	.59549	1.9787	1.1609	0.30095	.90162
0.40	.52903	.61515	1.9608	1.1566	0.31372	.90300
0.41	.54651	.63448	1.9428	1.1523	0.32658	.90442
0.42	.56376	.65345	1.9247	1.1480	0.33951	.90587
0.43	.58075	.67205	1.9065	1.1437	0.35251	.90736
0.44	.59748	.69025	1.8882	1.1394	0.36556	.90888
0.45	.61393	.70803	1.8699	1.1351	0.37865	.91044
0.46	.63007	.72538	1.8515	1.1308	0.39178	.91203
0.47	.64589	.74228	1.8331	1.1266	0.40493	.91366
0.48	.66139	.75871	1.8147	1.1224	0.41810	.91532
0.49	.67655	.77466	1.7962	1.1182	0.43127	.91702
0.50	.69136	.79012	1.7778	1.1140	0.4445	.91875
0.51	.70581	.80509	1.7594	1.1099	0.45761	.92052
0.52	.71990	.81955	1.7410	1.1059	0.47075	.92232
0.53	.73361	.83351	1.7226	1.1019	0.48387	.92416
0.54	.74695	.84695	1.7043	1.0979	0.49696	.92603
0.55	.75991	.85987	1.6860	1.09397	0.51001	.92794
0.56	.77248	.87227	1.6678	1.09010	0.52302	.92988
0.57	.78467	.88415	1.6496	1.08630	0.53597	.93186
0.58	.79647	.89552	1.6316	1.08255	0.54887	.93387
0.59	.80789	.90637	1.6136	1.07887	0.56170	.93592
0.60	.81892	.91670	1.5957	1.07525	0.57447	.93800
0.61	.82956	.92653	1.5780	1.07170	0.58716	.94012
0.62	.83982	.93585	1.5603	1.06821	0.59978	.94227
0.63	.84970	.94466	1.5427	1.06480	0.61232	.94446
0.64	.85920	.95298	1.5253	1.06146	0.62477	.94668

Table A.5 (*Continued*)

Rayleigh Line

(*a*) $k = 1.4$

M	$\dfrac{T_0}{T_0^*}$	$\dfrac{T}{T^*}$	$\dfrac{p}{p^*}$	$\dfrac{p_0}{p_0^*}$	$\dfrac{V}{V^*}$	$\left(\dfrac{T_0}{T_0^*}\right)_{\text{isoth}}$
0.65	.86833	.96081	1.5080	1.05820	.63713	.94894
0.66	.87709	.96816	1.4908	1.05502	.64941	.95123
0.67	.88548	.97503	1.4738	1.05192	.66159	.95356
0.68	.89350	.98144	1.4569	1.04890	.67367	.95592
0.69	.90117	.98739	1.4401	1.04596	.68564	.95832
0.70	.90850	.99289	1.4235	1.04310	.69751	.96075
0.71	.91548	.99796	1.4070	1.04033	.70927	.96322
0.72	.92212	1.00260	1.3907	1.03764	.72093	.96572
0.73	.92843	1.00682	1.3745	1.03504	.73248	.96826
0.74	.93442	1.01062	1.3585	1.03253	.74392	.97083
0.75	.94009	1.01403	1.3427	1.03010	.75525	.97344
0.76	.94546	1.01706	1.3270	1.02776	.76646	.97608
0.77	.95052	1.01971	1.3115	1.02552	.77755	.97876
0.78	.95528	1.02198	1.2961	1.02337	.78852	.98147
0.79	.95975	1.02390	1.2809	1.02131	.79938	.98422
0.80	.96394	1.02548	1.2658	1.01934	.81012	.98700
0.81	.96786	1.02672	1.2509	1.01746	.82075	.98982
0.82	.97152	1.02763	1.2362	1.01569	.83126	.99267
0.83	.97492	1.02823	1.2217	1.01399	.84164	.99556
0.84	.97807	1.02853	1.2073	1.01240	.85190	.99848
0.85	.98097	1.02854	1.1931	1.01091	.86204	1.00144
0.86	.98363	1.02826	1.1791	1.00951	.87206	1.00443
0.87	.98607	1.02771	1.1652	1.00819	.88196	1.00746
0.88	.98828	1.02690	1.1515	1.00698	.89175	1.01052
0.89	.99028	1.02583	1.1380	1.00587	.90142	1.01362
0.90	.99207	1.02451	1.1246	1.00485	.91097	1.01675
0.91	.99366	1.02297	1.1114	1.00393	.92039	1.01992
0.92	.99506	1.02120	1.09842	1.00310	.92970	1.02312
0.93	.99627	1.01921	1.08555	1.00237	.93889	1.02636
0.94	.99729	1.01702	1.07285	1.00174	.94796	1.02963
0.95	.99814	1.01463	1.06030	1.00121	.95692	1.03294
0.96	.99883	1.01205	1.04792	1.00077	.96576	1.03628
0.97	.99935	1.00929	1.03570	1.00043	.97449	1.03966
0.98	.99972	1.00636	1.02364	1.00019	.98311	1.04307
0.99	.99993	1.00326	1.01174	1.00004	.99161	1.04652

Table A.5 (*Continued*)

Rayleigh Line

(*a*) $k = 1.4$

M	$\dfrac{T_0}{T_0{}^*}$	$\dfrac{T}{T^*}$	$\dfrac{p}{p^*}$	$\dfrac{p_0}{p_0{}^*}$	$\dfrac{V}{V^*}$	$\left(\dfrac{T_0}{T_0{}^*}\right)_{\text{isoth}}$
1.00	1.00000	1.00000	1.00000	1.00000	1.00000	1.05000
1.01	.99993	.99659	.98841	1.00004	1.00828	1.05352
1.02	.99973	.99304	.97697	1.00019	1.01644	1.05707
1.03	.99940	.98936	.96569	1.00043	1.02450	1.06066
1.04	.99895	.98553	.95456	1.00077	1.03246	1.06428
1.05	.99838	.98161	.94358	1.00121	1.04030	1.06794
1.06	.99769	.97755	.93275	1.00175	1.04804	1.07163
1.07	.99690	.97339	.92206	1.00238	1.05567	1.07536
1.08	.99600	.96913	.91152	1.00311	1.06320	1.07912
1.09	.99501	.96477	.90112	1.00394	1.07062	1.08292
1.10	.99392	.96031	.89086	1.00486	1.07795	1.08675
1.11	.99274	.95577	.88075	1.00588	1.08518	1.09062
1.12	.99148	.95115	.87078	1.00699	1.09230	1.09452
1.13	.99013	.94646	.86094	1.00820	1.09933	1.09846
1.14	.98871	.94169	.85123	1.00951	1.10626	1.10243
1.15	.98721	.93685	.84166	1.01092	1.1131	1.10644
1.16	.98564	.93195	.83222	1.01243	1.1198	1.11048
1.17	.98400	.92700	.82292	1.01403	1.1264	1.11456
1.18	.98230	.92200	.81374	1.01572	1.1330	1.11867
1.19	.98054	.91695	.80468	1.01752	1.1395	1.12282
1.20	.97872	.91185	.79576	1.01941	1.1459	1.12700
1.21	.97685	.90671	.78695	1.02140	1.1522	1.13122
1.22	.97492	.90153	.77827	1.02348	1.1584	1.13547
1.23	.97294	.89632	.76971	1.02566	1.1645	1.13976
1.24	.97092	.89108	.76127	1.02794	1.1705	1.14408
1.25	.96886	.88581	.75294	1.03032	1.1764	1.14844
1.26	.96675	.88052	.74473	1.03280	1.1823	1.15283
1.27	.96461	.87521	.73663	1.03536	1.1881	1.15726
1.28	.96243	.86988	.72865	1.03803	1.1938	1.16172
1.29	.96022	.86453	.72078	1.04080	1.1994	1.16622
1.30	.95798	.85917	.71301	1.04365	1.2050	1.17075
1.31	.95571	.85380	.70535	1.04661	1.2105	1.17532
1.32	.95341	.84843	.69780	1.04967	1.2159	1.17992
1.33	.95108	.84305	.69035	1.05283	1.2212	1.18456
1.34	.94873	.83766	.68301	1.05608	1.2264	1.18923

Table A.5 (Continued)

Rayleigh Line

(a) $k = 1.4$

M	$\dfrac{T_0}{T_0{}^*}$	$\dfrac{T}{T^*}$	$\dfrac{p}{p^*}$	$\dfrac{p_0}{p_0{}^*}$	$\dfrac{V}{V^*}$	$\left(\dfrac{T_0}{T_0{}^*}\right)_{\text{isoth}}$
1.35	.94636	.83227	.67577	1.05943	1.2316	1.19394
1.36	.94397	.82698	.66863	1.06288	1.2367	1.19868
1.37	.94157	.82151	.66159	1.06642	1.2417	1.20346
1.38	.93915	.81613	.65464	1.07006	1.2467	1.20827
1.39	.93671	.81076	.64778	1.07380	1.2516	1.21312
1.40	.93425	.80540	.64102	1.07765	1.2564	1.21800
1.41	.93178	.80004	.63436	1.08159	1.2612	1.22292
1.42	.92931	.79469	.62779	1.08563	1.2659	1.22787
1.43	.92683	.78936	.62131	1.08977	1.2705	1.23286
1.44	.92434	.78405	.61491	1.09400	1.2751	1.23788
1.45	.92184	.77875	.60860	1.0983	1.2796	1.24294
1.46	.91933	.77346	.60237	1.1028	1.2840	1.24803
1.47	.91682	.76819	.59623	1.1073	1.2884	1.25316
1.48	.91431	.76294	.59018	1.1120	1.2927	1.25832
1.49	.91179	.75771	.58421	1.1167	1.2970	1.26352
1.50	.90928	.75250	.57831	1.1215	1.3012	1.26875
1.51	.90676	.74731	.57250	1.1264	1.3054	1.27402
1.52	.90424	.74215	.56677	1.1315	1.3095	1.27932
1.53	.90172	.73701	.56111	1.1367	1.3135	1.28466
1.54	.89920	.73189	.55553	1.1420	1.3175	1.29003
1.55	.89669	.72680	.55002	1.1473	1.3214	1.29544
1.56	.89418	.72173	.54458	1.1527	1.3253	1.30088
1.57	.89167	.71669	.53922	1.1582	1.3291	1.30636
1.58	.88917	.71168	.53393	1.1639	1.3329	1.31187
1.59	.88668	.70669	.52871	1.1697	1.3366	1.31742
1.60	.88419	.70173	.52356	1.1756	1.3403	1.32300
1.61	.88170	.69680	.51848	1.1816	1.3439	1.32862
1.62	.87922	.69190	.51346	1.1877	1.3475	1.33427
1.63	.87675	.68703	.50851	1.1939	1.3511	1.33996
1.64	.87429	.68219	.50363	1.2002	1.3546	1.34568
1.65	.87184	.67738	.49881	1.2066	1.3580	1.35144
1.66	.86940	.67259	.49405	1.2131	1.3614	1.35723
1.67	.86696	.66784	.48935	1.2197	1.3648	1.36306
1.68	.86453	.66312	.48471	1.2264	1.3681	1.36892
1.69	.86211	.65843	.48014	1.2332	1.3713	1.37482

Table A.5 (*Continued*)

Rayleigh Line
(*a*) $k = 1.4$

M	$\dfrac{T_0}{T_0{}^*}$	$\dfrac{T}{T^*}$	$\dfrac{p}{p^*}$	$\dfrac{p_0}{p_0{}^*}$	$\dfrac{V}{V^*}$	$\left(\dfrac{T_0}{T_0{}^*}\right)_{\text{isoth}}$
1.70	.85970	.65377	.47563	1.2402	1.3745	1.38075
1.71	.85731	.64914	.47117	1.2473	1.3777	1.38672
1.72	.85493	.64455	.46677	1.2545	1.3809	1.39272
1.73	.85256	.63999	.46242	1.2618	1.3840	1.39876
1.74	.85020	.63546	.45813	1.2692	1.3871	1.40483
1.75	.84785	.63096	.45390	1.2767	1.3901	1.41094
1.76	.84551	.62649	.44972	1.2843	1.3931	1.41708
1.77	.84318	.62205	.44559	1.2920	1.3960	1.42326
1.78	.84087	.61765	.44152	1.2998	1.3989	1.42947
1.79	.83857	.61328	.43750	1.3078	1.4018	1.43572
1.80	.83628	.60894	.43353	1.3159	1.4046	1.44200
1.81	.83400	.60463	.42960	1.3241	1.4074	1.44832
1.82	.83174	.60036	.42573	1.3324	1.4102	1.45467
1.83	.82949	.59612	.42191	1.3408	1.4129	1.46106
1.84	.82726	.59191	.41813	1.3494	1.4156	1.46748
1.85	.82504	.58773	.41440	1.3581	1.4183	1.47394
1.86	.82283	.58359	.41072	1.3669	1.4209	1.48043
1.87	.82064	.57948	.40708	1.3758	1.4235	1.48696
1.88	.81846	.57540	.40349	1.3848	1.4261	1.49352
1.89	.81629	.57135	.39994	1.3940	1.4286	1.50012
1.90	.81414	.56734	.39643	1.4033	1.4311	1.50675
1.91	.81200	.56336	.39297	1.4127	1.4336	1.51342
1.92	.80987	.55941	.38955	1.4222	1.4360	1.52012
1.93	.80776	.55549	.38617	1.4319	1.4384	1.52686
1.94	.80567	.55160	.38283	1.4417	1.4408	1.53363
1.95	.80359	.54774	.37954	1.4516	1.4432	1.54044
1.96	.80152	.54391	.37628	1.4616	1.4455	1.54728
1.97	.79946	.54012	.37306	1.4718	1.4478	1.55416
1.98	.79742	.53636	.36988	1.4821	1.4501	1.56107
1.99	.79540	.53263	.36674	1.4925	1.4523	1.56802
2.00	.79339	.52893	.36364	1.5031	1.4545	1.57500
2.01	.79139	.52526	.36057	1.5138	1.4567	1.58202
2.02	.78941	.52161	.35754	1.5246	1.4589	1.58907
2.03	.78744	.51800	.35454	1.5356	1.4610	1.59616
2.04	.78549	.51442	.35158	1.5467	1.4631	1.60328

Table A.5 (*Continued*)

Rayleigh Line

(*a*) $k = 1.4$

M	$\dfrac{T_0}{T_0{}^*}$	$\dfrac{T}{T^*}$	$\dfrac{p}{p^*}$	$\dfrac{p_0}{p_0{}^*}$	$\dfrac{V}{V^*}$	$\left(\dfrac{T_0}{T_0{}^*}\right)_{\text{isoth}}$
2.05	.78355	.51087	.34866	1.5579	1.4652	1.61044
2.06	.78162	.50735	.34577	1.5693	1.4673	1.61763
2.07	.77971	.50386	.34291	1.5808	1.4694	1.62486
2.08	.77781	.50040	.34009	1.5924	1.4714	1.63212
2.09	.77593	.49697	.33730	1.6042	1.4734	1.63942
2.10	.77406	.49356	.33454	1.6161	1.4753	1.64675
2.11	.77221	.49018	.33181	1.6282	1.4773	1.65412
2.12	.77037	.48683	.32912	1.6404	1.4792	1.66152
2.13	.76854	.48351	.32646	1.6528	1.4811	1.66896
2.14	.76673	.48022	.32383	1.6653	1.4830	1.67643
2.15	.76493	.47696	.32122	1.6780	1.4849	1.68394
2.16	.76314	.47373	.31864	1.6908	1.4867	1.69148
2.17	.76137	.47052	.31610	1.7037	1.4885	1.69906
2.18	.75961	.46734	.31359	1.7168	1.4903	1.70667
2.19	.75787	.46419	.31110	1.7300	1.4921	1.71432
2.20	.75614	.46106	.30864	1.7434	1.4939	1.72200
2.21	.75442	.45796	.30621	1.7570	1.4956	1.72972
2.22	.75271	.45489	.30381	1.7707	1.4973	1.73747
2.23	.75102	.45184	.30143	1.7846	1.4990	1.74526
2.24	.74934	.44882	.29908	1.7986	1.5007	1.75308
2.25	.74767	.44582	.29675	1.8128	1.5024	1.76094
2.26	.74602	.44285	.29445	1.8271	1.5040	1.76883
2.27	.74438	.43990	.29218	1.8416	1.5056	1.77676
2.28	.74275	.43698	.28993	1.8562	1.5072	1.78472
2.29	.74114	.43409	.28771	1.8710	1.5088	1.79272
2.30	.73954	.43122	.28551	1.8860	1.5104	1.80075
2.31	.73795	.42837	.28333	1.9012	1.5119	1.80882
2.32	.73638	.42555	.28118	1.9165	1.5134	1.81692
2.33	.73482	.42276	.27905	1.9320	1.5150	1.82506
2.34	.73327	.41999	.27695	1.9476	1.5165	1.83323
2.35	.73173	.41724	.27487	1.9634	1.5180	1.84144
2.36	.73020	.41451	.27281	1.9794	1.5195	1.84968
2.37	.72868	.41181	.27077	1.9955	1.5209	1.85796
2.38	.72718	.40913	.26875	2.0118	1.5223	1.86627
2.39	.72569	.40647	.26675	2.0283	1.5237	1.87462

Table A.5 (*Continued*)
Rayleigh Line
(*a*) *k* = 1.4

M	$\dfrac{T_0}{T_0{}^*}$	$\dfrac{T}{T^*}$	$\dfrac{p}{p^*}$	$\dfrac{p_0}{p_0{}^*}$	$\dfrac{V}{V^*}$	$\left(\dfrac{T_0}{T_0{}^*}\right)_{\text{isoth}}$
2.40	.72421	.40383	.26478	2.0450	1.5252	1.88300
2.41	.72274	.40122	.26283	2.0619	1.5266	1.89142
2.42	.72129	.39863	.26090	2.0789	1.5279	1.89987
2.43	.71985	.39606	.25899	2.0961	1.5293	1.90836
2.44	.71842	.39352	.25710	2.1135	1.5306	1.91688
2.45	.71700	.39100	.25523	2.1311	1.5320	1.92544
2.46	.71559	.38850	.25337	2.1489	1.5333	1.93403
2.47	.71419	.38602	.25153	2.1669	1.5346	1.94266
2.48	.71280	.38356	.24972	2.1850	1.5359	1.95132
2.49	.71142	.38112	.24793	2.2033	1.5372	1.96002
2.50	.71005	.37870	.24616	2.2218	1.5385	1.96875
2.51	.70870	.37630	.24440	2.2405	1.5398	1.97752
2.52	.70736	.37392	.24266	2.2594	1.5410	1.98632
2.53	.70603	.37157	.24094	2.2785	1.5422	1.99515
2.54	.70471	.36923	.23923	2.2978	1.5434	2.00403
2.55	.70340	.36691	.23754	2.3173	1.5446	2.01294
2.56	.70210	.36461	.23587	2.3370	1.5458	2.02188
2.57	.70081	.36233	.23422	2.3569	1.5470	2.03086
2.58	.69953	.36007	.23258	2.3770	1.5482	2.03987
2.59	.69825	.35783	.23096	2.3972	1.5494	2.04892
2.60	.69699	.35561	.22936	2.4177	1.5505	2.05800
2.61	.69574	.35341	.22777	2.4384	1.5516	2.06711
2.62	.69450	.35123	.22620	2.4593	1.5527	2.07627
2.63	.69327	.34906	.22464	2.4804	1.5538	2.08546
2.64	.69205	.34691	.22310	2.5017	1.5549	2.09468
2.65	.69084	.34478	.22158	2.5233	1.5560	2.10394
2.66	.68964	.34267	.22007	2.5451	1.5571	2.11323
2.67	.68845	.34057	.21857	2.5671	1.5582	2.12256
2.68	.68727	.33849	.21709	2.5892	1.5593	2.13192
2.69	.68610	.33643	.21562	2.6116	1.5603	2.14132
2.70	.68494	.33439	.21417	2.6342	1.5613	2.15075
2.71	.68378	.33236	.21273	2.6571	1.5623	2.16022
2.72	.68263	.33035	.21131	2.6802	1.5633	2.16972
2.73	.68150	.32836	.20990	2.7035	1.5644	2.17925
2.74	.68038	.32638	.20850	2.7270	1.5654	2.18883

Table A.5 (continued)

Rayleigh Line
(a) $k = 1.4$

M	$\dfrac{T_0}{T_0{}^*}$	$\dfrac{T}{T^*}$	$\dfrac{p}{p^*}$	$\dfrac{p_0}{p_0{}^*}$	$\dfrac{V}{V^*}$	$\left(\dfrac{T_0}{T_0{}^*}\right)_{\text{isoth}}$
2.75	.67926	.32442	.20712	2.7508	1.5663	2.19844
2.76	.67815	.32248	.20575	2.7748	1.5673	2.20808
2.77	.67704	.32055	.20439	2.7990	1.5683	2.21776
2.78	.67595	.31864	.20305	2.8235	1.5692	2.22747
2.79	.67487	.31674	.20172	2.8482	1.5702	2.23722
2.80	.67380	.31486	.20040	2.8731	1.5711	2.24700
2.81	.67273	.31299	.19909	2.8982	1.5721	2.25682
2.82	.67167	.31114	.19780	2.9236	1.5730	2.26667
2.83	.67062	.30931	.19652	2.9493	1.5739	2.27655
2.84	.66958	.30749	.19525	2.9752	1.5748	2.28648
2.85	.66855	.30568	.19399	3.0013	1.5757	2.29644
2.86	.66752	.30389	.19274	3.0277	1.5766	2.30643
2.87	.66650	.30211	.19151	3.0544	1.5775	2.31646
2.88	.66549	.30035	.19029	3.0813	1.5784	2.32652
2.89	.66449	.29860	.18908	3.1084	1.5792	2.33662
2.90	.66350	.29687	.18788	3.1358	1.5801	2.34675
2.91	.66252	.29515	.18669	3.1635	1.5809	2.35692
2.92	.66154	.29344	.18551	3.1914	1.5818	2.36712
2.93	.66057	.29175	.18435	3.2196	1.5826	2.37735
2.94	.65961	.29007	.18320	3.2481	1.5834	2.38763
2.95	.65865	.28841	.18205	3.2768	1.5843	2.39794
2.96	.65770	.28676	.18091	3.3058	1.5851	2.40828
2.97	.65676	.28512	.17978	3.3351	1.5859	2.41865
2.98	.65583	.28349	.17867	3.3646	1.5867	2.42907
2.99	.65490	.28188	.17757	3.3944	1.5875	2.43952
3.00	.65398	.28028	.17647	3.4244	1.5882	2.45000
3.50	.61580	.21419	.13223	5.3280	1.6198	3.01875
4.00	.58909	.16831	.10256	8.2268	1.6410	3.67500
4.50	.56983	.13540	.08177	12.502	1.6559	4.41874
5.00	.55555	.11111	.06667	18.634	1.6667	5.25000
6.00	.53633	.07849	.04669	38.946	1.6809	7.17499
7.00	.52437	.05826	.03448	75.414	1.6896	9.45000
8.00	.51646	.04491	.02649	136.62	1.6954	12.07500
9.00	.51098	.03565	.02098	233.88	1.6993	15.05003
10.00	.50702	.02897	.01702	381.62	1.7021	18.37500
∞	.48980	0	0	∞	1.7143	∞

Table A.5 (*Continued*)

Rayleigh Line

(*b*) $k = 1.0$

M	$\dfrac{T_0}{T_0{}^*} = \dfrac{T^*}{T}$	$\dfrac{p}{p^*}$	$\dfrac{p_0}{p_0{}^*}$	$\dfrac{V}{V^*}$
0	0	2.000	1.213	0
0.05	.00995	1.995	1.212	.00499
0.10	.03921	1.980	1.207	.01980
0.15	.08608	1.956	1.200	.04401
0.20	.14793	1.923	1.190	.07692
0.25	.2215	1.882	1.178	.1176
0.30	.3030	1.835	1.164	.1651
0.35	.3889	1.782	1.149	.2183
0.40	.4756	1.724	1.133	.2758
0.45	.5602	1.663	1.116	.3368
0.50	.6400	1.600	1.0997	.4000
0.55	.7132	1.536	1.0834	.4645
0.60	.7785	1.471	1.0679	.5294
0.65	.8352	1.406	1.0534	.5940
0.70	.8828	1.342	1.0402	.6577
0.75	.9216	1.280	1.0285	.7200
0.80	.9518	1.220	1.0186	.7805
0.85	.9740	1.161	1.0107	.8389
0.90	.9890	1.105	1.0048	.8950
0.95	.9974	1.0512	1.0012	.9488
1.00	1.0000	1.0000	1.0000	1.0000
1.05	.9976	.9512	1.0013	1.0488
1.10	.9910	.9049	1.0052	1.0951
1.15	.9807	.8611	1.0118	1.1389
1.20	.9675	.8197	1.0214	1.1802
1.25	.9518	.7805	1.0340	1.220
1.30	.9342	.7435	1.0498	1.257
1.35	.9151	.7086	1.0690	1.291
1.40	.8948	.6757	1.0919	1.324
1.45	.8737	.6447	1.1187	1.355
1.50	.8521	.6154	1.150	1.384
1.55	.8301	.5878	1.186	1.412
1.60	.8080	.5618	1.226	1.438
1.65	.7859	.5373	1.271	1.463
1.70	.7639	.5141	1.323	1.486

Table A.5 (Continued)

Rayleigh Line
(b) $k = 1.0$

M	$\dfrac{T_0}{T_0{}^*} = \dfrac{T}{T^*}$	$\dfrac{p}{p^*}$	$\dfrac{p_0}{p_0{}^*}$	$\dfrac{V}{V^*}$
1.75	0.7422	0.4923	1.381	1.508
1.80	0.7209	0.4717	1.446	1.528
1.85	0.7000	0.4522	1.519	1.547
1.90	0.6795	0.4338	1.600	1.566
1.95	0.6595	0.4164	1.691	1.584
2.00	0.6400	0.4000	1.793	1.601
2.05	0.6211	0.3844	1.907	1.616
2.10	0.6027	0.3697	2.034	1.630
2.15	0.5849	0.3557	2.176	1.644
2.20	0.5677	0.3425	2.336	1.657
2.25	0.5510	0.3299	2.515	1.670
2.30	0.5348	0.3179	2.716	1.682
2.35	0.5192	0.3066	2.942	1.693
2.40	0.5042	0.2959	3.197	1.704
2.45	0.4897	0.2857	3.484	1.714
2.50	0.4757	0.2759	3.808	1.724
2.55	0.4621	0.2666	4.175	1.733
2.60	0.4490	0.2577	4.591	1.742
2.65	0.4364	0.2493	5.064	1.751
2.70	0.4243	0.2413	5.602	1.759
2.75	0.4126	0.2336	6.215	1.766
2.80	0.4013	0.2262	6.916	1.774
2.85	0.3904	0.2192	7.719	1.781
2.90	0.3799	0.2125	8.640	1.787
2.95	0.3698	0.2061	9.699	1.794
3.00	0.3600	0.2000	10.92	1.800
3.50	0.2791	0.1509	41.85	1.849
4.00	0.2215	0.1176	212.71	1.882
4.50	0.1794	0.09412	1425	1.906
5.00	0.1479	0.07692	12519	1.923
6.00	0.10519	0.05405	$215(10)^4$	1.946
7.00	0.07840	0.04000	$106(10)^7$	1 960
8.00	0 06059	0 03077	$147(10)^{10}$	1.969
9.00	0.04818	0.02439	$574(10)^{13}$	1.976
10.00	0.03921	0.01980	$623(10)^{17}$	1.980
∞	0	0	∞	2.000

Table A.5 (Continued)

Rayleigh Line
(c) $k = 1.1$

M	$\dfrac{T_0}{T_0{}^*}$	$\dfrac{T}{T^*}$	$\dfrac{p}{p^*}$	$\dfrac{p_0}{p_0{}^*}$	$\dfrac{V}{V^*}$	$\left(\dfrac{T_0}{T_0{}^*}\right)_{\text{isoth}}$
0	0	0	2.100	1.228	0	0.95652
0.05	.01044	0.01097	2.094	1.226	0.00524	0.95664
0.10	.04111	0.04315	2.077	1.221	0.02077	0.95700
0.15	.09009	0.09449	2.049	1.213	0.04611	0.95760
0.20	.15444	0.16184	2.011	1.203	0.08046	0.95843
0.25	.2305	0.2413	1.965	1.190	0.1228	0.95951
0.30	.3144	0.3286	1.911	1.174	0.1720	0.96083
0.35	.4020	0.4195	1.851	1.157	0.2267	0.96238
0.40	.4898	0.5102	1.786	1.140	0.2857	0.96417
0.45	.5746	0.5973	1.717	1.122	0.3478	0.96621
0.50	.6540	0.6782	1.647	1.1040	0.4118	0.96848
0.55	.7261	0.7510	1.576	1.0867	0.4766	0.97099
0.60	.7898	0.8147	1.504	1.0702	0.5416	0.97374
0.65	.8446	0.8684	1.434	1.0550	0.6057	0.97673
0.70	.8902	0.9123	1.365	1.0412	0.6686	0.97996
0.75	.9270	0.9467	1.297	1.0291	0.7297	0.98342
0.80	.9554	0.9720	1.232	1.0189	0.7887	0.98713
0.85	.9761	0.9892	1.170	1.0109	0.8453	0.99108
0.90	.9899	0.9989	1.111	1.0050	0.8995	0.99526
0.95	.9976	1.0023	1.0538	1.0013	0.9511	0.99968
1.00	1.0000	1.0000	1.0000	1.0000	1.0000	1.00435
1.05	.9979	0.9930	0.9490	1.0013	1.0463	1.00925
1.10	.9919	0.9821	0.9009	1.0051	1.0901	1.01439
1.15	.9827	0.9679	0.8555	1.0116	1.1314	1.01977
1.20	.9710	0.9511	0.8127	1.0209	1.1703	1.02539
1.25	.9572	0.9322	0.7724	1.0331	1.207	1.03125
1.30	.9418	0.9118	0.7345	1.0483	1.241	1.03735
1.35	.9251	0.8902	0.6989	1.0665	1.273	1.04368
1.40	.9074	0.8678	0.6654	1.0880	1.304	1.05026
1.45	.8892	0.8449	0.6339	1.1130	1.333	1.05708
1.50	.8706	0.8217	0.6043	1.141	1.360	1.06413
1.55	.8518	0.7984	0.5765	1.173	1.385	1.07142
1.60	.8329	0.7753	0.5503	1.210	1.409	1.07896
1.65	.8141	0.7524	0.5257	1.251	1.431	1.08673
1.70	.7955	0.7298	0.5025	1.297	1.452	1.09474

Table A.5 (*Continued*)

Rayleigh Line
(c) $k = 1.1$

M	$\dfrac{T_0}{T_0{}^*}$	$\dfrac{T}{T^*}$	$\dfrac{p}{p^*}$	$\dfrac{p_0}{p_0{}^*}$	$\dfrac{V}{V^*}$	$\left(\dfrac{T_0}{T_0{}^*}\right)_{\text{isoth}}$
1.75	.7771	.7076	.4807	1.347	1.472	1.10299
1.80	.7591	.6859	.4601	1.403	1.491	1.11148
1.85	.7415	.6648	.4407	1.465	1.508	1.12021
1.90	.7243	.6443	.4224	1.532	1.525	1.21917
1.95	.7076	.6243	.4052	1.607	1.541	1.13838
2.00	.6914	.6049	.3889	1.689	1.556	1.14783
2.05	.6756	.5862	.3735	1.780	1.570	1.15751
2.10	.6603	.5681	.3589	1.879	1.583	1.16743
2.15	.6456	.5506	.3451	1.987	1.595	1.17760
2.20	.6313	.5337	.3321	2.106	1.607	1.18800
2.25	.6175	.5174	.3197	2.237	1.618	1.19864
2.30	.6042	.5017	.3079	2.380	1.629	1.20952
2.35	.5914	.4866	.2968	2.537	1.639	1.22064
2.40	.5790	.4720	.2863	2.709	1.649	1.23200
2.45	.5671	.4580	.2763	2.897	1.658	1.24360
2.50	.5556	.4444	.2667	3.104	1.667	1.25543
2.55	.5445	.4314	.2576	3.332	1.675	1.26751
2.60	.5338	.4189	.2489	3.581	1.683	1.27983
2.65	.5235	.4068	.2406	3.855	1.690	1.29238
2.70	.5136	.3952	.2328	4.156	1.697	1.30517
2.75	.5041	.3840	.2253	4.487	1.704	1.31821
2.80	.4949	.3733	.2182	4.851	1.711	1.33148
2.85	.4860	.3629	.2114	5.251	1.717	1.34499
2.90	.4775	.3529	.2049	5.692	1.723	1.35874
2.95	.4693	.3433	.1986	6.176	1.729	1.37273
3.00	.4613	.3341	.1927	6.710	1.734	1.38696
3.50	.3960	.2578	.1451	16.26	1.777	1.54239
4.00	.3496	.2040	.1129	42.42	1.806	1.72174
4.50	.3160	.1648	.0902	115.70	1.827	1.92500
5.00	.2909	.1357	.0737	322.33	1.842	2.15217
6.00	.2568	.09631	.05172	2508	1.862	2.67826
7.00	.2356	.07169	.03825	18430	1.874	3.30000
8.00	.2215	.05536	.02941	$123(10)^3$	1.882	4.01739
9.00	.2116	.04400	.02331	$743(10)^3$	1.888	4.83044
10.00	.2045	.03579	.01892	$401(10)^4$	1.892	5.73913
∞	.1736	0	0	∞	1.909	∞

Table A.5 (Continued)
Rayleigh Line
(d) $k = 1.2$

M	$\dfrac{T_0}{T_0^*}$	$\dfrac{T}{T^*}$	$\dfrac{p}{p^*}$	$\dfrac{p_0}{p_0^*}$	$\dfrac{V}{V^*}$	$\left(\dfrac{T_0}{T_0^*}\right)_{\text{isoth}}$
0	0	0	2.200	1.242	0	0.92308
0.05	.01094	.01203	2.193	1.239	.00548	0.92331
0.10	.04301	.04726	2.173	1.234	.02174	0.92400
0.15	.09408	.10325	2.141	1.226	.04820	0.92515
0.20	.16089	.17627	2.099	1.214	.08397	0.92677
0.25	.2395	.2618	2.047	1.199	.1279	0.92885
0.30	.3255	.3548	1.986	1.183	.1787	0.93138
0.35	.4147	.4507	1.918	1.165	.2350	0.93438
0.40	.5034	.5450	1.846	1.146	.2953	0.93785
0.45	.5884	.6343	1.770	1.127	.3584	0.94177
0.50	.6672	.7160	1.692	1.1078	.4231	0.94615
0.55	.7381	.7881	1.614	1.0895	.4884	0.95100
0.60	.8003	.8497	1.536	1.0722	.5531	0.95631
0.65	.8531	.9004	1.460	1.0563	.6168	0.96208
0.70	.8969	.9405	1.385	1.0420	.6788	0.96831
0.75	.9318	.9704	1.313	1.0296	.7388	0.97500
0.80	.9585	.9910	1.244	1.0191	.7964	0.98215
0.85	.9779	1.0032	1.178	1.0109	.8514	0.98977
0.90	.9907	1.0081	1.115	1.0049	.9037	0.99785
0.95	.9978	1.0067	1.0562	1.0012	.9532	1.00638
1.00	1.0000	1.0000	1.0000	1.0000	1.0000	1.01538
1.05	.9981	.9888	.9471	1.0013	1.0441	1.02485
1.10	.9927	.9741	.8972	1.0050	1.0856	1.03477
1.15	.9845	.9564	.8504	1.0114	1.1247	1.04515
1.20	.9740	.9365	.8065	1.0204	1.1613	1.05600
1.25	.9617	.9149	.7653	1.0322	1.196	1.06731
1.30	.9481	.8921	.7266	1.0467	1.228	1.07908
1.35	.9334	.8685	.6903	1.0640	1.258	1.09131
1.40	.9180	.8443	.6563	1.0843	1.286	1.10400
1.45	.9021	.8199	.6245	1.1077	1.313	1.11715
1.50	.8859	.7955	.5946	1.134	1.338	1.13077
1.55	.8695	.7712	.5666	1.164	1.361	1.14485
1.60	.8532	.7473	.5403	1.197	1.383	1.15938
1.65	.8370	.7237	.5156	1.234	1.404	1.17438
1.70	.8211	.7007	.4924	1.275	1.423	1.18985

Table A.5 (Continued)

Rayleigh Line

(d) $k = 1.2$

M	$\dfrac{T_0}{T_0{}^*}$	$\dfrac{T}{T^*}$	$\dfrac{p}{p^*}$	$\dfrac{p_0}{p_0{}^*}$	$\dfrac{V}{V^*}$	$\left(\dfrac{T_0}{T_0{}^*}\right)_{\text{isoth}}$
1.75	.8054	.6782	.4706	1.320	1.441	1.20577
1.80	.7900	.6563	.4501	1.369	1.458	1.22215
1.85	.7750	.6351	.4308	1.422	1.474	1.23900
1.90	.7604	.6146	.4126	1.480	1.490	1.25631
1.95	.7462	.5947	.3955	1.543	1.504	1.27408
2.00	.7325	.5755	.3793	1.612	1.517	1.29231
2.05	.7192	.5570	.3641	1.687	1.530	1.31100
2.10	.7063	.5391	.3497	1.767	1.542	1.33015
2.15	.6939	.5219	.3360	1.854	1.553	1.34977
2.20	.6819	.5054	.3231	1.948	1.564	1.36985
2.25	.6703	.4895	.3109	2.050	1.574	1.39039
2.30	.6591	.4742	.2994	2.159	1.584	1.41139
2.35	.6484	.4595	.2884	2.277	1.593	1.43285
2.40	.6381	.4453	.2780	2.405	1.602	1.45477
2.45	.6281	.4317	.2682	2.542	1.610	1.47715
2.50	.6185	.4187	.2588	2.690	1.618	1.50000
2.55	.6093	.4062	.2499	2.849	1.625	1.52331
2.60	.6004	.3941	.2414	3.021	1.632	1.54708
2.65	.5918	.3825	.2334	3.205	1.639	1.57131
2.70	.5836	.3713	.2257	3.403	1.645	1.59600
2.75	.5757	.3606	.2184	3.617	1.651	1.62115
2.80	.5681	.3503	.2114	3.847	1.657	1.64677
2.85	.5608	.3404	.2047	4.094	1.663	1.67285
2.90	.5537	.3309	.1983	4.359	1.668	1.69938
2.95	.5469	.3217	.1923	4.644	1.673	1.72638
3.00	.5404	.3128	.1864	4.951	1.678	1.75385
3.50	.4865	.2405	.1401	9.597	1.717	2.05385
4.00	.4486	.1898	.1089	18.99	1.743	2.40000
4.50	.4211	.1531	.08696	37.61	1.761	2.79230
5.00	.4006	.1259	.07097	73.64	1.774	3.23077
6.00	.3730	.08919	.04977	266.2	1.792	4.24615
7.00	.3557	.06632	.03679	875.9	1.803	5.44615
8.00	.3443	.05118	.02828	2621	1.810	6.83077
9.00	.3363	.04065	.02240	7181	1.815	8.40002
10.00	.3306	.03306	.01818	18182	1.818	10.15385
∞	0.3056	0	0	∞	1.833	∞

Table A.5 (Continued)

Rayleigh Line

(e) $k = 1.3$

M	$\dfrac{T_0}{T_0{}^*}$	$\dfrac{T}{T^*}$	$\dfrac{p}{p^*}$	$\dfrac{p_0}{p_0{}^*}$	$\dfrac{V}{V^*}$	$\left(\dfrac{T_0}{T_0{}^*}\right)_{\text{isoth}}$
0	0	0	2.300	1.255	0	.89655
0.05	.01143	.01314	2.293	1.253	.00573	.89689
0.10	.04489	.05155	2.270	1.247	.02270	.89790
0.15	.09803	.11236	2.234	1.237	.05028	.89958
0.20	.16726	.19120	2.186	1.224	.08745	.90193
0.25	.2482	.2828	2.127	1.209	.1329	.90496
0.30	.3363	.3816	2.059	1.191	.1853	.90866
0.35	.4270	.4822	1 984	1.172	.2430	.91303
0.40	.5165	.5800	1.904	1.152	.3046	.91807
0.45	.6015	.6713	1.821	1.131	.3687	.92378
0.50	.6796	.7533	1.736	1.1112	.4340	.93017
0.55	.7494	.8244	1.651	1.0919	.4994	.93723
0.60	.8099	.8837	1.567	1.0739	.5640	.94497
0.65	.8611	.9312	1.485	1.0574	.6272	.95337
0.70	.9029	.9673	1.405	1.0426	.6885	.96245
0.75	.9361	.9928	1.328	1.0299	.7473	.97220
0.80	.9614	1.0088	1.255	1.0193	.8035	.98262
0.85	.9795	1.0163	1.186	1.0109	.8569	.99372
0.90	.9914	1.0166	1.120	1.0049	.9075	1.00548
0.95	.9980	1.0108	1.0583	1.0012	.9552	1.01792
1.00	1.0000	1.0000	1.0000	1.0000	1.0000	1.03103
1.05	.9982	.9851	.9452	1.0012	1.0421	1.04482
1.10	.9933	.9669	.8939	1.0049	1.0816	1.05928
1.15	.9859	.9461	.8458	1.0111	1.1186	1.07441
1.20	.9765	.9235	.8008	1.0199	1.1532	1.09021
1.25	.9656	.8996	.7588	1.0312	1.186	1.10668
1.30	.9534	.8747	.7194	1.0451	1.216	1.12383
1.35	.9404	.8493	.6826	1.0617	1.244	1.14165
1.40	.9268	.8237	.6483	1.0809	1.270	1.16014
1.45	.9128	.7980	.6161	1.1028	1.295	1.17930
1.50	.8986	.7726	.5860	1.128	1.318	1.19914
1.55	.8843	.7475	.5578	1.155	1.340	1.21965
1.60	.8701	.7230	.5314	1.185	1.360	1.24083
1.65	.8560	.6990	.5067	1.219	1.379	1.26268
1.70	.8421	.6756	.4835	1.256	1.397	1.28521

Table A.5 (Continued)
Rayleigh Line
(e) $k = 1.3$

M	$\dfrac{T_0}{T_0{}^*}$	$\dfrac{T}{T^*}$	$\dfrac{p}{p^*}$	$\dfrac{p_0}{p_0{}^*}$	$\dfrac{V}{V^*}$	$\left(\dfrac{T_0}{T_0{}^*}\right)_{\text{isoth}}$
1.75	.8285	.6529	.4617	1.296	1.414	1.30841
1.80	.8153	.6309	.4413	1.340	1.430	1.33227
1.85	.8024	.6097	.4221	1.387	1.445	1.35682
1.90	.7898	.5892	.4040	1.438	1.459	1.38204
1.95	.7776	.5695	.3870	1.493	1.472	1.40792
2.00	.7659	.5505	.3710	1.552	1.484	1.43448
2.05	.7545	.5322	.3559	1.615	1.495	1.46172
2.10	.7435	.5146	.3416	1.683	1.506	1.48962
2.15	.7329	.4977	.3281	1.755	1.517	1.51820
2.20	.7227	.4815	.3154	1.832	1.527	1.54745
2.25	.7129	.4659	.3034	1.915	1.536	1.57737
2.30	.7034	.4510	.2920	2.003	1.545	1.60797
2.35	.6943	.4367	.2812	2.097	1.553	1.63923
2.40	.6855	.4229	.2710	2.197	1.561	1.67117
2.45	.6771	.4097	.2613	2.303	1.568	1.70378
2.50	.6690	.3971	.2521	2.416	1.575	1.73707
2.55	.6612	.3850	.2433	2.536	1.582	1.77103
2.60	.6537	.3733	.2350	2.664	1.588	1.80565
2.65	.6465	.3621	.2271	2.800	1.594	1.84096
2.70	.6396	.3513	.2195	2.944	1.600	1.87693
2.75	.6329	.3410	.2123	3.096	1.606	1.91358
2.80	.6265	.3311	.2055	3.258	1.611	1.95090
2.85	.6203	.3216	.1990	3.429	1.616	1.98889
2.90	.6144	.3124	.1928	3.611	1.621	2.02755
2.95	.6087	.3036	.1868	3.804	1.626	2.06689
3.00	.6032	.2952	.1811	4.007	1.630	2.10690
3.50	.5582	.2262	.1359	6.806	1.665	2.54397
4.00	.5265	.1781	.1055	11.57	1.688	3.04828
4.50	.5037	.1435	.08417	19.44	1.704	3.61982
5.00	.4867	.1178	.06866	32.06	1.716	4.25862
6.00	.4639	.08335	.04812	76.97	1.732	5.73793
7.00	.4496	.06192	.03555	191.3	1.742	7.48621
8.00	.4402	.04775	.02732	413.4	1.748	9.50345
9.00	.4336	.03792	.02164	833.4	1.753	11.78968
10.00	.4289	.03082	.01756	1582	1.756	14.34483
∞	.4083	0	0	∞	1.769	∞

Table A.5 (Continued)

Rayleigh Line

(f) $k = 1.67$

M	$\dfrac{T_0}{T_0{}^*}$	$\dfrac{T}{T^*}$	$\dfrac{p}{p^*}$	$\dfrac{p_0}{p_0{}^*}$	$\dfrac{V}{V^*}$	$\left(\dfrac{T_0}{T_0{}^*}\right)_{\text{isoth}}$
0	0	0	2.670	1.299	0	.83292
0.05	.01325	.01767	2.659	1.297	.00665	.83362
0.10	.05183	.06896	2.626	1.289	.02626	.83571
0.15	.11243	.1490	2.573	1.276	.05790	.83920
0.20	.19020	.2506	2.503	1.259	.10011	.84408
0.25	.2794	.3653	2.418	1.239	.1511	.85036
0.30	.3742	.4849	2.321	1.216	.2089	.85803
0.35	.4693	.6018	2.216	1.192	.2715	.86710
0.40	.5606	.7103	2.107	1.168	.3371	.87756
0.45	.6448	.8062	1.995	1.144	.4040	.88942
0.50	.7201	.8870	1.884	1.1202	.4709	.90267
0.55	.7853	.9519	1.774	1.0981	.5366	.91732
0.60	.8402	1.0010	1.667	1.0778	.6003	.93337
0.65	.8853	1.0354	1.565	1.0597	.6614	.95081
0.70	.9213	1.0565	1.468	1.0438	.7195	.96964
0.75	.9491	1.0662	1.377	1.0303	.7744	.98987
0.80	.9697	1.0660	1.291	1.0193	.8260	1.01150
0.85	.9842	1.0578	1.210	1.0108	.8742	1.03452
0.90	.9935	1.0432	1.135	1.0048	.9192	1.05893
0.95	.9985	1.0235	1.0649	1.0012	.9611	1.08474
1.00	1.0000	1.0000	1.0000	1.0000	1.0000	1.11195
1.05	.9987	0.9736	.9398	1.0012	1.0361	1.14055
1.10	.9952	0.9454	.8839	1.0046	1.0695	1.17054
1.15	.9899	0.9158	.8321	1.0103	1.1005	1.20193
1.20	.9833	0.8855	.7842	1.0181	1.1292	1.23472
1.25	.9757	0.8550	.7397	1.0280	1.156	1.26890
1.30	.9674	0.8246	.6985	1.0400	1.181	1.30447
1.35	.9586	0.7946	.6603	1.0540	1.204	1.34145
1.40	.9495	0.7652	.6249	1.0700	1.225	1.37981
1.45	.9403	0.7365	.5919	1.0880	1.245	1.41957
1.50	.9310	0.7087	.5612	1.108	1.263	1.46073
1.55	.9217	0.6818	.5327	1.130	1.280	1.50328
1.60	.9125	0.6559	.5062	1.154	1.296	1.54723
1.65	.9035	0.6309	.4814	1.179	1.311	1.59257
1.70	.8947	0.6069	.4583	1.206	1.324	1.63931

Table A.5 (Continued)
Rayleigh Line
(f) $k = 1.67$

M	$\dfrac{T_0}{T_0{}^*}$	$\dfrac{T}{T^*}$	$\dfrac{p}{p^*}$	$\dfrac{p_0}{p_0{}^*}$	$\dfrac{V}{V^*}$	$\left(\dfrac{T_0}{T_0{}^*}\right)_{\text{isoth}}$
1.75	.8862	.5840	.4367	1.235	1.337	1.68744
1.80	.8779	.5620	.4165	1.266	1.349	1.73696
1.85	.8699	.5410	.3976	1.299	1.360	1.78789
1.90	.8621	.5209	.3799	1.334	1.371	1.84021
1.95	.8546	.5018	.3633	1.370	1.381	1.89392
2.00	.8474	.4835	.3477	1.408	1.391	1.94903
2.05	.8405	.4660	.3330	1.448	1.400	2.00553
2.10	.8338	.4493	.3192	1.490	1.408	2.06343
2.15	.8274	.4334	.3062	1.534	1.415	2.12273
2.20	.8213	.4183	.2940	1.580	1.423	2.18341
2.25	.8154	.4038	.2824	1.628	1.430	2.24550
2.30	.8097	.3899	.2715	1.678	1.436	2.30897
2.35	.8043	.3767	.2612	1.729	1.442	2.37385
2.40	.7991	.3641	.2514	1.783	1.448	2.44011
2.45	.7941	.3521	.2422	1.839	1.454	2.50778
2.50	.7893	.3406	.2334	1.897	1.459	2.57684
2.55	.7847	.3296	.2251	1.956	1.464	2.64729
2.60	.7803	.3191	.2173	2.018	1.469	2.71914
2.65	.7761	.3090	.2098	2.082	1.473	2.79239
2.70	.7721	.2994	.2027	2.148	1.477	2.86703
2.75	.7682	.2902	.1959	2.216	1.481	2.94307
2.80	.7644	.2814	.1895	2.287	1.485	3.02049
2.85	.7608	.2730	.1834	2.360	1.489	3.09932
2.90	.7574	.2649	.1775	2.435	1.493	3.17954
2.95	.7541	.2571	.1719	2.512	1.496	3.26115
3.00	.7509	.2497	.1666	2.587	1.499	3.34416
3.50	.7251	.1897	.1244	3.521	1.524	4.25100
4.00	.7072	.1484	.09632	4.716	1.541	5.29736
4.50	.6943	.1191	.07669	6.213	1.553	6.48321
5.00	.6848	.0975	.06246	8.044	1.561	7.80860
6.00	.6721	.06870	.04368	12.86	1.573	10.87789
7.00	.6642	.05092	.03224	19.44	1.580	14.50526
8.00	.6590	.03920	.02475	28.07	1.584	18.69067
9.00	.6553	.03110	.01959	39.05	1.587	23.43419
10.00	.6528	.02526	.01589	52.66	1.589	28.73566
∞	.6414	0	0	∞	1.599	∞

Table A.6

Mach Number and Mach Angle
vs.
Prandtl-Meyer Function for Perfect Gas*

(a) $k = 1.4$

ω	α	M	ω	α	M
0.0	90.0000	1.0000	25.0	30.8469	1.9503
0.5	72.0988	1.0509	25.5	30.5355	1.9682
1.0	67.5741	1.0818	26.0	30.2293	1.9862
1.5	64.4505	1.1084	26.5	29.9281	2.0044
2.0	61.9969	1.1326	27.0	29.6316	2.0226
2.5	59.9500	1.1553	27.5	29.3397	2.0409
3.0	58.1805	1.1769	28.0	29.0524	2.0593
3.5	56.6139	1.1976	28.5	28.7694	2.0778
4.0	55.2048	1.2177	29.0	28.4906	2.0964
4.5	53.9204	1.2373	29.5	28.2158	2.1151
5.0	52.7383	1.2565			
5.5	51.6419	1.2753	30.0	27.9451	2.1339
6.0	50.6186	1.2938	30.5	27.6782	2.1528
6.5	49.6583	1.3120	31.0	27.4149	2.1718
7.0	48.7528	1.3300	31.5	27.1552	2.1910
			32.0	26.8991	2.2103
7.5	47.8957	1.3478			
8.0	47.0818	1.3655	32.5	26.6464	2.2297
8.5	46.3065	1.3830	33.0	26.3970	2.2492
9.0	45.5660	1.4004	33.5	26.1507	2.2689
9.5	44.8570	1.4177	34.0	25.9076	2.2887
			34.5	25.6675	2.3086
10.0	44.1770	1.4349			
10.5	43.5233	1.4521	35.0	25.4304	2.3287
11.0	42.8940	1.4692	35.5	25.1962	2.3489
11.5	42.2869	1.4862	36.0	24.9648	2.3693
12.0	41.7007	1.5032	36.5	24.7361	2.3898
			37.0	24.5101	2.4105
12.5	41.1338	1.5202			
13.0	40.5849	1.5371	37.5	24.2866	2.4313
13.5	40.0529	1.5540	38.0	24.0657	2.4523
14.0	39.5366	1.5709	38.5	23.8473	2.4734
14.5	39.0350	1.5878	39.0	23.6313	2.4947
			39.5	23.4176	2.5162
15.0	38.5474	1.6047			
15.5	38.0730	1.6216	40.0	23.2061	2.5378
16.0	37.6108	1.6385	40.5	22.9969	2.5596
16.5	37.1605	1.6555	41.0	22.7900	2.5816
17.0	36,7212	1.6725	41.5	22.5852	2.6038
			42.0	22.3824	2.6261
17.5	36.2925	1.6895			
18.0	35.8739	1.7065	42.5	22.1816	2.6487
18.5	35.4648	1.7235	43.0	21.9828	2.6714
19.0	35.0648	1.7406	43.5	21.7860	2.6944
19.5	34.6735	1.7578	44.0	21.5911	2.7176
			44.5	21.3980	2.7409
20.0	34.2904	1.7750			
20.5	33.9153	1.7922	45.0	21.2068	2.7644
21.0	33.5479	1.8095	45.5	21.0174	2.7882
21.5	33.1877	1.8269	46.0	20.8297	2.8122
22.0	32.8344	1.8443	46.5	20.6437	2.8364
			47.0	20.4594	2.8609
22.5	32.4879	1.8618			
23.0	32.1478	1.8793	47.5	20.2767	2.8856
23.5	31.8138	1.8969	48.0	20.0956	2.9105
24.0	31.4859	1.9146	48.5	19.9160	2.9356
24.5	31.1637	1.9324	49.0	19.7380	2.9610
			49.5	19.5615	2.9867

* These data are reprinted with permission from J. H. Keenan and J. Kaye, *Gas Tables*, 1948, John Wiley and Sons, Inc.

Table A.6 (Continued)

(a) $k = 1.4$

ω	α	M		ω	α	M
50.0	19.3865	3.0126		70.0	13.3247	4.3390
50.5	19.2129	3.0388		70.5	13.1913	4.3821
51.0	19.0408	3.0652		71.0	13.0587	4.4258
51.5	18.8700	3.0919		71.5	12.9268	4.4702
52.0	18.7005	3.1189		72.0	12.7955	4.5152
52.5	18.5324	3.1462		72.5	12.6649	4.5610
53.0	18.3657	3.1738		73.0	12.5349	4.6076
53.5	18.2002	3.2016		73.5	12.4055	4.6549
54.0	18.0360	3.2298		74.0	12.2768	4.7029
54.5	17.8730	3.2583		74.5	12.1487	4.7517
55.0	17.7112	3.2871		75.0	12.0212	4.8014
55.5	17.5506	3.3162		75.5	11.8943	4.8519
56.0	17.3911	3.3457		76.0	11.7680	4.9032
56.5	17.2328	3.3755		76.5	11.6422	4.9554
57.0	17.0757	3.4056		77.0	11.5170	5.0085
57.5	16.9196	3.4361		77.5	11.3924	5.0626
58.0	16.7646	3.4669		78.0	11.2683	5.1176
58.5	16.6107	3.4981		78.5	11.1447	5.1736
59.0	16.4579	3.5297		79.0	11.0217	5.2306
59.5	16.3061	3.5616		79.5	10.8992	5.2887
60.0	16.1552	3.5940		80.0	10.7772	5.3479
60.5	16.0053	3.6268		80.5	10.6558	5.4081
61.0	15.8564	3.6600		81.0	10.5348	5.4694
61.5	15.7085	3.6936		81.5	10.4143	5.5320
62.0	15.5615	3.7276		82.0	10.2942	5.5959
62.5	15.4154	3.7620		82.5	10.1746	5.6610
63.0	15.2703	3.7969		83.0	10.0555	5.7274
63.5	15.1260	3.8323		83.5	9.9369	5.7950
64.0	14.9826	3.8681		84.0	9.8187	5.8640
64.5	14.8400	3.9044		84.5	9.7010	5.9345
65.0	14.6983	3.9412		85.0	9.5837	6.0064
65.5	14.5574	3.9785		85.5	9.4668	6.0799
66.0	14.4174	4.0163		86.0	9.3503	6.1550
66.5	14.2781	4.0547		86.5	9.2342	6.2317
67.0	14.1396	4.0936		87.0	9.1185	6.3101
67.5	14.0019	4.1330		87.5	9.0032	6.3902
68.0	13.8650	4.1730		88.0	8.8884	6.4720
68.5	13.7288	4.2136		88.5	8.7740	6.5558
69.0	13.5934	4.2548		89.0	8.6599	6.6415
69.5	13.4587	4.2966		89.5	8.5462	6.7292
				90.0	8.4328	6.8190

index